To

Émile

From

San Ferri

THE FINAL REFUGE

THE FINAL REFUGE

Ian Ferri

Book Guild Publishing
Sussex, England

First published in Great Britain in 2014 by
The Book Guild Ltd
The Werks
45 Church Road
Hove, BN3 2BE

Typesetting in Garamond by
Keyboard Services, Luton, Bedfordshire

Printed in Great Britain by
CPI Group (UK) Ltd, Croydon, CR0 4YY

A catalogue record for this book is available from
The British Library.

ISBN 978 1 84624 967 9

To my late wife Fiona
With grateful thanks
For her help and patience
And skilful editing, without
Which this work might never
Have been completed.

*Much gratitude to John Neill,
My good and always reliable friend,
Who gave much of his time
Checking the final editing.*

1

Leaving her place of work, Linda Johnstone stared past the scurrying crowd around her towards the street outside. It was snowing. She shrugged her shoulders and walked calmly towards the factory doors. I won't have to put up with this for much longer, she thought.

Linda smiled almost cynically and took stock of her situation. Here we go again. Another day's work behind me, thank God. Her feelings were of relief, thinking that at last her time was once more her own as she drifted into thoughts of the evening ahead, Well, where to now? What exciting prospects lie before me? I wonder what they're doing in Florida right now. Lying back on the proverbial sun-kissed beach I suppose or languishing under a palm tree. Wouldn't that be a great way to spend an evening? But I guess it's back to the telly for me. Her contemplation was abruptly disturbed by the sudden rush of cold wind and snow as she left the factory and stepped out onto the street. She controlled her thoughts by confining them to her immediate surroundings.

Linda's companion walked silently beside her, preoccupied with threading her way through people and traffic as they crossed the street. They approached a flight of steps which led to a pedestrian crossing on the main road. They silently climbed the steps to the top and stopped for a moment at the crossing. During this pause, Linda's mind wandered again, with thoughts of warmer climes. This is strange indeed, she thought. Here I am, wrapped up for winter, fighting my way through the wind and snow, and I bet there's somebody over there in Florida getting bronzed in a deck chair. Gee, I wish! Having safely reached the other side of the road, they made for her companion's car. As they approached, Linda's thoughts were distracted again by the jingling of the keys that her friend had produced. She listened to their rhythmic sound as they jingled to the pace of her walk. Linda waited by the car as her friend quickly got in and opened the door for her. She was sharply reminded of the bitter weather as she made contact with the cold seat.

Her friend uttered her first words by drawing attention to the dirty windscreen, commenting on her forgetfulness to refill the windscreen washer. Linda momentarily considered her partner's self-rebuke, but became distracted once more as the car drew away from the kerb. America dominated her thoughts once more. It was not by chance that she should be thinking along these lines, because that's where she was destined to go in the near future – although it wasn't sunny Florida that she was heading for, but Washington DC. Linda would often dream of the US and what it would be like in real life; it was a form of escapism for her. She didn't go out much, and there was little else for her to do. But she had never seriously believed she would ever actually go there. When her father first broached the subject she could hardly believe her ears, for it was beyond her wildest dreams. The drone of the engine was all Linda was aware of until it stopped, her friend nudged her, and Linda automatically opened her door. She was home.

Linda Johnstone was a young Scottish girl, who was not too happy about her social prospects. She lived in a small mining town near Edinburgh and was daughter to William Johnstone, a miner who had suffered the consequences of the confrontation between the Thatcher government and the National Union of Mineworkers. The dispute was to last 18 bitter months only to end in the complete capitulation of the miners. Willie Johnstone hated Maggie Thatcher, the Tory government and all that they stood for. He had seen many right-wing governments in his time but none quite so extreme as this one.

Willie was passionate and radical in his union beliefs, always first on hand for picket duty. He believed in the closed shop and that if the union didn't have the unity of the men there was no point in having one. It was only a matter of time before he got himself involved in a fight with one of the strike breakers. Willie was fired and therefore not able to return to work when the strike was over. Twenty years down the drain thought Willie, and not a bloody thing to show for it. Bastards!

Willie Johnstone was a bitter man who did not hide his feelings or political views from anyone. There were some who would say that his forthright attitude was directly responsible for his present situation. Willie was determined to salvage what he could from his predicament. He had a teenage daughter whom he was determined to shield from the poverty that was bound to follow. He had withdrawn all his savings from the bank and given the money to Linda, with the intention that she should emigrate to America and start a new life with his brother George and his family in Washington.

A month of preparation and farewells went by. Linda would soon be on her way to start a new life. Until now Linda had not been a very happy girl; introverted and shy, she didn't mix much with other girls her own age. Her somewhat sullen nature was probably due to her strong-willed, domineering father's strict control over her since she was a child. Willie had been determined that his only child was going to be given a better chance in life than he ever had. There would be no getting married at 18 to some local miner's son who was going to piss his wages against the wall every Friday night after going to the local. None of them were good enough for her.

Consequently, Linda didn't know much about boys, nor was she allowed to associate with many of the local girls. This sheltered environment meant that Linda was quite simply not streetwise in her own town, yet here she was about to embark on a lone adventure to the vast country of America.

A farewell party was held two days before her departure. Mrs Johnstone was bent on giving Linda a send-off to remember, and spent days shopping and hours cooking and preparing for the celebrations. Nothing was too good for her Linda, and it was to be a sit-down meal for everyone. There would be none of these fast food buffets and paper cups in her house. Linda had other ideas about the kind of party she wanted, but she didn't have the heart to tell her mother, who had worked so hard arranging everything on her own. Linda could see the joy on her mother's face as she scurried about, assiduously preparing the house for her party. She had never seen her mother so happy and there was no way that she was going to spoil it for her.

Margaret Johnstone, a gentle and religious woman, was inwardly heartbroken at the thought of her only child emigrating to America. Linda's mother was 50 years old and her hair had turned grey. She was still a good-looking woman despite her mature years, although she always seemed to have a sad face, particularly now when she was about to lose her only daughter. She had prayed very hard that her daughter should get a better chance in life than herself, and almost despaired when Willie lost his job and all their prospects seemed to be dashed.

Margaret hadn't had an easy life, especially with such an argumentative, domineering husband as Willie. Not that he had always been like that. Margaret could remember him as a young, very handsome lad with a shock of curly red hair. He was boisterous then, and forever teasing her. Young Willie Johnstone had a heart of gold and would never see anybody in need, not if he could do something about it. That's why he had become so involved in the Union. It was the mines that had soured him. He had seen his own father die of silicosis just two weeks before he started in the mines himself.

Margaret had lost her second baby in childbirth. It had been a boy, and oh how she had longed for a wee boy. A wee lad would have made her family complete. It would have been the answer to all her prayers. But it was not to be. There were complications that threatened Margaret's life as well as the child's and the doctor had to make a quick decision. It was either the mother or the child, and the mother had the best chance of survival.

Margaret remembered the pregnancy well. How she nurtured dreams of what the child would be like, even made plans in her mind for its future, in anticipation of a boy. She often wondered what dreadful deed she had committed to deserve the awesome punishment of losing a child. Months were spent in vain, trying to determine why. Even so, she continued to blame herself for the loss of the child and sometimes wished that she had died in its place, for this, to Margaret, was a living purgatory.

It took years for Margaret to get over her feelings of emptiness and unfulfilment. Years of tender care and attention by Willie, who was a devoted and attentive husband throughout this bitter experience for them both. But eventually, she was persuaded of her innocence and even came to terms with her inability to have another child, due to the hysterectomy that followed. But Margaret knew within herself that she could never again face even the risk of repeating such an awful experience. For even now, she had the occasional nightmare when she relived the whole ordeal. Such was the trauma of this agonising episode in her life.

The big day had arrived at last for Linda. It was time to go to Waverley Station. She had to get a train to London where she would pick up a flight to New York, then on to Washington where, hopefully, she would be met by her uncle.

It was a really exciting day for all who were involved in this adventure, and to Linda that's exactly what it was: an adventure. There were three car loads of people at the station. Her father wondered where all these people had come from, considering how restrictive he had been of Linda's movements. He didn't reckon on her having so many friends, most of them coming from work. There was much hugging and kissing at the station and Linda thought she would never stop crying.

Even her father had tears in his eyes when they said their goodbyes. 'Remember and write every week lass and don't worry about us. We'll be all right. Phone us as soon as you get to George's house so that we know you arrived safely.'

'Aw stop fussing, Willie,' said Margaret. 'Can't you see the lassie's upset enough without you embarrassing her? Of course she'll phone us. She knows fine we'll be worried until we hear from her.'

5

2

When Linda touched down in Washington she was already on a tremendous high from her first experience of flying, coupled with her brief but exhilarating adventure in New York flying over the Statue of Liberty and the Empire State Building. These were just names in a book before, but this was 'the real thing' as the advert said. If only she had someone to share it with.

Clutching her suitcases, she eagerly fought her way through the crowded terminal, among the noise and bustle. She was busy observing everybody, looking at their clothes, listening to them talking. Sometimes she would lapse into a dream-like trance as she looked at their faces, hoping to recognise someone she had seen on the telly.

Linda's trance was interrupted by the repetition of her name in a voice that she had never heard before. 'Linda. Linda. Linda Johnstone. Are you Linda Johnstone from Edinburgh?' Suddenly, the trance was broken and a face loomed before her, a vaguely familiar face, one that she had seen only in photographs.

It was George Johnstone, her uncle, who was just as excited about meeting Linda as she was about meeting him. They greeted each other with a big hug, the kind of hug you only see at airports or railway stations.

'How was the trip?' said George. 'I bet you're glad to be back on the ground. Never did like flying myself.'

'Oh no, it was absolutely fabulous!' shrieked Linda. 'That's one experience I will never forget.'

Her uncle smiled. The expression on her face said it all. 'Let's find the rest of your luggage and get you home. Your Aunt Mary and the kids are awful anxious to meet you.'

George was an engineer who had left Scotland 20 years before when he was 28. He escaped work in the mines because his father was determined to save at least one of his sons from mining. So George was sent off to Edinburgh to learn electronics and become an engineer.

'Not far now,' said George as he drove onto the state highway. 'Well, what do you think of America so far? Does it come up to your expectations?'

'This is just as I imagined,' said Linda. 'I used to think that people didn't really talk and dress the way they do on the telly. Somehow, I thought it was all exaggerated. But it's true. They really do talk and look like that.'

'And what's wrong with the way we dress and talk? Don't you like my clothes, then?' teased George.

'I didn't mean that. It's just ... just so different.'

'I know what you mean,' said George trying to save her further embarrassment.

When they arrived at the house, Aunt Mary, young David and little Dorothy were outside waiting for them, brimming with excitement and chattering non-stop.

'What took you so long? Oh it's so good to see you Linda,' cried Mary.

It didn't take long for Linda to settle down with her new family, especially as they were such caring people. She was treated as a daughter and she loved every minute of it, becoming more affable, even chatty, and eager to learn new things. David and Dorothy were absolutely delighted with their new cousin from Scotland. They loved to hear her talk, for the Scottish accent was music to their ears. 'You must tell us about Scotland. I want to know everything,' said Dorothy. Linda kept them awake many a night telling them stories about when she was a wee girl. She was now part of a new and happy family, and this gave her the confidence upon which to build a new life.

It wasn't long before she started work in a department store called

Styles situated at the local mall. While working in Styles, Linda met and befriended a young Irish girl called Kathy Conners. Kathy had been in America for four years now and was pretty well established in the American way of life, or so it seemed. Kathy had a blue Pontiac convertible, her own flat, and always wore good-quality clothes. Considering that she was earning much the same salary as Linda, Linda never ceased to wonder how Kathy managed to stretch her salary so far.

Kathy first came to North America when she was 19. She had had a whirlwind romance with a young Egyptian lad called Abdul Rassid. Abdul and Kathy had married in Ireland against the wishes and advice of parents on both sides. Abdul's father however yielded to the inevitable, but suggested that the young couple should start their lives together in a new country, and offered them a sum of money as a wedding present to be used to this end. Kathy and Abdul decided on Canada as the place to start their new lives together and were soon on their way. However, the money didn't last long and Abdul was having difficulty in finding work. Kathy soon realised Abdul was an extremely proud individual who was not prepared to do manual work. The fact that he had no formal skills to turn to didn't seem to bother him.

Abdul's reluctance to compromise his ambitions with their needs led to many arguments and much fighting between them. This culminated in Abdul absconding with what little money they had left, never to be seen again. Fortunately for Kathy there were no children involved and she was free to move around looking for work. She had always wanted to go to America and saw this as her chance. After working in a department store in Toronto for several months, doing lots of overtime and exercising a great deal of thrift, she managed to save enough money to move to Washington.

Despite their very different experiences in life, and different personalities, Kathy and Linda had a good relationship and were very good friends. Linda was able to draw upon Kathy's hard-earned schooling in life, such as her ability to stand on her own two feet and her adroitness in difficult situations. Kathy knew what she wanted out of life and was prepared to work hard to get it. It didn't take her long to adopt the American ethic of 'go for it', which was a driving force that Kathy responded to with zest.

Linda, on the other hand, had developed into a very charming and tranquil young woman who was acutely aware that her good fortune and new lifestyle were the result of her parents' sacrifices, together with the efforts of her new family who had turned out to be wonderful foster parents. She was not slow to show her gratitude. She wrote home frequently and sent presents at every possible opportunity: birthdays, anniversaries, Christmas. She never missed an occasion.

Kathy, at first, could not understand Linda's selfless, giving nature and often suggested that she was too giving, that she would one day regret her kindness when she met people who would take advantage of her. But deep down, Kathy found Linda's personality refreshing and comforting, especially after her raw experiences with Abdul and a few others since. Linda's generous disposition meant that she was also trusting and caring, two things that Kathy longed to be. She was therefore able to find some refuge in Linda from the highly competitive aspects of living in a capitalist system. Linda and Kathy complemented each other, and they developed a close relationship. Even when they were with boyfriends, one or the other would try to arrange a foursome so that they could all be together.

During one of these foursomes, Linda was introduced to Gregg Donoghue, Kathy's date for that evening. Gregg was a well-built, athletic six-footer who was slightly balding, or as Gregg would put it, he was still growing when his hair stopped. He was a 32-year-old government official who didn't like talking about his work. He claimed that work was a social interruption, and seemed to be more interested in food, women and keeping in shape – in that order. He was always quite happy to let others do all the talking, for he was a good listener and, according to Kathy, almost interrogative on occasion. Kathy told Linda that Gregg worked out of town a lot and that she only saw him once a month, sometimes less. She suspected that he was married but never pushed the issue.

In fact, Kathy had actually met Gregg through the Mayfair Agency

– a high-class escort agency, the biggest in the state. When Kathy first came to Washington, she found that life in the big city could be very lonely for a young woman living on her own. While flicking through one of the local magazines her eye was caught by an ad that was looking for 'Young, attractive, intelligent women with six hours a week to spare, with high earning potential'.

Kathy considered that it might be an escort agency, but had thought, what the heck, where's the harm in that? This could be a golden opportunity to meet a nice young eligible bachelor. At the very least, I'm gonna meet new people, get a free night out and get paid for it. Let's face it, this is the state capital. There must be lots of important people in town who have left their wives behind and are looking for a partner to attend some of these state functions.

It didn't take Kathy long to figure out that this was a call-girl racket under the guise of a highly sophisticated escort agency, with an exclusive clientele. Washington is a much-visited city, with lots of through traffic of extremely important people. Being the country's capital, there are many politicians and associated agencies representing the country's biggest industries. This also means that there is a large turnover of high-earning, lonely men, many of whom are looking for a partner for at least one evening while they're on the loose from their wives. This was the sales pitch that Kathy was being given. This and many other cogent arguments were persuasively put forward in their efforts to recruit her.

Perhaps it was the chance to meet high-earning, influential men that could lead to a more permanent relationship, or maybe it was the money. Let's face it, 100 bucks for an hour's work is sure easy money. OK, so the house takes 50 per cent. After some of the hard times I've been through, thought Kathy, what the heck? This could well be a short cut to some real money. Maybe it's time I had a spell on easy street. Anyway, at these rates, I won't have to stay with it for long, only until I have earned enough money for a stake in a legitimate business of my own.

Kathy was persuaded. Who'd have thought of Kathy Conners, a young Catholic girl from Connemara, becoming a call-girl to some of the most influential men in the capital? Her mother would be turning in her grave. And so, Kathy became a member of the Mayfair Escort Agency, or as some of her in-house friends would say, 'She works for Auntie Mae.'

This is how Kathy was able to drive a convertible, own her flat and always have a well-heeled appearance. This was a side of Kathy that Linda never knew, for Linda thought Kathy a nice girl with high morals and would definitely not approve. OK, it was none of her business anyway, but Kathy valued Linda's friendship and didn't want to risk losing it. Good, reliable friends are hard to come by in this world and Kathy thought Linda one of the best.

As soon as Kathy met Gregg she suspected him of being an FBI agent. It was the gun that did it. Some of Kathy's other clients carried guns too, but there was something about the way Gregg handled his that looked very professional. For one thing, it was never out of his sight, even at the most intimate moments. OK, America can be a rough country, and probably half the population carry weapons. Washington in particular could certainly be a violent city: the locals claimed that in Washington, even the robbers get mugged on their way back to the getaway car. Gregg was reluctant to discuss his work and always managed to parry any questions in that direction by steering the conversation away from himself and back to Kathy. This was probably how he got to know so much about her.

They had a strange relationship. Gregg was certainly not an emotional type. He didn't display many feelings, but it was obvious that he liked her very much for he always asked for Kathy when he was in Washington, and he really enjoyed taking her out. They had good fun together. Kathy, on the other hand, had made a point of keeping a certain calculated distance from her clients, as involvement invariably led to complications, but she did allow Gregg a bit more licence than any of the others. Perhaps it was living for the day with no past, no tomorrow. Perhaps this was the common denominator that was the secret of their relationship. Kathy had warned Gregg never to let Linda know about her connection with the agency, and Gregg respected that confidence; he was good at keeping secrets.

'Kathy tells me you're from Scotland, Linda. What brings you to the U S of A? Have you been here long?'

'Doesn't everyone want to come to America?' replied Linda. 'My first introduction to the "U S of A", as you put it, was through soap operas like *Dallas*, *Dynasty* and *The Colbys*. Who could resist the opportunity to see it for real? So when my father offered me the chance to come and stay with my uncle, I just jumped at it. That was two years ago and I still love it. Mind you, I haven't met a movie star yet, but I guess I'll survive that one. Anyway, who needs movie stars when we can meet the real thing, like you, Gregg?' teased Linda.

Little did Linda know that one day she would see Gregg in a different light for she would become embroiled in some terrible events, events that would dramatically change her destiny, and put her life and the lives of her loved ones at stake.

3

Just off the Florida coast, somewhere in Apalachee Bay, a luxury yacht had just dropped anchor. On board were three very influential people. Tom Casey, the eldest of the three and the owner of the yacht, was a large, rotund man whose 250lb body weight was more than a match for his expensive cashmere blazer. Tom was head of a large corporation whose main business was radar installations and associated military equipment. The corporation also had several subsidiary companies, including its own airline. Tom Casey's two guests were Senator Brian Mitchell of South Carolina and Frank Mariano of the CIA.

The three had been having a relaxed discussion over drinks and a cigar. Tom contemplated the white flaky ash on the end of his cigar while he waited for an appropriate break in the conversation. His aim was to lift the discussion onto a higher plane and extend its parameters. He was concerned about the current political situation in Europe and what the Russian response might be to certain proposed military changes in England.

'Well, Frank,' said Tom. 'The Ruskies sure seem to be having a bad time right now, wouldn't you say? Are you aware of the problems those guys are having at the moment? They've got political unrest in Poland, heavy losses in Afghanistan and on the domestic front, there are severe grain shortages. I would say that adds up to one hellova headache, wouldn't you?'

Frank Mariano, a thickset, good-looking young man, pushed a hand of thick fingers through his jet black wavy hair, while contemplating a response to the question. He was the junior of the three by at least a decade. Frank was more interested in what Tom was leading up to, than the current debate, so he decided to encourage his line of argument rather than challenge it.

13

'You gotta be right there Tom,' replied Frank. 'They're also doing a lot of bitchin' over the Star Wars programme. I guess they're getting worried, eh?'

'That's just the problem,' said Tom. 'Worried people can be pushed into doing desperate things. What with the kinda pressure that's on these guys right now, there's no tellin' what they'll do next. What do you say, Senator?'

Senator Mitchell, a tall, refined, white-haired Southern gentleman, was also wearing a blazer, though in stark contrast to Tom's its fit was impeccable. The Senator leaned heavily on his silver-topped cane as if to give emphasis to his response.

'Let's not go flying off the handle, sir. These Ruskies have been in far tougher jams than this. It's not as if we have a red alert situation here, now do we? Besides, these people have been known to have one or two trump cards up their sleeve, which I'm sure Frank here will testify to.'

Tom, determined not to be put off his train of thought, continued his argument. 'What do you think of this pinko then that's running for election in England?'

'I don't think that it's fair, Tom, callin' the gentleman a pinko. I take it you mean Steve Tulloch, the Labour candidate?'

'Yeh, that's the guy,' said Tom. 'A pinko if ever I saw one. As a matter of fact, that whole organisation – what do you call them, the Labour Party are all a bunch of reds if you ask me. They don't call themselves socialists for nothin' you know.'

Frank interceded. 'Steady on, Tom. These guys may make a lot of noise when they're campaigning for election, but believe me, what they say they're gonna do, and what they end up doing, don't always amount to the same thing.'

'Don't gimme that! That guy's gonna close down all our bases and kick our asses outa there. He's gonna do away with our nuclear force and lay Europe wide open, and with the Ruskies being so desperate at the moment, they're liable to make their move now. What're we gonna do about it, Senator?'

Tom was getting just a bit volatile and Brian, who by now was finding himself straining to contain the situation, tried to bring him down to a simmer.

'Now, Tom. You've heard of the Special Relationship, haven't you, hands across the sea and all that? We daren't interfere with British internal politics. The repercussions could be enormous and no tellin' where it might lead.'

Frank interrupted at this point, 'Who knows? It just may be, one of their own might decide to intervene, especially if they feel it's as serious as you seem to think it is.'

'What do you mean by that?'

'Well, didn't the IRA have a go at taking out Mrs Thatcher and her Cabinet not so long ago? Pity you don't have a friendly IRA man up your sleeve,' said Frank jokingly. Or was he joking? Frank's reference was to a bomb planted by the IRA in a Brighton hotel during the Tory Party Conference, when three people were killed and many were wounded. Was Frank planting a little seed in a fertile place, thought Tom, or just exercising a dry sense of humour?

Frank Mariano was well aware of Tom's sympathies with the IRA. He was also aware of the massive contributions that Tom's corporation had made to the Cause. There was also some doubt whether these contributions were restricted to financial ones, or were perhaps of a more material nature like weapons. Tom certainly had access. The Agency was still investigating that one.

Of course, Tom had certainly not put all his cards on the table. What he didn't say was that his corporation was in the middle of negotiating a $5 billion contract with the US government, to update all the American radar bases in the UK. If Steve Tulloch was to be elected, there wouldn't be any bases left to update. Naturally, Tom Casey was hoping that the administration was going to take steps to remedy the situation by taking some preventative action. However one phrased it, it still amounted to interfering with the internal affairs of another state, and one that happens to be America's closest ally.

Tom Casey's stratagem had failed. His ploy, transparent as it was to his guests, was to invite them on this trip with the sole intention of pumping them for information about the government's attitude to Steve Tulloch's proposal. Whether he overestimated their friendship or underestimated their integrity was unclear, but the point remains, that if the administration had a contingency plan for such a scenario, then nobody was saying, much to Tom's extreme aggravation.

Tom appreciated that he had gone a bit far with his probing, and that he had been less than subtle with his remarks. He also realised he was being stonewalled and so considered it would be prudent to defuse the situation somewhat. Just because they wouldn't provide him with the information that he was seeking, was no reason to make enemies of these people. No, that wouldn't do, thought Tom.

'Hey, guys, I'm sorry if I was gettin' a bit uptight there. I reckon that this good Napoleon brandy is startin' to get the better of an old man. I guess I just can't hold my liquor like I used to.' Tom may have been in his sixties but was far from being in the condition he implied.

It was the Senator who grabbed hold of the olive branch. 'Don't be silly, Tom, I reckon we've all had more than enough brandy for an evening. It serves you right for plying us with such good-quality liquor. Joking aside though, there's really no need for apologies. You haven't said anything to offend me. In fact, it's been one hellova trip. I've enjoyed every minute of it. I don't often get the chance to go sailing on a luxury yacht so let me take this opportunity to thank you for your hospitality.'

Frank joined in at this point, saying, 'I'd like to endorse that. It's been a fun trip. Hope we can do it again. Well, I don't know about you guys, but I'm gettin' a bit tired. I think I'll turn in. It's gettin' late.'

'I think it's time I hit the sack as well,' said the Senator.

'OK. See you people in the morning,' said Tom.

Next morning, the yacht tied up at the north shore of Pensacola, where the three said their goodbyes. Tom Casey headed for Mobile, where he caught a flight to Washington DC. It was a three-hour flight and he was weary, tired and angry by the time the plane touched down in the capital. He'd had three hours to mull over the previous night's discussions, and the more he thought about it the angrier he became. Such a bloody waste of time, thought Tom. The total futility of the whole exercise was getting to him, and he could hardly wait to get to his office where he was planning to organise his own remedy. All right, maybe the Administration are prepared to lie back and let a bunch of limey reds walk all over them, but I'm not. It's time to put away the kid gloves. No more niceties. If they think I'm going to let a multimillion dollar contract go out the window without a fight, they've got another think coming.

As Tom Casey's plane taxied up the runway at Washington airport, Kevin McGuire, a young Irishman, was just arriving in New York on a flight from London. Destination: the National Bank of New York. His objective: to draw funds from a secret bank account that he had established five years before. Kevin was deceptive in appearance, for his overall lean look belied his muscular athleticism. He had shoulder-length fair hair that combined with a dark moustache to form a curious frame for his steely blue eyes. There was no time to waste, for Kevin was on the run and he knew it was only a matter of time before his pursuers extended their search to New York.

While in the taxi from the airport he was already making plans for his next move, which was to make contact with an Italian immigrant called Joseph Deponio. Deponio, being a Catholic, had certain sympathies with the Cause and had often assisted in fundraising exercises in New York. Kevin had deliberately cultivated a relationship with Deponio on previous visits. His intention was to try and establish a safe house in America, or at least a stop-over point that would allow him time to make provision for a more permanent arrangement. As the cab got closer to the city centre, the increasing familiarity of the scenery triggered off thoughts of a previous journey to the Big Apple. He allowed himself the luxury of a wry smile as he remembered with quiet satisfaction how he'd had the temerity and foresight to make provisions for such a contingency. His thoughts were interrupted by the cab driver sliding back the adjoining window.

'Hey, we're approaching the city centre now, fella. Where exactly do you want to go?'

'Em ... I'm heading for the National Bank of New York,' replied Kevin.

'Yes, well that's about three blocks from here.'

'OK driver. Why don't you pull over at the next block and I'll walk the rest. It'll give me a chance to stretch my legs, after that long flight.'

As Kevin walked away from the cab, he tried to recapture the thoughts that had been in his mind before he was interrupted. This minor indulgence was quickly dispelled however, as the urgency of his more immediate predicament interrupted his thoughts. Kevin was not more than 20 feet from the bank, when he suddenly realised that there was a tall, thin, swarthy-looking character standing close to the entrance, watchfully monitoring the bank's customers.

Kevin stopped in his tracks. He needed time to think. Closer examination revealed a familiar face, which he soon recognised as Joseph Deponio. This was the very man he had hoped would harbour him during his stay in the city. But there was something wrong: this was too much of a coincidence.

Kevin's highly developed sense of suspicion was aroused, but his desperate need for help, coupled with his natural risk-taking propensity, overcame the danger signals. He decided to take the chance and continued towards the man in question. At that moment the guy turned towards Kevin, giving him a full view of his face. The tall man's eyes widened with recognition then abruptly turned into a frown. That was Kevin's first warning: the frown! He decided to make a run for it and made a sudden turn in an attempt to retrace his steps. As he was side on, halfway through his turn, his right eye caught a glimpse of a gun being raised and pointed towards him. At this point, the irate pedestrian Kevin had stumbled into decided to make an issue of the situation and grabbed him by the lapels. He spun him around, saying, 'Hey! Wait a minute fella. What's your hurr...' He never did finish the sentence. The man dropped like a stone in front of him. Kevin didn't stop to see the blood that was oozing from the gaping hole in the back of the man's head. He just ran.

He had covered three blocks, dodging and stumbling his way through a crowded street, when suddenly a vehicle screeched to a halt alongside him. Two policemen jumped out and grabbed him. There was nothing he could do. Within moments, he was facing a wall with both hands cuffed behind his back.

Kevin's next destination was the hustle and bustle of the police station. After his interrogation, during which he denied all knowledge of his would-be assailant, he decided to make a bid for political asylum. By now, he had figured that his only hope was with the authorities.

Tom Casey was still muttering to himself when he entered his private limousine which he had prearranged to collect him at the airport. 'Straight to the office, and I'm in a hellova hurry.' He picked up the limousine phone which gave him a direct line to the office, and barked into it. 'Get me Roy Stirling immediately.'

'I don't think he's in his office sir, but I'll...'

Tom didn't wait for the secretary to finish the sentence and again barked into the phone. 'I don't care where the hell he is. I want him in my office by the time I get there. OK?' He didn't wait for a reply, but slammed the phone down.

Roy Stirling was head of security for CLC Industries and one of the few men that Tom Casey trusted. There was nothing that he wouldn't do for Tom. Roy was a rugged looking character with a pock-marked face and dark, deep-set eyes. Although he was softly spoken, it in no way concealed his obnoxious manner. He was a Vietnam vet, one of the killing machines who had survived to kill again. Any scruples or morals that Roy might have had before Vietnam, he had left behind.

He was waiting for Tom when he arrived at his office. 'Did you have a good trip, sir?'

'No, as a matter of fact I did not. Sit down, Roy. There's a lot of work to be done and I'm anxious to get started. Are you aware of the contract we are negotiating to update radar installations in the UK?'

'I sure am,' replied Stirling. 'It was me who arranged the security for the initial survey of their equipment and the test trials for our...'

'Yes, OK,' said Tom, interrupting. 'It seems that a major obstacle has appeared on the horizon that could prevent further developments. Indeed, it could be that steps are taken to remove our existing equipment and facilities in that part of the world.'

'That's gotta be some obstacle! I should think that only the British government can exercise that kind of clout. Is that what we're dealing with?'

'Well, prospective government would be more accurate.'

'I see. You say an obstacle. Am I to understand that it's a surmountable one?'

'That's what we're about to find out. But first we need to find a suitable candidate for a very special task.'

'Can you be a bit more specific, sir?'

'An assassin, damn you, a bloody assassin! Have I got to spell everything out for you?'

'Sorry sir. I just wanted to make sure that we were both thinking along the same lines.'

'Here's what I want you to do. Arrange a meeting with these Irish people we've been dealing with. You know who I mean, the ones I've been funding all these years. Perhaps it's time we got some returns on that investment. Root around a bit and see if they've got anybody over here that might be willing to do some work for us. But as far as they're concerned, it's a local job. I don't want these people knowing what we're up to. What I'm after is a list of IRA members who have taken refuge over here, preferably recent arrivals, as they won't have had time to make many contacts. Oh, by the way, have you still got that phoney CIA identification we gave you?'

'Yes sir.'

'That's OK. Keep it handy. You may well have a chance to use it on this project. That reminds me, I also want you to get a hold of that FBI fella we have on our books. What's his name?'

'Donoghue sir. Gregg Donoghue.'

'Yea, that's the guy. You two are gonna be working together on this case. He's got some very useful connections that I want to take advantage of. Well that's it for the moment Roy. Get back to me as soon as you can. Now remember, I want priority on this one for there isn't much time. It's only two months until the general election takes place and I want this job in gear way before that happens.'

Tom Casey was now calling in some of his loyal and trusted lieutenants. He was about to arrange a feasibility study for one of the biggest hits this century. He sat back in his chair contemplating the situation. I'll bet you that Frank Mariano was just trying to set me up. He's gonna be makin' the balls and wants me to fire them, so that if anything goes wrong, I'm to be the fall guy. Well, have I got a surprise for you, Mr Mariano.

Tom Casey was looking for a suitable candidate for this particularly demanding operation. Such a candidate would have to fit a specific profile. He'd already decided that he should be an IRA member, but one who had no qualms about making a hit on a VIP, and preferably one so full of hatred for the English that the task would be its own reward. He also needed a plan of operation that would work in the UK.

The man most suitable for such an undertaking, would be Alex Stenton, the Security Chief for Atlantic Air, the corporation's own airline. His suitability for such an assignment lay in the fact that he was a former member of the SAS. Stenton was dishonourably discharged from the service for being overenthusiastic in the field. He had developed a taste for killing to such an extent that few were willing to work with him. He had also killed one of his own recruits during an unarmed combat exercise. Accidents such as this can happen while training to such a high level of skill, but it was more the way he responded at the inquiry that was the deciding factor. Stenton's attitude at the inquiry seemed to be one of callous indifference to what he had done. He showed no regret for taking the life of one of his own men. This, coupled with his repeated undisciplined behaviour in the field, suggested that further investigation into this man was warranted. Sentence was suspended pending a psychiatric investigation, but Stenton refused point blank to cooperate. As they were unable to examine him further, he was dishonourably discharged from the service.

Tom Casey collected reprobates the way some people collect fine art. He knew how to deal with these people and how to get the best from them. Given the right motivation and the appropriate rewards, they tended to respond well to delicate tasks, and were not too concerned about the 'why'. Alex Stenton was just the man to deal with this operation. But he had to be dealt with personally.

Tom buzzed his secretary and said, 'Locate Alex Stenton for me. He's security chief for Atlantic Air. Arrange for him to come to Washington on Thursday.'

Alex Stenton duly arrived on Thursday morning. He was a burly 6 foot 4, the sort who looks awkward in a suit and more at home in a sweatshirt and jeans. He wondered what could be so important that it required his flying to Washington at such short notice. The old man must have a real problem on his hands this time. He arrived at Tom Casey's office just in time to see Gregg Donoghue going into the room.

'Oh, Mr Stenton?' said the secretary questioningly.

'Yes, that's me.'

'Just go right in. Mr Casey's expecting you.'

Tom Casey wasn't a man to waste time on preliminaries, so after the briefest of introductions it was straight down to business. Three hours and about 15 cups of coffee later, Tom decided to call a halt.

'OK, Alex. I didn't expect a foolproof plan after just three hours' discussion, but by now, you should be aware of the kind of operation I have in mind. I'm leaving you to work out the details at the UK end. Just let me know when you're ready to go. Now I've got a very special type of candidate in mind for this task, but I want you to plan the operation, and it'll be your responsibility to see that he gets back here in one piece. It's important that he should be kept on ice for a while, just in case anything should go wrong. You, Gregg, will be responsible for things at this end of the operation. I want you to arrange a safe house for our candidate's return, where you can look after him for a while. Oh, and by the way, you'll also be working with Roy Stirling on this. I believe you've met before?'

'Yes,' said Gregg. 'We've worked together before.'

'Right, I'll give you the details later. OK, fellas. That's all for now, you've got two months to get this operation under way. We can't afford to wait any longer. Keep in touch and let me know if you need anything – and I mean anything. Good luck.'

Roy Stirling and Gregg Donoghue met up with Tom Casey's Irish associates in an office in New York and were pleasantly surprised to find out how cooperative they turned out to be. After only two hours' consultation, Roy was handed a list containing four names of recent Irish immigrants to America. At the top of this list was Kevin McGuire, who came highly recommended by these people. There was one major snag however: Kevin McGuire was at present in custody in a New York police cell.

What Gregg and Roy didn't know was that these people were in the process of trying to eliminate Kevin McGuire, and had already made an attempt on his life. Roy's request was seen as a golden opportunity to get McGuire back on the streets again, thus enabling them to make their own attempt at disposing of him. There would be no mistakes this time. Gregg did some checking around. The Irish 'friends' weren't being so honest. Hell, what does that word mean anyway? British sources revealed that this man was on the run, not only from the UK authorities, but also from the IRA who had already put out a contract on him.

This new development proved opportune to Gregg's purpose, as it meant that Kevin McGuire was now completely isolated and badly in need of a friend, thus making him that much easier to deal with.

4

No response had been given to Kevin McGuire's plea for asylum and he was being held under guard in an interrogation room. Two days had gone by since he was first arrested, during which time he had experienced a short respite from the chaos that had gone before. But there had also been time to think back and relive the nightmare of his arrest. He could hardly believe that so much had happened in so little time.

He was still trying to collect his thoughts when the door suddenly opened and in walked a rough-featured, pock-marked character who flashed an ID card at the guard as he came into the room. 'My name's Roy Stirling, Kevin. You can relax now, you're among friends.'

The door opened yet again revealing a tall, balding but youthful-looking guy, who was in the process of putting an FBI card back in his pocket. 'Hello, Kevin, I'm Gregg Donoghue. Roy here and myself are gonna be looking after you for a while. I understand you're claiming political asylum?'

'Yes I am, but no one seems to be taking me seriously around here, at least not until you people came along.'

'Don't worry, these things take time to organise. We would like you to come with us for a while. We've got some questions we would like to ask you.'

Kevin was whisked away in a big black limousine to an unknown destination somewhere in the New York suburbs. Gregg showed him around the house and acquainted him with all the facilities.

'OK, Kev. This is where you'll be staying for a while. We want you to get a good night's sleep and we'll come back in the morning and have a nice long talk. By the way, don't try to leave the building. We've got a man outside, but just holler if you need anything.'

Once more, Kevin was left on his own to reflect on recent events. How did I get myself into this mess in the first place? he thought as he lay on the bed looking up at the ceiling. It seemed a thousand years since he had left Ireland.

By the time Gregg and Roy returned the next day, Kevin was ready with a string of questions. For one thing, he had had access to some newspapers and was surprised to see that there was no mention of either the shooting incident or of anyone being arrested for it. His claim for political asylum was also ignored, even though the precinct had been full of press men when he was arrested. He was beginning to think that somebody was trying very hard to keep the lid on this, and he hadn't a clue as to why. He wasted no time waiting to be fobbed off yet again: as soon as they came into the room, he began firing questions at them.

'Hold it, Kev. Not so fast,' said Donoghue. 'We said we'd talk this morning, didn't we? OK, the short answer to most of your questions is quite simply that there are people with a lot of influence who don't want this kind of information to get out. It's as simple as that. And also, Mrs Thatcher, your Prime Minister, has just successfully convinced our government against the wisdom of granting political asylum to people like you. So, when you're released to the proper authorities, I'm afraid it's gonna be extradition and I guess that leaves you in limbo for the time being. What do you suggest, Kevin?'

'Come on, guys, gimme a break. You've got to know that by now I'm a wanted man back home.'

'Oh we sure do!' said Roy. 'We sure do!' as if he was savouring every word.

'Why, you're wanted by all sides, aren't you? By the IRA, the British government and, as it stands now, by the American government. Now look at it from our point of view, son. You're here illegally on a false passport, with no work permit, nowhere to stay and no visible means of support. I guess that makes you a vagrant as well as an illegal immigrant, not to mention what dastardly deeds you've committed back home. Well, Kevin, what have you got to say about that?'

'Then why've you brought me here in the first place? Why have I been sitting around all this time?'

'Well, we were trying to help you,' said Donoghue. 'But I'm afraid that events have rather overtaken us and it now appears to be out of our control.'

'Come on, fellas, you can't just hand me over like that. You know I'm done for if they get hold of me.'

'You should have thought about that a long time ago,' said Roy. 'You're not asking us to break the law, now are you?'

'Look, I'll do anything. Just let me go. Give me a chance. I promise you won't hear from me again.'

'Gee, we sure would like to help, Kev, but that would put us on the wrong side of the law now, wouldn't it?'

'All right. All right fellas. What exactly do you want from me anyhow? Let's stop playin' games. You people haven't covered up a murder rap for nothin', and you certainly didn't keep me tucked up here for no reason either. Just what is it that you have in mind?'

'Well, Kev,' said Roy. 'What was it you did in England that upset so many people? Tell us about it, maybe we can help you. Take your time. We've got all day before we hand you over. Well, if we hand you over. That just might depend on you. Tell us about the cop you killed in England.'

Kevin knew by now that these guys meant business. They owed him nothing and seemed to know a lot about him.

'How would you like a new identity and American citizenship, Kevin? And what if we were to give you a large capital sum, just enough to start up a small business somewhere, let's say in the Midwest. How would you react to that?' said Gregg.

Kevin took a long time responding, especially now that he knew they were about to get down to the nitty-gritty. He thought they must want something real bad to go to all this trouble. Eventually Kevin spoke. 'Just what is it that you people want from me? Who is it you want dead?'

'Now, it's not as if we're askin' you to put away one of your friends. As a matter of fact, you and your compatriots have been fighting the likes of these guys for years now, so we figure we're gonna give you a helpin' hand this time, that's all.'

'Who do you have in mind?' asked Kevin hesitantly.

'We want Steve Tulloch out of the picture.'

This time, it was clinically put to him. The games were over, they meant business. Kevin was at first hesitant to respond and then a sudden feeling of panic welled up inside of him, building up to an almost uncontrollable pressure. Then he spoke, his voice pitched higher than normal.

'That's the Labour leader you're talking about! You've gotta be joking! These people are covered day and night wherever they go, especially now that the election is coming up.'

'Take it easy, relax. The programme's been set for you. It's already arranged. We can get you in and out again inside twelve hours, by which time you'll be on your way back here, as free as a bird.'

'Why him?' asked Kevin, by this time sounding just a little bit desperate. 'He might not even get elected.'

'That's one of the conditions on this exercise, you don't ask questions unless they're operational. Now we want your answer tonight. We're gonna leave you alone for a few hours, but when we get back, we want an answer. OK?'

They both left the room, not waiting for a reply.

Kevin sat down on a chair. He was quite numb. The whole thing raced through his mind over and over again as he frantically searched for a way out of his predicament, but these people had been very thorough. They seemed to have covered all the options. What could he possibly do? It wasn't that he was against killing, he had done it before and, let's face it, they were the enemy. But this was real risky. They'd be waiting for him, especially after the Brighton incident.

Kevin's mind soon drifted away from the core of his problem. He reached further back into his mind as if trying to escape the present and reaching out for refuge in the past. He was thinking of home and his family. He wondered what they would be doing right now. Oh, how he longed to be with them. Why hadn't he taken his brother's advice, he asked himself. Why was he always at odds with his family?

Kevin had always been an impetuous child, he wanted things to happen now, he didn't like waiting for anything. Yes, Kevin was impatient and people who are impatient adopt suitable logic and lifestyles to accommodate their impatience; and what could be more suitable than gambling? Kevin was a risk-taker, always trying to speed up the returns from life. It really wasn't surprising that he had joined the fight for the Cause when he was old enough, for this was his chance to help change the system. There was no way that Kevin was going to wait for political change to improve things. No, not if he could do anything to speed things along. His brother had often warned him that his impatience would get him into trouble, but Kevin was never one to take advice, especially from a brother who was only a year older.

Kevin's brother Kieran was more of an investor than a gambler. He wasn't afraid to invest time and energy on a long-term basis. Kieran was a marathon runner, a stamina man who ran 10 miles a day. Although disciplined in the martial arts, running was in his blood, that's what gave him the mental and physical strength he craved.

Kieran had never got involved with the IRA because he felt that the odds were way against them, not that he didn't agree with many of their arguments. Anyway, Kevin always seemed to carry enough hate against the system for both of them and had grown up distrusting advice. He figured that it was just another ploy to slow him down, and when he joined the IRA he learned to distrust all kinds of officialdom, government agencies and police authorities in particular, not without some justification. But Kevin's distrust grew considerably, verging on the extreme, perhaps even paranoia, for eventually Kevin had found it necessary to kill a policeman who had him cornered when he was on the run. He was eventually tracked down and captured by the authorities when he was working on a job in London. Kevin claimed that considerable pressure had been put on him then to become a supergrass in exchange for a new life abroad. However, fearing that the police would not uphold their promises, and not wanting to give evidence against his compatriots, he had taken advantage of the trial situation to make good his escape. This is how he came to be in New York, and here he was being offered, yet again, another new lifestyle, this time in exchange for murder. Kevin felt that all his previous suspicion of officialdom and government agencies was being endorsed, and on reflection he felt justified in joining the war against a corrupt system.

Indeed, this reflection helped him arrive at his decision to work with them. What the hell, he thought. I've been fighting the system all my life and I've always ended up in a corner. This time, I'm going to work with them. Besides, there doesn't seem to be many alternatives at this point. I can't see these guys letting me loose now after telling me who the target is. It looks like my only chance is to play along. Kevin's thoughts had been so intense and exhausting that he fell asleep in his chair and it wasn't until the door slammed with Roy and Gregg's return that he woke up.

'Hey, dig this, Gregg,' said Roy sarcastically. 'We sure gotta cool one here. We offer this guy what's gotta be the toughest deal in his life, and what does he do, he just lies back in his chair and goes to sleep. Yeh, that's what I call cool.'

'You got an answer for us, Kevin?' said Gregg sternly.

'Yes,' said Kevin. 'I've decided to go along with it. Besides, if this is going to be my last job, I may as well go out in style.'

'That's the attitude, boy,' said Gregg.

'Yeh! You're my kinda guy,' said Roy.

And so the plot to kill Steve Tulloch, the leader of the opposition party in the United Kingdom, was finally hatched.

Meanwhile, in the UK, Alex Stenton had completed his interim report for Tom Casey. Three weeks after the original meeting, Alex Stenton returned to Washington to give Tom a briefing.

'Well, Tom, it looks as if this operation's going to be a bit more complicated than we originally thought. For one thing, it looks like we've got two targets to deal with, not one. My investigations reveal that Rob Paterson, who is Steve Tulloch's running mate for this election, is just as credible a candidate as Steve Tulloch. The Party see them as the Dream Team or the Dream Ticket for this election. Apparently there have never been two candidates of such calibre whose politics are so close to each other. So you see, the elimination of just one of them would probably have little effect on the expected course of events. To hit both men at the same time would mean finding a location where they are both likely to be present and that suggests an attack on the actual location. Yes Tom, explosives or possibly a bomb.'

'That's not the way we usually do things over here, Alex.'

'Precisely, but this is the way the IRA operates. What could be better? And you don't need to guess who'll get the publicity! Besides, it'll suit our candidate down to the ground. There's no reason why we can't repeat the Brighton affair at Blackpool. By the way, it would be useful if we could arrange some Labour anti-IRA publicity just prior to the event. It would make the response appear more authentic.'

'How do you intend shipping our candidate back over to the UK?'

'That's already taken care of. He'll be standing in as a co-pilot on one of our scheduled flights to London.'

'Of course,' said Tom thoughtfully. 'Atlantic Air has a regular flight to Heathrow. Good work, Alex. No one is going to be looking for an IRA man wearing an American civil airline uniform.'

'That's right, sir, and it makes shipping him out again that much easier.'

'Have you met the candidate yet?'

'No, no need. I've got his profile though. Gregg Donoghue sent me a copy. Besides, the fewer people he knows to be involved, the better. I've already been in touch with Gregg and Roy Stirling. We had a meeting a week ago. I've given them a report on the operation, together with a cramming programme for our candidate. I don't think I should discuss the fine details with you; the less you know the better. But I expect you'll get a full report from the British press after the event.'

'I like it, Alex. It sounds fine. You're doing a good job. Anything I can do for you just let me know.'

'Well there is something, sir. It's that anti-IRA publicity. If you have some influence with anyone in the British press, it could be real useful.'

'Leave it with me, son. It's time I called in a few favours from some friends of mine. I'm pretty sure it can be arranged.'

Meanwhile Roy Stirling and Gregg Donoghue had been briefing Kevin McGuire on the operation and his new identity at the safe house just outside New York. Kevin was becoming more and more sceptical about the operation the more he heard about it, and was starting to show signs of stress.

'What! A co-pilot on a plane. You guys are mad, you've gotta be kiddin'. I get airsick every time I step on a plane, never mind sittin' in a cockpit, and what if something goes wrong during the flight? There's no way I could fly the bloody thing.'

'Look, Kevin,' said Gregg. 'Nothin's gonna go wrong. There's gonna be two pilots on board already, one of whom is acting as a navigator.'

'Why can't I just go as a steward or something?' came back Kevin.

'No way! We need you to keep a low profile. We can't have you wandering up and down the aisles simply because we don't want you exposed to the passengers. The less people who see you the better it will be. Listen. We're gonna get some training film and some manuals for you to look at, so that by the time you get on board, you'll be fully acquainted with airline flight deck procedures.'

'Hey, do we really have to go that far?' jumped in Kevin impatiently.

'Yes we do!' barked Roy as he grabbed Kevin by the collar, pulling him out of his chair until his face was no more than an inch from his own. 'As far as the rest of the crew are concerned, you're gonna be one bona fide co-pilot. But I'm getting just a bit pissed off with your objections anyway. Maybe you ain't up to the job Paddy. Maybe you're all mouth! How about we just ship you home again to good old Ireland where guys like you seem to be in big demand, you stooly bastard!'

'All right, OK, I get the picture,' said McGuire, dangling from Stirling's fist. 'I'm sorry. I was just gettin' a bit tetchy being cooped up in this house all the time. When am I going to get out of here before I start talkin' to the furniture? At least get me a woman or something. It's driving me up the wall.'

'Take it easy, Kevin. Relax,' said Gregg. 'Leave it with me. I'll see what I can do. OK Roy, let's go, give the guy a break. We don't want Kevin to think we're unfriendly now do we. Bye, Kev! See you in a couple of days. Who knows, if you're really good, I might have a prezzy for you. Wait and see.'

Kevin was really angry. He was particularly angry with Roy Stirling who seemed to enjoy getting a bit physical. Although it may well have been a Mutt and Jeff act, with Donoghue playing the good guy. Whatever, Kevin was getting just a bit cheesed off by this time. He figured that they didn't have to play it that way anyhow. He would have been more cooperative had they put up a straightforward proposition instead of all this blackmail and bullying.

He began to wonder if they had any intention of bringing him back, let alone bringing him back alive. They may represent a government agency, thought Kevin, but that needn't stop them from getting rid of a potential embarrassment, especially when the man in question was already on the run. The more he thought about it, the more convinced he became of their potential treachery.

Kevin decided that it was time he took out a little insurance, and scanned the room looking for pen and paper. Instead, he found a stereo cassette recorder. He quickly raked around to see if there were any tapes lying about. Minutes later, he was sitting down recording everything he knew about the operation, including the names of the participants in the plot. Kevin's next move was to arrange somehow for the tape to be posted to his brother in Ireland, as insurance should anything happen to him.

5

When Gregg Donoghue returned to Washington, his intention was to meet up with Kathy Conners, but he was having some difficulty tracing her. The agency claimed that she was out with a very important client that very evening, but she had told Gregg that she never worked on a Sunday. It was her way of keeping faith with her religion, and Gregg remembered teasing her about it. He was starting to get a bit suspicious and concerned, so he decided to phone Linda Johnstone in an effort to track her down.

'Hi! Linda, Gregg here. How are you?'

'Oh! Hello Gregg, great to hear from you. I'm fine, how are you?'

'I just arrived in Washington this evening. I'm trying to get hold of Kathy. Have you seen her lately?'

'Why yes,' said Linda. 'Kathy and I went out for a meal just last week. Tuesday I think it was. Yes, Tuesday. She had arranged to meet me today. We were going to take in a film, but she called this afternoon and cancelled.'

'Oh,' said Gregg hopefully. 'Did she say where she was going?'

'No, not exactly. She just said something had cropped up that she had to attend to. If it's any help, she has arranged to meet me on Tuesday.'

'No, that's OK, Linda. I'll try her place again tomorrow. Thanks for your help. I'll see you later.'

Meanwhile, Kathy had indeed been out with an important client. It was Gerry Austin, the Senator from Massachusetts. Senator Austin had recently been in a car accident on his way to Washington. Fortunately for the Senator, there was little physical damage other than a deep leg wound which caused the loss of a considerable amount of blood. By the time he arrived at the hospital, Gerry was greatly in need of a blood transfusion. This was to be the start of a sequence of events that would lead to terrifying consequences for the unsuspecting participants in the drama that was to follow.

Prior to the Senator's accident, there had been a major freeway pile-up involving many cars. Consequently, a great number of people had been taken to this particular hospital, and its blood bank had been considerably depleted. Unfortunately for Gerry, whose blood group was type O, one of the most common blood groups, this particular type had been exhausted. The Senator's aide who was travelling with him decided to exercise some initiative and recruited a volunteer from the hospital lobby. He was a young friendly teenager who happened to have the same blood group. This overenthusiastic aide, anxious and eager to get a quick supply of blood for his Senator, had taken it upon himself to engage the teenager instead of waiting for the hospital staff who were trying to organise a special delivery of blood from another hospital. The Senator agreed because he was equally anxious to have his treatment completed as quickly and as discreetly as possible.

After the blood transfusion, when the Senator was on the road to recovery, he confided in his aide that he was a bit concerned that the press might find out about his hospitalisation. This would mean his wife finding out and wanting to join him, a prospect which he didn't exactly relish.

'Heck!' he said. 'The only break I get from my wife is when I travel to Washington. The last thing I want is her following me down here. See if you can book me into a hotel for the night. I want out of here before the scavengers arrive.'

'But the doctor said...' the concerned aide started to say.

'I don't care what the doctor said,' replied the agitated Senator. 'My goodness man, it's only a minor leg wound. I've had a lot worse happen to me in my time, especially during the war when there was nobody to fuss and mollycoddle me. I know what I'm doing, so get me a room and book me in under another name. I don't want these vultures tracking me down for an interview.'

Gerry Austin was booked into a small hotel on the outskirts of Washington and the next call his aide made that night was to the Mayfair Agency, asking specifically for Kathy Conners.

'Yes, I know she doesn't usually work on a Sunday. My client usually sees her on a Saturday when he's in Washington, but he got held up this trip. He's a very wealthy man, you know, and is prepared to compensate your agency for any inconvenience. No, I'm afraid he wouldn't like to meet one of your other girls. He insists on Kathy. OK, we'll wait.'

The agency managed to locate Kathy that afternoon and persuaded her to make a one-off exception. So Kathy agreed to meet the Senator later that evening. When she arrived at the hotel, she was surprised to see Gerry Austin in bandages halfway up his thigh.

'My word, Senator, what have you been up to?'

'Oh, just a little accident on my way here, but no way was I gonna let it stop me from seeing you.'

'Why, you're nothin' but an old flatterer. Now tell me all about it. What happened?'

'Oh that's a long story, babe, but I'm sure we can think of better things to do than talk about my little ole accident now, can't we.'

Kathy spent that night with Gerry Austin. She didn't like stopping over with clients but the Senator was a good customer and he paid well.

It was Monday afternoon before Gregg finally managed to get in touch with Kathy, and he arranged to take her out that evening for a meal at the Sheraton. He wanted Kathy to go to New York with him to spend a couple of nights with Kevin McGuire. He considered that it was extremely important to keep McGuire happy and in a proper frame of mind for the task that was to follow. Besides, Kathy with her Irish background might just be the ideal partner to help him unwind.

Gregg wasn't too sure how Kathy would react to his proposition.

He expected her to bitch a bit at the beginning, but he figured she would come round in the end.

'You've gotta nerve,' said Kathy angrily. 'I haven't seen you for six weeks and you've got the cheek to ask that kind of favour from me!'

'Look, Kath. We're talkin' big bucks here. There's gonna be a big bonus in it for you. Believe me, you'll be well rewarded. Come on, Kath. Just this one time, I promise you won't regret it.'

'Who is this guy anyway?' asked Kathy. 'And what's so special about him?'

'He's one of your countrymen and we're keeping him in protective custody for a while. I'm afraid that's all I can tell you.'

'All right, I'm gonna do this one favour for you but don't you ever ask a favour of me again, got it? And another thing, if this guy turns out to be some kind of weirdo, then you can forget it. How long did you say I've got to spend with him?'

'Well, I figure a couple of days should do it, but if there's a hold-up somewhere along the line, then I would like you to stay on a bit longer.'

'How much will I be gettin' for this favour?' snapped Kathy.

'Give us a break. This is a very good business deal for you.'

'How much?' asked Kathy impatiently.

'Seven hundred fifty bucks a day and we'll cover all your expenses.'

'Make it a thousand plus expenses and you've gotta deal,' said Kathy.

'All right Kath. You're on,' said Gregg. 'Let's shake on it.'

Gregg suggested to Kath that she should take a couple of days to sort out her affairs in Washington, and told her to be discreet about her absence. He didn't want anyone knowing where she was going, not even to what city. They arranged to meet on Thursday at the airport. Gregg decided not to hang around too long, just in case Kathy should change her mind. He could see she was in a foul mood, so he said his goodbyes and left.

Kathy certainly was in a foul mood. She was furious. Secretly, she had nursed the idea that she and Gregg had an ongoing relationship that might one day lead to something. But this proposition made it plain to see that he had had no such ideas. OK Kath, she said to herself, snap out of it, this is business. You said you were not going to get involved with any of your clients, and that's all Gregg is, he's just another client, certainly from now on.

Kathy and Gregg arrived in New York on the Thursday evening. Gregg, not wanting to waste time, had briefed her on the plane. He gave her some minor details about McGuire and again cautioned her about being discreet.

As they were walking towards the terminal, Gregg said, 'Oh, by the way, I forgot to tell you that we'll be travelling to the location in an enclosed van, so don't be alarmed. It's just a precaution. There's no way we can take a chance on his location being discovered by the wrong people.'

'You're kidding,' said Kath. 'Do you people really behave like this?' she added mockingly. 'I mean all this cloak and dagger stuff! I thought this sort of thing only happened in cheap detective stories.'

Kathy was letting off steam. Her sarcasm was her way of punishing Gregg for using her this way. Gregg didn't take the bait. He knew what she was up to, and he didn't intend giving her any more ammunition.

They were picked up at the airport by Roy Stirling who was driving the van. Gregg didn't introduce her to Roy. He figured that it wasn't in her interest to know who he was, so they travelled in silence for the rest of the journey.

It wasn't until they arrived at their destination that Gregg made his final comment. 'Remember what I said, Kath. All I want you to do is keep him sweet for two or three days. You know what I mean. Help him unwind, and don't worry, it won't take long. You'll be back in Washington before you know it.'

Meanwhile, Kevin had been getting extremely agitated during Gregg's absence. For one thing, Gregg had intimated that he'd be back in a couple of days and this was four days later. Or was it five? Kevin was losing track of time and getting very edgy. He still hadn't been allowed further than the bottom of the driveway, and Roy Stirling hadn't made things any easier either. He had got a bit rough in Gregg's absence and insisted that Kevin should spend all day learning the flight deck procedures manual. Kevin was practically at breaking point by the time Gregg arrived with Kathy.

'Hey, how you doing, Kev?' shouted Gregg. 'Just you wait and see what I've got for you. Looky here now,' he said as he gently pulled Kath into the room. 'This is Kathy and she'll be your companion for a couple of days, so I hope you two will get on together.'

Kathy took a long lingering look at McGuire, and thought to herself that this poor guy was in one hell of a mess. By this time, Kevin's eyes had disappeared somewhere into the back of his head. He had bruises on both sides of his face and his clothes looked as if they hadn't been changed for a month. Boy have I got my work cut out, she thought.

'OK,' said Gregg. 'I'll leave you two guys to get acquainted. See you later.' He and Roy then left them together.

6

Back in Washington, Alex Stenton received an urgent coded communication from his UK contacts. After decoding, it read as follows:

> Steve Tulloch and Rob Paterson, in anticipation of a June election, are planning to open their campaign in Edinburgh two weeks tomorrow. Edinburgh party members, who are students of the Edinburgh University, have arranged for the election campaign to coincide with the local Students' Charity Parade. The Edinburgh Students Union has recently taken on a pinkish hue due to recent cuts in student grants. This has created a fertile breeding ground for leftist students to become prominent campaigners against present government policies. The Edinburgh Students Union, who organise an annual Charity March through the streets of Edinburgh, have invited Steve Tulloch and Rob Paterson to lead the Students' Charity Parade. This new development may present a golden opportunity for a more rewarding and fertile reception for our people. Suggest that you join me for further investigation, as this may prove to be a more favourable environment for a less volatile reception.

Alex Stenton had a lot of faith in his UK connections, and was sure that they wouldn't send such a message unless convinced that a new strategy was warranted. Besides, he wasn't 100 per cent happy about his current programme, especially since it involved explosives. There tended to be too many imponderables, such as the failure of the device to explode when it should, or it being discovered by the authorities who were getting more and more efficient at detecting such things. Alex decided to explore this new development further, and had his secretary book him on the first available flight for Scotland.

'I'm afraid you may have to go via London, sir, and take a connection from there to Edinburgh.'

'Is that a company flight, Alice?'

'Oh yes, sir. Would you like me to try one of the other lines?'

'No, that's OK,' said Alex. 'Are we talking Washington – New York – London and then Edinburgh?'

'Yes. That's right sir, but you may get a more direct flight elsewhere.'

'No. Fine, leave it at that. I'll call in at our London office while I'm there.'

Alex had never been to Edinburgh before, even when he was working with the SAS. Most of his field training took place further north, in the Highland region, when they were flown in directly by helicopter. Still, he was looking forward to seeing the UK again. It had been nine years since he left. He thought that it would be good to hear an English accent again, and then he remembered. Oh no! I better watch that, the Jocks get a bit humpy if you refer to them as English, and that won't do if I'm looking for their cooperation.

Alex arrived at Edinburgh Turnhouse Airport on a Friday morning. It was a beautiful day with a clear blue sky. He was half expecting to be feeling the cold by now, but knew this was always a popular misconception about Scotland. The English tended to think of Scotland as being further north that it really was, but in fact Edinburgh is only 400 miles north of London and by American standards that's a relatively short distance and doesn't necessarily warrant a weather shift.

Alex was met at the airport by Dave Simpson who ran E&F Securities, a Glasgow-based agency that was owned indirectly, through a series of other companies, by CLC Industries. E&F Securities traded in information. Its function was to identify and list known communists, militant unionists and political activists in general. It boasted 300,000 names on file, and local industries such as the larger electronic companies used its facilities for screening their employees.

Dave was the man who had sent Alex the report of the new development.

'Good to meet you, sir. Did you have a good flight?'

'The flight was fine. I'm sure relieved to find some sunshine though. It was raining real heavy when I left New York and London was overcast with black clouds yesterday.'

'I've booked you in at the Clifton Hotel, sir. It's quite central but discreet. Will you require a rest before you start?'

'No, we may have wasted enough time already. I want to start right away, as soon as you get me booked into the hotel. Have you got your preliminary report with you?'

'Yes, I have it with me.'

'Good, I'll look it over in the car.'

Dave's report proved extremely interesting reading. Apparently the Charity Parade was planned in such a way as to cover the more prominent streets of the city, and there was a limited window in time given for it, so optimum coverage of the city was essential. Saturday was considered to be the day when the city was most congested with people. So, this was the day chosen for parades. The local police had introduced a rule stipulating that the Charity Parade should be completed by one o'clock and the people dispersed by two. This was to minimise inconvenience to city traffic. To make sure that these rules were adhered to, the police, together with the organisers, had arranged that the parade should finish at Parliament Square in the High Street at one o'clock. This ensured that Princes Street, the most prominent and busiest street in the city, would be cleared by then. To underline this rule, it was also agreed that the one o'clock gun should mark the end of the parade. This, reasoned the police, gave the crowds one hour to disperse, so that by two o'clock the city would be returned to some semblance of normality. The report went on to say:

The one o'clock gun is an old Edinburgh tradition and time mark that takes place each day. One of the cannons in the castle is fired at precisely one o'clock every day. This ritual can be utilised to our advantage, as the tremendous noise of the cannon can be used as a cover for the rifle shots fired by our candidate. A further advantage of this location is that we not only know where the parade will finish, but also at exactly what time it will finish. In other words, we know precisely where our targets will be at a particular point in time. All that remains is to locate an appropriate vantage point for our candidate in or around the area in question.

Two days ago I surveyed the area and discovered an ideal vantage point. At the very top of the High Street, close to the gates of the castle, there is a tower situated at the top of a building which has been used for over 100 years as a Camera Obscura. The implications of this are extremely advantageous to our requirements. This tower looks directly down the High Street, and progress of the whole parade can be observed under cover, using the Camera Obscura. It is an exceptionally well-placed observation point and one that by its very nature was designed to observe the major areas of our concern. Indeed under ideal conditions all that our candidate would have to do would be to enter the Camera Obscura at the appropriate time and monitor a parade, led by his targets, that was destined to finish not more than 300 or 400 yards from his concealed position. A further advantage is its proximity to the city's railway station, the Waverley. This is no more than half a mile from the tower, a distance which could be covered in eight minutes on a pushbike moving at an inconspicuous rate. Such a vehicle could be concealed at the base of the tower to the rear of the building. This drops down to a much lower level than the High Street.

I have checked the train timetables, and there is a train leaving for Glasgow 1.10 pm every Saturday. It would be quite feasible for our candidate to catch this train. It would then be a simple matter for him to take a regular flight from Glasgow to London.

I have considered some details that might further facilitate his escape. A rope might be put to our advantage in this situation, as it could be used to speed up his escape from the tower. If he was to lower himself down from the rear of the tower to ground level, which happens to be an unused garden leading on to Ramsay Place, he could have quicker access to a bicycle which had already been concealed there for him. This would give him adequate time to vacate the area and rendezvous with the train.

These are all the positive advantages of this location, but there are some disadvantages that require further exploration before we could proceed. For example, the Camera Obscura is a very popular tourist attraction in the city and it would be of particular interest to tourists during a parade in the area. We would have to find a way of putting it temporarily out of commission, at least as far as the tourists are concerned. Secondly, it will not have escaped the notice of the local constabulary that it presents itself as a vantage point for unwelcome visitors, especially during a parade led by such distinguished politicians. These are going to be difficult obstacles to overcome, but I suspect that they are not insurmountable.

Alex was astonished at the amount of work that Dave had done in so little time, and how thorough he had been. This looks like an excellent plan, he thought to himself. We would be fools to pass up this opportunity.

When they arrived at the hotel, Alex wasted no time before congratulating Dave on his report. 'This is what I call a good brief. In fact, it's gotta be one of the best I've ever seen.'

'Well thank you, sir,' responded Dave modestly. 'When I first heard on the grapevine that Tulloch and Paterson were coming to Edinburgh, I thought it wouldn't do any harm to investigate the lie of the land. I was quite surprised myself when I saw how well things were fitting together.'

'Have you had any more thoughts on overcoming the obstacles in your report?' asked Alex.

'I'm afraid not, sir. There just hasn't been enough time.'

'Well,' said Alex gleefully, 'from now on, you and I are gonna make time. First thing tomorrow, I want you to take me to this Camera Obscura so I can see for myself what the problems might be and how we're gonna solve them. When I was in the service, my business was puttin' things out of commission.'

'Yes, that could be very useful, but we'll be requiring this facility later ourselves,' said Dave cheekily.

'I'm well aware of that, Dave,' said Stenton firmly, in an attempt to put Simpson back in his place.

'I'm sorry, sir. I didn't mean any offence. Honestly.'

'That's OK, forget it. I better get word back to the States to warn them that there might be a change in the programme. I'll make out a message tonight and you can get your own people to code it and send on to Head Office in Washington. Can you do that?'

'Oh yes, we can arrange that.'

Back in Washington, Kevin and Kathy were doing a bit of soul-searching and reminiscing about Ireland. Kathy had done her job well. Kevin had become almost a different man overnight. For a start, he was much cleaner, and she had had one of the guards arrange to get him some new clothes. For Kevin's part, he was just so relieved to find someone he felt that he could talk to; and who better than a girl from back home.

Kevin told Kath about his brother, and how they had always been at loggerheads with each other, a relationship that their mother had always found heartbreaking. She used to say that if she hadn't given birth to them herself, she would never have believed that they were members of the same family. But despite their differences, Kevin loved his brother Kieran. He was a real steady guy who seemed to know exactly what he wanted out of life and he always stuck to his religious beliefs.

'How are you on the religious side, Kath? Do you still believe?'

'Why of course I do! What kind of a fool question is that to ask now? And one of these days, I'll be gettin' right back to doing something about it. Just you wait and see,' she said emphatically. 'I didn't start out in America doing this sort of work, you know. I was married when I first came over here. Well, I say here, but it was Canada where I started. Boy, did I have dreams then. I was gonna have at least four children, one of each.'

'One of each?' said Kevin mockingly, with a big grin on his face.

'Why sure,' said Kath. 'I wanted a boy and a girl with red hair like mine, and a boy and a girl with black hair like their father's and we were all going to go to Mass every Sunday.'

'Well what happened?' asked Kevin impatiently.

'Oh, the rest is oh so boring,' said Kath. 'Let's talk about your brother again. He sounds like a real nice guy.'

Kath was trying hard to change the subject as she was already getting flashbacks of the more unsavoury aspects of her marriage, which is why she had tried to avoid discussing that aspect of her life.

During this discussion, it suddenly occurred to Kevin that Kathy was the ideal person to look after his tape for him. He could give her instructions to post it off to Ireland if she didn't hear from him by a certain date.

7

On the third of June, Alex Stenton returned to Washington where he had arranged to meet Tom Casey, Gregg Donoghue and Roy Stirling at Head Office. Alex was last to arrive because his New York flight was delayed due to bad weather. By the time he got there, Tom was showing signs of concern.

'Ah Alex, I see you made it then,' said Tom displaying his impatience.

'Yes, I'm sorry to keep you waiting, but I was held up at the airport.'

'OK. Sit down and tell us what this is all about. As you can see, we got your message, but it didn't tell us very much other than advising us to suspend operations.'

'Yes. There's been a new development in the UK which I think warrants further investigation. Personally I believe it's a golden opportunity that we can't afford to ignore.'

'Don't tell me you're gonna change your plans this late in the day?'

'That's exactly what I'm suggesting we should do, sir. But don't worry, we've got all the details worked out. If you can just hold fire until you hear my report, I'm sure you'll agree.'

Alex spent the next two hours explaining the advantages of the new situation and gave an in-depth report of the new arrangements that he and Dave Simpson had prepared in Edinburgh. They were all very much impressed, especially Tom, who thought it was certainly imaginative, even ingenious. Alex's only concern now was how Kevin McGuire would respond.

'Well, Gregg, you're the one who knows our man best by now. How is he shaping up? Do you think he can handle this new approach?'

'I'm sure he can,' said Gregg. 'As a matter of fact, I think he would prefer using a rifle to setting up explosives.'

'Good, then our only problem now is time. We've got seven days to get organised. How soon can you get our man over there?'

'Oh, that shouldn't be a problem since he's going by the company airline and they have a scheduled flight every day. All you have to do is fix the date and we'll do the rest.'

'OK,' said Alex. 'We don't want him over there too early in case he gets recognised. By the way, have you done anything about his appearance?'

'Yes, we've taken care of that. We aged him a little, gave him some snow on top and a new make-up job. With that and his new rig-out, he looks more American than I do.'

'Good. OK, here's what we do. I want him in Edinburgh four days before the Parade. That should be long enough for him to get acquainted with the lay out. Dave Simpson will take care of him as soon as he arrives. He's a good man, and very reliable. Since most of this operation was planned by him, it will be in his interest to see that it runs smoothly.'

'What about getting him out again?' Tom interjected.

'That's taken care of. I've arranged for one of my men to meet him at Glasgow Airport and fly down with him to London. I figured that anyone travelling on his own after the main event will be treated with suspicion. Once there, we can revert back to the original plan when he joins one of our own aircraft as a crew member. If there are no more questions, sir, I'd like to get this thing moving right away.'

Kevin McGuire wasn't too pleased about the last-minute changes but he was itching to get it over with so he didn't make much of a fuss. Besides, the new set-up certainly had a lot going for it, and he figured that he had a better chance of getting out. Kevin was feeling pretty good by this time: Kathy had spent the best part of four days with him and had agreed to see him again when he returned.

Kevin arrived at Heathrow the following Wednesday without

arousing any suspicion regarding his real identity. It hadn't been too difficult modifying his Irish accent to make it sound American, as the Irish are often mistaken for Americans when travelling abroad. Clearing customs was a breeze. Of course his US civil airline uniform had a lot to do with that. After customs Kevin made his way directly to the men's room where he quickly changed into civilian clothes. From there, he headed straight over to Terminal One to catch the next shuttle to Edinburgh. Kevin was already feeling squeamish from the flight over but had managed to keep it under control. He was not looking forward to another flight so soon after the first but knew that he had no option because the shuttle timing had been designed to connect with the New York flight to accommodate passengers travelling to Scotland.

Kevin was on the shuttle and back in the air within the hour. By this time his queasiness was catching up on him and he felt the blood drain from his face as his stomach began to churn. He decided to pop a couple of pills and tried to sleep through an hour of the journey. Fortunately for him it was only an hour and 20 minutes flying time to Edinburgh, although to Kevin it seemed an eternity.

Kevin was met at Turnhouse airport by Dave Simpson whom he managed to identify from a photograph given to him by Alex Stenton. Dave drove him straight to the Sheraton, one of the newest and most prestigious hotels in the city. Dave had figured that a high profile can often be a more effective disguise than a low profile. After all, the guy you see swanning around the hotel in an expensive lounge suit is not the sort of person you expect to find on a roof top with a rifle.

Dave allowed Kevin to rest for a few hours in his hotel room until nightfall as this would be the best time for Kevin to have his first look round the area. It also meant that he could go to bed that evening with a picture in his mind of the target area.

Nine o'clock that night Kevin found himself wandering up the Royal Mile, with Dave pointing out the more relevant aspects of the district. They even stopped for a drink in one of the local pubs.

The city was absolutely teeming with tourists, and the local bars were having a field day. Dave pointed out the Camera Obscura to Kevin in passing but they didn't linger as it was not the sort of place that you could hang around inconspicuously at that time of night. They then went round the back of the tower and down Ramsay Place, allowing Kevin to see the building from a different angle. From there they walked straight down and along Market Street to the Waverley Station with Dave explaining the significance of the route and giving him various landmarks. They stopped for a while at the station restaurant where they had coffee and Dave pointed out the platform that Kevin would be making for after the event.

By then it was time to get a taxi back to the hotel, where Kevin spent a few minutes studying photographs of his targets. He then went to bed and tried to recapture in his mind the route that he had walked that day. But he was very tired. It had been an extremely busy and exhausting day for him so it didn't take long before he fell fast asleep.

The next morning when Kevin awoke he discovered some brochures and booklets that had been left on his desk by Dave. He picked them up and, scanning through them, discovered that it was all information relating to the Royal Mile and the Camera Obscura. As the building housing the Camera Obscura was a historical one there were many pictures of it from almost every angle. There was even an aerial view which Kevin thought might be useful. Kevin took the brochures to breakfast with him so that he could browse over them while he was eating. After all, the Camera Obscura was a popular tourist attraction and it would look quite natural for him to be seen studying such material.

Dave met Kevin in the hotel reception at ten o'clock that morning as arranged and they both set off once more for the High Street. This time they walked all the way from the hotel through Princes Street, down to the Waverley and up the High Street towards the Camera Obscura. It was a fabulous day with brilliant sunshine. Kevin and Dave had walked the major part of the parade route in less than an hour. This time they bought tickets and went into the Camera Obscura.

Kevin was quite fascinated by an exciting display of holograms in the anteroom leading to the stairs of the tower. There were three flights of stairs to the tower and on each landing was a photographic display, including one on pinhole photography. At the top of the stairway there was a roof-top terrace, where tourists could take pictures of the magnificent view while waiting their turn to enter the Camera Obscura. This room was situated at the top of a separate stairway and, although it was only a very small room, surprisingly it could hold about 15 to 20 people at a time.

Kevin and Dave deliberately held back from entering with the first group. This gave them time to hover around the terrace, as it was from here that the shooting was to take place. Dave knew that Kevin would want to inspect every minute aspect of the area. Kevin spent some of this time taking pictures looking down the Royal Mile, covering the vicinity where the targets were expected to be. By the time the first group returned from the Camera Obscura room, Kevin was starting to feel perfectly at home on the terrace.

Finally the doors swung open and the first party began to leave the room. Dave and Kevin joined the second party. The second tour guide manoeuvred himself into position and then beckoned the next group to follow. When, finally, everybody had entered the Camera Obscura, the doors were closed and every speck of light was blotted out. Kevin had never experienced such total darkness before. The tour guide dramatically removed a black cover from the top of the display table and light flooded into the room, revealing a magnificent colour spectacle. The only source of light allowed to enter the room was directed through a series of prisms and lenses by means of a device that could only be described as a periscope.

This light was ultimately emitted onto a display table, exposing a brilliant panoramic view of the west side of the city. By a simple manual turning of the lens casing the guide was able to pan through 360 degrees, exposing vast scenic views of the city. While conducting this manoeuvre the tour guide was giving a short lecture on the historical significance of each part of the city viewed. It was quite a fascinating experience for Kevin, who had never seen anything quite like it before.

Once the tour was over, Kevin and Dave left the building. Dave decided to take Kevin down the back route again by way of Ramsay Place. This was to give him another look at the rear of the building, but this time in daylight. Today, he drew Kevin's attention to the unkempt green area at the back of the tower building that was basically a piece of waste ground. Although it was walled in, access was by means of a large iron gate that was quite scalable. This was to be the escape route, using a rope dropped from the top of the tower.

After a quick reconnaissance they again walked along Market Street for a daylight view of the rest of the escape route. When they got to the station Kevin decided that he wanted to walk the rest of the way on his own. He told Dave that he wanted to get used to finding his own way around. The truth was that he needed some breathing space and he was finding it difficult to relax with Dave always being around giving him instructions. Dave agreed to give him some time on his own and said he would meet him at his hotel at six o'clock that evening.

Kevin was quite surprised that Dave took his request so well. He had thought that Dave was under orders to chaperone him throughout the whole exercise. Dave had warned him not to spend too much time on the streets just in case a policeman should recognise him. Nevertheless, Kevin decided it was time he did some sightseeing on his own. After all, Edinburgh was a fascinating city, rich in culture and steeped in history.

He started up towards Princes Street and worked his way along this well-known historic mile. Looking beyond the Floral Clock, Kevin caught sight of the stunning architecture of Ramsay Gardens. Standing in stark contrast to the grey slate rooftops of the surrounding area is a cluster of beautiful, tall, white-walled buildings, capped with steeply sloping red roofs. The windows of these five-storey structures are trimmed with red bricks, giving an almost Disney World quality to the whole ensemble. The scene viewed from Princes Street is perhaps one of the more spectacular examples of Patrick Geddes' contribution to the Edinburgh skyline.

Kevin's next stop was at the Scot Monument, a grand Gothic structure towering 150 feet above Princes Street. Inside the structure is a spiral staircase that goes all the way to the top of the monument, with look-out balconies every 20 feet. For a small entrance fee tourists could climb this famous spiral stairway thus giving them a most splendid platform from which to view the city.

Kevin couldn't resist the temptation to investigate, so up he went. While he was up there it occurred to him that this would be an even better vantage point for the task that he was here to do, but he quickly realised that there would be major difficulties in retreating from the area.

Kevin spent the next hour wandering about the city. He even ventured into one of the local pubs, that he was surprised to find open at that time of day. Before recent changes in the licensing laws, Scotland had once had a reputation for having very strict regulations. Drinking houses were strictly controlled and bars were not allowed to sell alcohol between the hours of two and five o'clock. Kevin only had two drinks. He decided that it was prudent to keep a clear head for the duration of his stay in Edinburgh. When he had finished his drinks it occurred to him that he had indulged enough and it was time to get back to the hotel. He planned to have his meal first, then go back to his room to do some serious thinking about the operation that lay ahead.

At six o'clock that evening, Kevin's phone rang, waking him with a start. He had decided to take an afternoon nap and had slept through his meeting time with Dave Simpson. It was Dave phoning him from the hotel lobby, and he sounded just a little bit agitated.

'What the hell are you doing? I've been waiting in this lobby for half an hour already.'

'Oh, I'm sorry about that,' said Kevin in a rather sleepy voice. 'I guess I slept in. I'll be down in just a moment to pick you up.'

By the time Kevin got to the hotel lobby Dave Simpson was

drumming his fingers and looked as if he had spent all of his patience. He had a large, elongated package under his arm which he was holding very awkwardly, and was looking decidedly conspicuous. He was determined not to make a scene in the hotel lobby, but his extremely red complexion conveyed the limits of his control.

'What on earth have you got there?' said Kevin quite unthinkingly and still half-asleep.

'What the hell do you think it is?' replied Dave, losing all self-control, and by this time looking considerably embarrassed. 'I think we had better continue this conversation in your room,' he said, thinly disguising his temper.

'Oh!' said Kevin, suddenly coming to his senses and realising what the package must contain, 'Oh! Right. Yes, that's a good idea. Let's go up to my room.'

Dave exploded within seconds of arriving in Kevin's room. It was a controlled explosion, but one with an ever increasing intensity. It took 20 minutes before Kevin got him to calm down. Maybe it was the whisky, but Kevin probably prevented a major cardiac problem for Dave that evening, albeit that he was the one responsible for raising the man's blood pressure in the first place.

They spent a further hour getting Kevin acquainted with the rifle. It was a type he had never seen before and the Lord knows he had seen a lot of rifles during his time in the IRA. The rifle was a Belgian make and a beautiful machine. By the time the hour was up Kevin was quite familiar with the new weapon and was able to take it apart and reassemble it in less than three minutes.

It was now time to talk about getting access to the tower and out again after the main event. The plan was that, the evening before the parade, Dave Simpson would set off a small explosive device in the stairwell of the Camera Obscura building. This would not only restrict passageway to the upper terrace but would cause enough damage and commotion that the authorities would be forced to close the place down. After the explosion, Kevin's task was to get into the tower under cover of darkness. He would spend the remainder of the night there and by morning would be well placed to observe the parade when it started and perfectly poised to strike his targets at the appropriate time.

'OK, Kev. It's time to go over the programme and see if there's anything we've missed. First of all, have you got all your equipment ready?'

'Yes. It's all in that holdall apart from the actual weapon.'

'Yeh, but what have you actually got in the bag?' asked Dave.

'I've got a rope, a glass cutter, a two-way radio and a jemmy. OK?'

'All right, that's fine. Let's go over your time sequence starting from tomorrow morning.'

Dave and Kevin spent the better part of four hours going over every conceivable aspect of the project. Dave was determined to make sure that he knew every move that Kevin would make. He wanted to be in a position to know precisely where he would be every moment over the next two days. It was almost midnight before they had exhausted all the possibilities they could think of and Dave decided to leave and let Kevin get some sleep.

The next morning was Friday, the day before the parade. Kevin was up bright and early. He had a quick wash to take the sleep out of his eyes then went straight down to the gym for a 30-minute training session. He wanted to make sure that he was going to be mentally and physically alert that day. The gym was empty at that time of the morning so he was able to get through his routine without interruption. He managed to work up a good sweat and was feeling really fit by the time he left the gym. All that remained now was a shower and some breakfast. Then he would be ready to make a final tour of the tower block.

This time Kevin wanted to pay particular attention to the windows, as that was to be his means of entry. Dave had assured him, in no uncertain terms, that there was no alarm system, for he had checked himself. He could still hear Dave's assurances ringing in his ears. 'Yes, I know it's a popular tourist attraction, but believe me, there's nothing in there worth stealing, so it doesn't warrant the cost of an expensive alarm system.' Kevin had built up a lot of trust in Dave

Simpson by this time, and had been very impressed by his meticulous efficiency. Dave had got him tuned up for this job and he was feeling good and ready to get started.

Kevin had long since come to terms with the idea that he was going to kill. There had been plenty of time to think about that in New York. OK, he had killed before, but that was because he had been cornered and it was either the policeman or himself. This time it was different. His unwitting victims were not threatening him, although there were others who were. As far as Kevin was concerned there was no room left for emotional considerations. He had been put in a vice and the only way out was to do this job and do it right.

Kevin spent 15 to 20 minutes in and around the tower block acting like an inquisitive tourist, but that was about all the time he could afford: any longer might well have attracted unwelcome attention. Fortunately for Kevin there was no need. His trip had not been in vain. As a matter of fact, it had been an exceedingly worthwhile exercise for he had noticed this time that the window he was interested in was open. This was excellent news as it meant that there would be fewer problems that night. Having seen all that he was interested in, Kevin made his way back to the hotel.

Dave joined Kevin for a meal at the hotel. He wanted an update on Kevin's progress and made his inquiry during lunch.

'Everything go all right this morning?'

'Sure did. As a matter of fact, it couldn't have worked out better. Getting into that place is gonna be a piece of cake.'

'That easy!' said Dave mockingly.

'Since you're so smug, when are you gonna play your part anyhow? If you ask me, you're sure cuttin' it fine.'

'Oh, no need to worry about me son, I'll hold up my end. Just you wait and see.

'Wait a minute!' said Kevin, as he suddenly downed his cutlery and looked at his watch thoughtfully. 'Any second now,' he said raising his finger to his forehead, 'Six, five, four, three, two, one.' At that very instant, a loud report was heard in the distance. 'And right on the button!' It was the one o'clock gun, and Kevin was making sure that his watch was synchronised to it.

'How did you get into this business anyway, Dave? You don't look like the sort of person who would be doing this kind of work. I had you figured for a retired colonel when I first set eyes on you. I bet you got army training though.'

'Yes, you're right about one thing, I am retired from the army, but I never made Colonel. I was with the security forces during the war. Part of my job was to filter out the Nazis and the Communists who tried to get into this country during and just after the war.'

'Catch any?' asked Kevin.

'Oh, we caught a few.'

'What did you do with them?'

'Most of them were sent back to Germany. Only the ones that had form were dealt with over here and some of them were later sent back for the Nuremberg Trials. But if I had had my way, I would have shot the lot of them. Scumbags, parasites, that's what they were. One lot were feedin' on the dead, stealin' gold teeth and anything else they could lay their thieving hands on, and the other lot were feedin' off the system and trying to convert the rest of us to their corrupt ways. I became quite good at identifying the bastards though.'

Dave had a distant look in his eyes. The words had obviously triggered off some bad memories. Kevin was quite surprised. He had found it hard in the past to get Dave to talk about anything other than the job at hand. That was one of the things that impressed him. Kevin realised that he had opened up a can of worms here and wasn't too keen on pursuing this line of discussion. He tried to get the conversation back onto a lighter note.

'So what did you do after the army?'

'Oh, well I started up my own security business. I figured that there were already a lot of commies in this country and it was my job to identify the scum,' said Dave with some venom. 'And when that Labour lot got into power after the war, all hell broke loose. That's when this country really went to the dogs.'

'What do you mean by that?'

'You know what I mean. They started to nationalise everything. They even gave power to the unions and these bastards have been running this country ever since.'

'So I guess you've got a particular axe to grind with this operation Dave, eh? I mean knocking off the Labour leadership is right up your street then, isn't it?'

'You bet your life it is,' said Dave, almost spitting it out.

Dave realised he had said too much already and decided that he didn't want to pursue this line of conversation any further. Anyway it was time to move and get ready to carry out his part of the operation. 'Well, some of us don't have time to sit around and gas all day. Some of us have work to do,' he said jokingly. 'You won't be seeing me after this. This is probably the last chance we'll have to socialise. However, I want to wish you luck. Keep your cool and everything will be all right. I'll be watching your every move until you get on that train, just in case you need me. Remember, I'm on the other end of that two-way radio. Any problems, talk to me, but save it strictly for emergencies. We don't want the police tuning in on our wavelength now do we?' Dave stood up and reached out his hand in a formal gesture.

Kevin grabbed hold of it, and shaking it firmly said, 'Thanks, Dave, for all your help. I want you to know that I really appreciate having you around on this operation. I couldn't think of a better guy for a back-up. If anything goes wrong with this operation, it certainly won't be your fault.'

That Friday afternoon the Camera Obscura was extremely busy with visitors. It had been a glorious day and it seemed that everybody was out taking advantage of the sunshine. Dave Simpson was one of these visitors. During the melée he was able to secrete a small explosive device in the stairwell of the tower, which could be detonated by remote control. His intention was to retreat to a safe distance within sight of the building and then trigger off the mechanism just after closing time at five o'clock, thus making sure that no one would be injured by the explosion. The last thing he needed was a murder investigation on his hands at this stage. All he wanted was to create enough disturbance to close the place down for a couple of days.

When five o'clock arrived there was one hell of a bang inside the tower block. People came running from all over the place. Sirens sounded and it wasn't long before both the police and the fire brigade arrived on the scene. Fortunately for all concerned there was no fire, and it didn't take long for the police to get things under control. Eventually they managed to disperse the crowds that had gathered around the building.

After a somewhat lengthy investigation, taking the better part of two hours, the building was made secure and the police and tour officials left the premises. Later, a sign was erected, indicating that the premises would be closed until further notice. This was exactly what Dave had anticipated. It couldn't have worked out better. At 7.30 that evening Dave phoned Kevin's number giving the prearranged signal indicating that it was all clear to move on to the next stage of the operation.

Immediately after the call Kevin organised a taxi to take him to Waverley Station. It took him half an hour to pack his luggage, get changed and check out of the hotel. At approximately 8.15 pm, Kevin arrived at Waverley where he booked in his luggage for the next day's 1.30 train for Glasgow. Kevin's next stop was the ABC cinema where he spent the next two hours watching a film while he waited for nightfall.

Meanwhile, Dave was spending his time checking on Steve Tulloch and Rob Paterson, making sure that they had arrived on schedule. He also sent a signal to the States telling Alex Stenton that they were in a ready position. This was a contingency plan that Alex had insisted upon, providing him with a chance to abort the operation should it be necessary.

In the ABC cinema, Kevin was having great difficulty concentrating on the film. Up until now, he had been kept pretty busy familiarising himself with his new environment and preparing for the task at hand, but the sheer enormity of what lay before him was starting to filter through. His thoughts were becoming more and more preoccupied with the imminence of the cold-blooded murder he was about to perpetrate. He broke into a cold sweat, and for a while his whole body trembled uncontrollably. He tried desperately to contain the turmoil that was taking place inside him.

Kevin was displaying symptoms of delayed shock. His physical reaction was a classic response to the mental conflict he was beginning to experience. He was thankful that he was in the darkness of the cinema. He tried harder to concentrate on the film but this only made matters worse as he was watching a comedy. A bloody comedy, he thought to himself, how the hell can I laugh with all this going on? He tried to control his trembling by taking long, deep breaths and after a few minutes of this the shaking began to subside, allowing him at least some temporary respite.

If this happens to me when I'm up in that bloody tower, I'm done for, well and truly done for, he thought. Kevin realised that the trembling was starting up again and steadily getting worse. He was almost in a state of panic by this time but was quick to realise that it was self-induced. He again tried to control his breathing and this time his thinking as well. I must concentrate on something else. Keep my mind off the job. Look at the film and keep taking deep breaths. Eventually the shaking subsided again and he felt that this time it was under control. He could feel the warmth rushing through his body as he gradually began to relax.

Kevin looked at his watch. It was just after eleven. Another half hour and I'm on my way, but I must use this time to get a grip on myself. Stay cool, Dave said. I'm glad he's not around to see this. By sheer determination, he was able to bring his mental and body processes under control and even managed to take in a little of the film.

At 11.30 pm the film ended and Kevin left the cinema and made his way on foot to the High Street. On his way to the tower block he was trying to console himself by thinking that all he really needed was some sleep, and he would get this in the Camera Obscura.

When he eventually arrived at the tower he found the place

deserted. There was not a soul to be seen in the area. He found the climb up onto the window ledge an easy one and gaining access through the second level window was no major obstacle either. This took him well above the damaged area of the staircase. Once inside it was a simple matter to climb the rest of the stairway and out onto the terrace. All that remained now was to jemmy open the doors to the actual Camera Obscura. As it was an old mortise lock, this too presented no major problem. It was now midnight and Kevin had achieved his first major objective. He was feeling very pleased with himself as it had taken him less than 15 minutes to gain entry.

The adrenalin that he generated had stimulated Kevin considerably and he was on quite a high by the time he reached the interior of the observation room. This proved to be a problem as he found his ability to sleep was now impaired. All things considered, this was by far a much easier problem to deal with than the one he had had in the cinema. He decided to do exercises in an attempt to relax and it wasn't long before this succeeded. Kevin looked at his watch again. It was now 1.15 am, time to signal Dave and let him know that he was now in a ready position. He took out his two-way radio and made the signal. It was just one word 'Amber', and he repeated it once more, 'Amber'. He then switched over to Receive and immediately got the reply, 'Amber acknowledged'.

Unknown to Kevin, Dave Simpson had watched him make his entry into the tower. He had wanted to be on hand should anything go wrong, but this was as far as he could go. This time it was up to Kevin. Now he was on his own. Having satisfied himself that Kevin was now safely in place, he decided to leave the area. He knew that Kevin would try and get some sleep now and it was time he did the same, for he wouldn't be needed again until the following day.

Saturday morning was pretty bleak. The sky was overcast and a fine drizzle was falling. Steve Tulloch looked out of his window and wondered about the wisdom of going on a parade on such a day. What have I let myself in for? He had done a great deal of campaigning in his time and put up with a lot of bad conditions but it was never easy trying to be cheerful on a dreich day, especially when you were totally exposed to the elements. Never mind, this kind of political exposure was not to be turned down, especially in Edinburgh, the capital. It was also the first time ever that such a parade would be led by political dignitaries, guaranteeing wide media coverage. He wondered what Rob thought their prospects would be on a day like this.

Steve joined Rob Paterson for breakfast that morning.

'And a good morning to you, sir!' said Rob with a big grin on his face.

'Hey! You're looking bright and cheerful,' said Steve.

'What have you got to be so chirpy about?'

'What do you mean? It's going to be a fine day today. I can feel it in my bones.'

'You've got to be joking! Have you seen that weather out there? It's absolutely pouring down.'

'Don't be daft, man. That's just drizzle and the forecast predicts that it will probably clear up by late morning. Anyway, the weather should be the least of our problems. Edinburgh for a long time now has been a Tory stronghold, as this is where the money is. Campaigning in Edinburgh has never been easy for Labour candidates, especially in the city centre, and here we are presented with this golden opportunity to campaign direct, in full view of the media. Right in the heart of Auld Reekie itself! I tell you, man, I can't wait to get out there and get at them.'

That morning, Kevin McGuire woke up at about nine o'clock. He wondered if there was any chance of the parade being cancelled because of the weather, but he soon dismissed that thought. There was simply too much money and organisation put into these things to cancel them because of a bit of rain. Besides, he had never heard of a parade or march being put off because of the weather, and he had seen a few marches in his time.

Kevin looked at his watch and thought mournfully, four hours to go. I'm never gonna last four hours in this cold and draughty place. The cold had wakened him, for there was a strong draught through the gap left by the door that he had jemmied open and been unable to close properly the night before. However, he had another go, and this time managed to jam it. He unwrapped a bar of chocolate for his breakfast and settled down to study the view on the Camera Obscura as he ate.

The town was bustling with people and there were already crowds gathering on the edge of the pavement, taking up position for the parade that was still three hours away. Kevin manipulated the lens and looked at other areas of the city. He tried to remember some of the lecture he had heard days before which described some of the breathtaking views that he was now observing. The bright light of the screen surrounded by the total darkness of the room produced a hypnotic effect on Kevin.

While watching the screen Kevin's mind wandered back, his thoughts triggered off by the view. As he drifted off into bygone days of his childhood the chaos of the screen became a blur and his thoughts drifted into deeper pastures of his mind. After a while he somehow felt disturbed, as if his thoughts were being distracted, but he didn't know why. This became irritating and he found it difficult to focus his concentration.

Then suddenly he realised that the previously blurred screen had begun to clear and appeared to be different. Kevin wasn't quite sure at first why it was different, but then it struck him. What had previously been chaos was now order. The screen was showing an orderly pattern, though its significance had not yet struck him. Then out of the blue, a word popped into his head. 'Parade! That's it! It's the parade! It's begun! My God, I've been sleeping!'

The bulk of the parade had already covered the length of Princes Street and was now starting to turn into the Bridges, leading to the Royal Mile. Kevin immediately unpacked the rope and moved out on to the terrace. At the edge of the terrace, looking out over the battlement, was a tourist telescope. He anchored one end of the rope to the base of the telescope stand and then, moving to the rear of the tower, he carefully lowered the other end to the ground. Having made ready his escape route he returned to the Camera Obscura for the rifle, which he unpacked and assembled with fluent expertise. He then moved over to the edge of the terrace, taking care to remain behind the battlement. He gently placed the rifle barrel over the edge of the crenelle, one of the indentations in the battlement and, looking through his telescopic sight, lined it up on the parade.

Kevin's heart was pumping, fast and furious. He could clearly see the parade snaking round into the High Street and slowly making its way towards him. He looked at his watch: it was two minutes to one. He removed the watch from his wrist and placed it on the parapet before him so that he could see it with his other eye. He then readjusted the sight, lining it up on the leader of the parade who was just coming into focus. Kevin could see the sun glinting on the bald head of the parade leader. It was Steve Tulloch. Kevin had a quick pan round, looking for Rob Paterson, and found him 4 feet behind and to the left of Tulloch. Kevin's other eye glimpsed the watch again.

The second hand was just approaching the zero point. He thought to himself, no time to realign on Tulloch. I'll take out Paterson first. He lined up on Rob Paterson's forehead and squeezed the trigger. At that precise moment a deafening explosion erupted. It was the one o'clock gun. Paterson dropped to the ground.

Kevin's timing had been perfect. The noise was still echoing in his ear as he lined up the gun on Steve Tulloch and again squeezed the trigger. Tulloch also fell to the ground. The timing between rifle shots and the cannon had been so close as to be almost indistinguishable.

Kevin dropped the gun where he lay and quickly moved to the rear of the terrace, and grabbing hold of the rope he climbed over the battlement and abseiled to the ground, an exercise that took just 90 seconds.

Before making his next move Kevin paused just long enough to look through the railings of the iron gate to see if there was anyone there. He then scaled the gate and dropped down into Ramsay Place where a bicycle was waiting for him, propped against the wall. Dave Simpson had placed it there just minutes before. Kevin quickly stripped off the tracksuit which he had been wearing over a cycling outfit, and stuffed it into the saddlebag strapped to the rear of the bike.

Three minutes had now passed since he fired the rifle and there were only seven minutes left to get to the station. Kevin made the Waverley in four and a half minutes, giving him just two and a half minutes to load his bike and himself on to the train. He had made it. The Glasgow train pulled out on time and Kevin was on his way.

8

Kevin McGuire was shivering with cold by the time he reached Glasgow Queen Street Station. He had spent 40 minutes in a draughty carriage dressed in only a cycling shirt and shorts. He was met at the train by Stan Hunter, one of Dave Simpson's men. Stan helped Kevin organise his luggage, which they carried to Stan's car.

On the way, Kevin stopped and said, 'Wait a minute, the bike, what about the bloody bike? I've still to pick that up yet!'

'No,' said Stan. 'Leave it. They'll take it to Lost Property. Can you think of a better place to lose something?'

'That's good thinking, Stan.'

Kevin changed into his regular clothes in the back of the car on their way to the airport. He was still shivering somewhat and feeling the cold even when fully dressed. This wasn't too surprising, considering that he had spent all night in the Camera Obscura with the door partially open. On top of this he had only eaten a bar of chocolate that day and was by now decidedly hungry.

They arrived at Glasgow Airport at 2.15 and their flight wasn't due to leave until three o'clock. Kevin welcomed this waiting period as it gave him time to get something to eat at the airport restaurant. Stan had taken it upon himself to organise the food but, because of the queues, it was 20 minutes before he returned. Kevin was still in the process of eating a hamburger when the tannoy system announced their flight, asking all passengers to board the plane.

There was still 15 minutes to wait after they had boarded the plane, a fact that seemed to worry him for, having satisfied his hunger, he was now anxious to leave and was beginning to get agitated. Stan sensed this and told him to relax, that everything was going to be all right. By this time Kevin had remembered his propensity to be airsick. While he was torturing himself with such thoughts the engines revved up and the plane started to move, leaving him with a whole bag of mixed feelings.

However, once in the air, he began to settle down a bit. The fact that he was getting further and further away from Edinburgh played a major part in overriding any other feelings. Kevin didn't do much talking on the flight down to London. He was too preoccupied, reliving the events that had gone before. Everything seemed to have happened so fast.

Stan Hunter interrupted Kevin's mental rerun by giving him an update on what was to take place when they landed at Heathrow. 'It's been arranged that you'll be going back to New York on one of Atlantic Air's flights. She'll be ready to go as soon as you're on board. They should have been away an hour ago but they've managed to hold the flight back on some pretext or other until you arrive.'

The flight to London took just under an hour and 20 minutes. The weather was good so there were no hold-ups. On leaving the plane and entering the terminal both Kevin and Stan were on the lookout for particularly inquisitive-looking observers but there were none obvious. Kevin was at his most apprehensive at this point for he knew that if they were on to him, this is where they would make their move to arrest him. He kept saying to himself, if only I can make it to the men's room where I can change into my Civil Airline uniform then everything will be all right. He was in luck. After saying his goodbyes to Stan he was able to slip into the men's room to make his change, after which it all went pretty well according to plan. Kevin was on board and in the air within the hour. For the first time in 48 hours he felt that he could really relax. He was now on his way to New York.

Meanwhile, back in Edinburgh, all hell had broken loose. Rob Paterson was dead on arrival at the Edinburgh Royal Infirmary, and Steve Tulloch was in intensive care. No one seemed to know what his condition was. Police were restricting all movements in and out of that part of the hospital. It had taken 15 minutes after the shooting before the police were able to establish what had taken place. The timing of the shooting to coincide with the one o'clock gun had been a very successful ploy indeed.

Although there were police lining the route, and even some in civilian clothing taking part in the parade, they were having great difficulty getting through the crowds, as the congestion at that part of town which marked the end of the parade was at its maximum. Many people had seen Rob Paterson fall to the ground when the one o'clock gun went off but a number of them thought it was some kind of stunt, especially when Steve Tulloch dropped to the ground almost immediately after him. The massive crowd that had accumulated at that point, instead of dispersing, gathered around the two victims of the shooting. It took the police quite a while to fight their way through and it took even longer for the ambulance to clear a passage to the site. The chaos enabled Kevin to clear the area unimpeded. It was more than half an hour before road blocks were established and rail and airport routes checked. By which time, Kevin was well on his way to Glasgow and freedom.

There was a news blackout on Steve Tulloch's condition, but Rob Paterson's death hit the six o'clock news headlines. It was already on the CBS news bulletin in New York by the time Kevin McGuire arrived. He was able to see it on the seven o'clock news in the airport arrivals lounge while waiting to collect his luggage. Kevin was concerned that Steve Tulloch hadn't been reported dead. He tried to think back, to recall the shooting. Was it possible that he had only wounded him? If so, his mission had failed. Kevin felt shivers up his spine when he thought about the possibilities. They wouldn't. No they wouldn't send me back over there again, would they?'

He was picked up at the airport by Gregg Donoghue. 'Welcome home, Kev. Hey, don't look so glum. You've done a fine job and we're all proud of you. Come on now, cheer up. What's wrong with you?' shouted Gregg as they got into the car.

Kevin slid silently into his seat and said nothing for a full two minutes.

'What if I missed?'

'Hey, what are you talkin' about? Rob Paterson's a dead man. He's real dead.'

'But Tulloch, there's been no report on Tulloch,' said Kevin almost despairingly.

'Aw, don't you be worrying about that now. Chances are if he isn't dead now he soon will be. Chances are, he won't last the night. You did go for a head shot, didn't you?'

'Yeh, of course I did.'

'Well then. What's there to worry about? In a few minutes, we'll have you back in our safe house where you can lie low for a while until we get something sorted out for you. Who knows, we may even organise another woman for you while you're waiting, eh? What do you think about that?'

That remark triggered off thoughts of Kathy Conners in Kevin's head. He missed her very much and hoped that he would be able to see her soon. He wondered what she was doing right now. He and Kathy had become quite close during the short time they had spent together. Besides which, Kathy was the closest, if not the only friend he had made in a long, long time.

By this time, unknown to Kevin or Gregg, Kathy had been shipped into hospital in Washington with suspected pneumonia. This had taken place two days before and she was not responding well to treatment. While in hospital, she saw a TV report about Gerry Austin which was giving her great cause for concern. The report said that war veteran Gerry Austin, the Senator for Massachusetts, who had been in hospital for eight days now, had just been diagnosed as suffering from an extremely virulent form of AIDS. It went on:

> According to experts the disease normally takes 12 to 15 months to manifest itself in any distinguishable form but this is considered to be a new strain, which the experts claim they have never

encountered before. This is yet another chilling chapter in the AIDS controversy and doctors say that they are alarmed at how quickly this new strain can develop. The Senator claims that he was recently involved in a car accident on his way to Washington and that this entailed him being taken to a nearby private hospital where he was given an emergency blood transfusion.

Linda Johnstone was visiting Kathy at the time of the news bulletin and was surprised to see tears well up in Kathy's eyes as she watched the item.

'What's wrong, Kath? Why are you crying? You're going to be all right, you know. Pneumonia is no big deal nowadays.'

'I think I've got AIDS,' she said, sobbing. 'I really do.'

'Don't be silly, Kathy. You're illness was diagnosed as pneumonia. You heard the doctor.'

'Don't treat me like a bloody child,' said Kathy angrily. 'I know what I'm talking about.'

'Take it easy. Take it easy. I'm your friend, remember. I'm on your side.'

At that moment, Kathy burst into floods of tears punctuated by bouts of sobbing. Linda had never seen her so distressed.

'Linda, oh Linda, what am I going to do?'

Linda was beginning to realise now that this was something more than a hysterical reaction to a news bulletin. 'Tell me. Take your time, now, and tell me what this is all about,' said Linda, putting a comforting arm around her shoulders.

Kathy's sobs were easing a little by now as she attempted to talk through her tears. 'Linda, I've not been the friend to you that you thought I was. I'm ... I'm afraid that there's another side to my life that I never told you about.' Kathy gave Linda an account of her involvement with the agency, going into great detail about some aspects of it, although she tended to gloss over the nastier side of the business.

Linda was utterly astonished at what she was hearing, although she managed to conceal this from Kathy. She had known that Kathy was a bit worldly and suspected that she had packed a lot of experience into a short period of her life, but she had never dreamt that Kathy would get involved with such an agency. As Linda thought back, one or two things fell into place. There had been areas of Kathy's lifestyle that had simply puzzled Linda, and of course she now realised how Kathy was able to afford such a relatively good lifestyle. Linda had rationalised this by assuming that Gregg Donoghue was responsible. Then again, Linda was such a trusting soul that she had a tendency to believe most, if not all, of what Kathy had told her. After all, Kathy was her best friend.

It was a long time before Kathy got round to telling Linda about Senator Gerry Austin, but by that time she was starting to work herself up again. It was understandable, as this was the reality of her present situation. Confessing her past sins had acted as a kind of release valve and had allowed her some short-term relief, especially as Linda was proving to be so understanding. But the latter episode of her life, leading to her suspicion of having AIDS, had reopened the wounds. It was something that Kathy just could not come to terms with. By this time, she was crying uncontrollably and Linda wasn't having much success in her attempts to console her. She was clearly grateful and very much relieved when a doctor burst into the room inquiring what all the crying was about.

Between Linda and the doctor they eventually managed to get Kathy under some kind of control and to calm her down. Linda had convinced her that she had better tell the doctor about her suspicions. Linda then left while Kathy explained to a now white-faced but extremely attentive doctor, who was possibly as much concerned about his own exposure to the disease as he was about Kathy's.

Linda's head was still reeling when she got home. She had been totally bewildered by Kathy's revelations. She daren't mention it to the family. Not that they wouldn't be sympathetic, for Kathy was also considered to be a friend of the family, but Kathy had made Linda swear that she would tell no one. Linda wanted time to think.

In fact she desperately needed time to think. Kathy hadn't helped matters with her crying because it prevented Linda from taking proper stock of the situation. So much had taken place in such a short time. Now she was trying to work out the implications of the situation and to determine what, if anything, she could do to help her best friend. It was so typical of Linda not to give even a second thought to the possible dangers that she herself might have been exposed to. She was solely concerned about Kathy and what she could do to alleviate some of her suffering.

Linda suddenly had a horrifying thought. What about Gregg Donoghue? Had he been in touch with Kathy since? Not too long ago, he had been desperately trying to locate her. Linda thought to herself that she must discuss this with Kathy tomorrow. Meantime, she would try to get hold of all the information that she could on this dreadful disease. Poor Kathy, thought Linda. Underneath that ultra-confident exterior was a very frightened young woman.

Meanwhile, Kevin was being debriefed by Roy Stirling in a safe house in New York, where they were getting a bit concerned about the fact that there had been no reports on Steve Tulloch's death. If he survived, then the whole organisation would have been put in jeopardy for nothing. Roy was all for sending Kevin back in again, but Gregg was dead set against it. He figured that a second attempt so soon after the first would be too risky, if not downright foolhardy. Besides, it would be prudent to wait and see what happened to Tulloch as they couldn't keep his condition secret indefinitely, especially with him being hospitalised.

'I reckon,' said Gregg, 'we'll probably have a news report on his condition sometime tonight.'

'If we've put our necks on the line for nothing,' said Roy, 'I personally will take that little Irish bastard out. I might have guessed he'd louse it up.'

'Cool it, Roy. For now, we're gonna adopt a wait-and-see posture. Meanwhile I've got to get in touch with Washington. They're waiting on my report. I'll find out what they want us to do next. You stay here and look after McGuire while I'm away, and for crying out loud, see if you can keep your hands off him. OK?'

Before this discussion took place Kevin McGuire had gone to bed, claiming that he wasn't feeling too well. He seemed to think that he had developed some kind of fever. Roy Stirling had suggested sarcastically that it was probably Yellow Fever.

In Washington, Tom Casey and Alex Stenton were practically at panic stations. They had just received word from the UK that Steve Tulloch had not only survived the attack but was on the road to recovery. Apparently the bullet had struck his skull a glancing blow. As a consequence of this he had suffered severe concussion and had been unconscious for six hours. He was now said to be responding well to treatment and the police were expected to interview him shortly. A spokesman for the police had said that at present they had no information regarding the assassin, but were convinced that the explosion that took place in the Camera Obscura the day before was in some way connected to the shooting.

Tom shouted impatiently at Alex, 'Where the hell's Gregg Donoghue? He's supposed to report to me today. Can none of you guys turn up on time? Sometimes I wonder what I pay you people for!'

Just then Tom Casey's intercom buzzed. It was his secretary announcing Gregg's arrival.

'Well, speak of the devil,' said Tom.

Gregg was surprised to find out that Steve Tulloch was alive and on the road to recovery. He had convinced himself that Tulloch was at the very least critically injured. It occurred to him that it was a good thing that Roy Stirling was as yet unaware of this information, for he didn't rate McGuire's chances if there was no one around to stop him. Gregg reported Kevin's story in detail to Tom Casey and Alex Stenton and received a mute response.

Alex broke the silence. 'Look, the guy hit both targets in the head and killed one of them. I figure it was surely divine intervention that saved that guy Tulloch. I reckon our man did his job. We've nothin' to reproach him for.'

'That,' said Tom, 'is as maybe, but it still leaves us with a major headache.'

At that moment the intercom went yet again and Tom's secretary announced that there was a call on the line from New York. It was Roy Stirling to tell them that Kevin's fever had developed further. He was now shaking uncontrollably and sweating profusely. Roy had panicked and phoned Washington because he didn't know what to do with McGuire. All he knew was that it looked serious and he didn't want to touch him in case it was contagious. Tom gave him a number to call, where he could locate one of the firm's doctors. After the call Tom asked Gregg what he thought could be wrong with Kevin.

'All I know, sir, is that he told me that on the night before the hit he slept on top of the tower and had been exposed to the weather. It may just be the flu, or at worst pneumonia.'

'OK, Gregg. You get back there tomorrow and keep a tight rein on things. Find out what's happening. I'll be in touch as soon as we decide what we're gonna do next.'

When Gregg left Tom's office that night he decided to look up Kathy Conners while he was in Washington. But when he arrived at her place he was again confronted with a closed door. He decided to phone Linda to see if she knew where Kathy was.

'Oh Gregg! I'm glad you've called. I take it you haven't heard about Kathy yet?'

'What do you mean?' said Gregg sharply.

'I'm afraid she's in hospital.'

'What! Where? What's happened to her?' said Gregg, in a concerned manner.

'Look, why don't you come round here and I'll tell you all about it? Then we can both go and see Kathy together.'

When Gregg arrived at Linda's she prepared a quick meal for him whilst she told him about Kathy's pneumonia. She didn't mention a word about AIDS to Gregg. First of all, she had given her word to Kathy that she would tell no one of her fears; and secondly, it hadn't been verified and it was still possible that Kathy was panicking without cause. Besides, the latest reports on the subject seemed to emphasise just how difficult it was to catch the disease.

After the meal Linda and Gregg drove over to St Columba's Hospital to see Kathy. When they arrived they were both surprised to find out that she had been moved to an isolation room. The doctor said that it was just a precaution and was very reluctant to let them in, but Gregg insisted. The doctor relented, provided they both wore masks and gowns. When they got into the ward Linda could see that Kathy looked a little better, although it was obvious she was under some kind of sedation.

'Well, Kath. What on earth have you been up to?' said Gregg as he approached the bed.

Kathy was startled at first and very surprised to hear his voice. When she saw that Linda was with him she began to worry whether Linda had told him about the AIDS situation. It was obvious from Gregg's conversation however that he knew nothing. Kathy inwardly heaved a sigh of relief. 'When did you get into Washington, Gregg?'

'Oh, just today as a matter of fact. What's with this isolation stuff then?'

'I'm not quite sure myself,' said Kath. 'The doctor suspects that there may be some kind of virus that's complicating things. They're just taking no chances. I'm here until they get all the results of my tests. But how are you, Gregg? Where have you been hiding yourself?'

All three exchanged small talk for about half an hour and then Linda left the ward to see if she could have a word with the doctor. While she was out Kathy took the opportunity to enquire about Kevin.

'By the way, how's Kevin? Is he back from his mission yet?'

Gregg had anticipated that Kathy might enquire about Kevin and had decided in advance that it was in everyone's interest that she and Kevin shouldn't get together again. Especially now that the mission was over and there was a flap on about its limited success. So Gregg had already concocted a story for Kath to cover such a contingency.

'I'm afraid I've got some bad news for you Kath. Kevin didn't make it back from that mission.'

'You don't mean he's...?'

'Yes, I'm afraid we fear the worst.'

Kathy was stunned into silence. She didn't know what to think. She and Kevin had become pretty close during their short stay together, and there was a good chance that if she had contracted AIDS then Kevin might well have caught it too. Perhaps it was a blessing in disguise, thought Kath. But she remembered that from the way Kevin had talked he hadn't trusted Gregg and his party, especially that guy Roy Stirling. The way things had turned out, it looked as if Kevin had been on a hiding to nothing.

My God, she thought, this sure has been an eventful month. I do some guy a favour and end up catching AIDS. For the first time in my life I get very close to perhaps the only guy in this world that I have anything in common with, only to lose him again in the same month.

Gregg had no way of knowing what he was about to unleash as a direct result of his statement to Kathy regarding Kevin McGuire. Kathy had been instructed by Kevin to send the package to Ireland should anything happen to him. Having thought all this through, Kathy decided that, all things considered, she should despatch the package as soon as possible.

While she was trying to figure out how she was going to go about this Linda returned to the ward. 'Gregg. Do you mind if I have a word alone with Linda before you two leave? Just girl talk, you know.'

'Sure,' said Gregg. 'I'll wait outside. You look after yourself now. I'll be back in Washington again as soon as I can.'

When Gregg left the room Kathy indicated to where her purse lay and asked Linda to bring it over.

'What's all this mystery about?' said Linda, as she handed the purse to her. 'Girl talk indeed.'

Kathy produced a small parcel from her purse. 'Linda,' she said. 'Would you do a favour and post this package? It's very important that it goes today.'

'Yes of course, but why did you ask Gregg to leave?'

'Oh, I wanted to ask you if you had told him about the AIDS thing.'

'You know I wouldn't do that. I promised, didn't I? Have you ever known me to break a promise?'

'No. I'm sorry, Linda. You've been a good friend to me. Forgive me for doubting you.'

'OK. But I must go now. I'll drop in and see you tomorrow.'

As Linda and Gregg walked down the corridor towards the exit an alarm buzzer suddenly went off, giving a loud continuous tone. Both Linda and Gregg stopped in their tracks. They turned around in time to see a commotion as doctors and nurses rush into Kathy's room.

Linda screamed, 'Oh no!'

She ran back down the corridor only to be stopped at the door by a nurse who held her back and shaking her head said, 'I'm afraid she didn't make it.'

'But ... but she couldn't have. I was speaking to her only minutes ago.'

A doctor appeared in the doorway, and took Linda aside and walked her towards a chair in the corridor. Linda was crying uncontrollably by this time. Gregg joined the doctor and assisted him in helping Linda to a chair.

The doctor turned to Gregg and said, 'Look, I know it was sudden and must have been an awful shock to you both but we were expecting it I'm afraid. Miss Conners was suffering from an extremely virulent form of AIDS.'

Gregg involuntarily recoiled at that point, and the doctor was quick to register this. 'Don't be alarmed, sir. One would have to have intimate contact before being in any danger of contracting the disease.'

'I thought that it took at least eighteen months for this disease to manifest itself doctor?' asked Gregg anxiously.

'Yes, this was the prevalent view, but just recently there have been two reported cases of this new strain in Washington and Miss Conners is the third.

'We don't know yet why it acts so quickly but the first two patients died within three weeks of contracting the disease. So far the symptoms seem to be quite consistent; fever, lymph node swelling and a rash, followed three weeks later by an overwhelming rare form of pneumonia. That's when the lungs quite suddenly collapse and we are unable to reflate them again. It's really quite extraordinary.'

Linda's tears by this time had subsided to bouts of sobbing as she tightly clasped the package that Kathy had given her just moments before. This had suddenly taken on a new significance because it was the last point of contact between Kathy and herself.

Gregg turned to Linda and, seeing her distressed state, he reached out to comfort her and said, 'Come, Linda. Let's leave now while we still have good thoughts of Kathy.'

'No. I want to see her before I go.'

The doctor intervened at this stage and said, 'Please take your companion's advice and leave with good memories of your friend, believe me, you would not like to see her as she is now.'

Linda stood up at this point and made for the exit. Gregg put a comforting arm around her and tried to cheer her by reviving memories of some of the good times they had once had together when they went out on foursomes.

They left the hospital and as they approached the car, Linda said, 'Just a minute, Gregg. I want to post this package for Kath.'

As she walked over to the mailbox outside the hospital, Gregg, intrigued by the mention of a parcel from Kath, followed her over. His training had made him very observant, and he just managed to get a glimpse of the latter part of the address on the parcel before Linda let it drop into the mail box.

'What's this? Kath sending home food parcels, eh?' said Gregg jokingly.

'I shouldn't think so,' replied Linda. 'Not unless it's a bar of chocolate.'

'I just saw Ireland on the address so I just assumed. I didn't quite catch the name though but it didn't look like Conners to me.'

'No it wasn't,' said Linda, innocently playing into Gregg's hands. 'It was McGuire. It's probably a family connection.'

'McGuire?' said Gregg. 'Are you sure?'

'Yes. Don't tell me you're acquainted with her relations back in Ireland?'

'Oh. I just heard her mention the name once.'

9

Back in New York, Roy Stirling had called in one of the firm's doctors to look at Kevin McGuire, whose condition had rapidly deteriorated.

'This man needs immediate hospitalisation,' said the doctor. 'He's running a temperature of 102 degrees and has obviously got a fever. I strongly suspect pleurisy or pneumonia.'

'No can do,' replied Roy. 'He stays here where we can keep an eye on him.'

'But I must insist,' said the doctor. 'I won't be responsible if this man's condition deteriorates further.'

'That's OK by me, Doc, but he's not moving from this room.'

The doctor hastily made out a prescription and handed it to Roy saying, 'That should combat his temperature for a little while, but he's your responsibility now.'

Gregg Donoghue arrived the next day, much to the relief of Roy Stirling who wasn't quite sure what to do next. He was also terrified in case it was something contagious.

'What's the score then? How is he doing?'

'It's bad. The doc thinks it may be pneumonia or pleurisy. Whatever, he sure don't look good. What are we gonna do with him now?'

Gregg had a look at McGuire and agreed with Roy's apprehension. Kevin was unconscious by this time, but shortly before Gregg had arrived he had been fighting for breath and panting very heavily, as his lungs craved for air. Gregg decided to phone Washington to inform Tom Casey of the situation.

'What's the story, Gregg? You think he's gonna make it?'

'Not unless we get him to a hospital. I don't think he'll make it through the night, sir. It may be very risky putting him in a hospital though, because if he gets delirious and starts talkin' through the fever we could all be in real trouble.'

'OK. Maybe we should let nature take its course. Put Roy on. I'll get him to make the necessary arrangements. Roy's good at that sort of thing. If there is nothing more you can do at that end, get yourself back here. We may have some tidying up to do.'

On the flight back to Washington Gregg was aware of something constantly nagging at the back of his mind. He gave his full attention to resolving it and tried to retrace his movements over the last couple of days. Quite suddenly, it struck him – the package. That's what it was, Linda was posting a package for Kathy Conners. What could it possibly be? Why would Kathy want to send a parcel to McGuire's family in Ireland?

Gregg tossed this question around in his mind for a while. There was something ominous about this whole situation, he thought. He had noticed that Kevin and Kathy had got along remarkably well, considering how little they knew about each other. But these things can happen when two people try to condense a whole relationship into a short period of time. Besides, they had a lot in common. For starters they both came from Ireland, from troubled backgrounds, and had tried to resolve their problems by coming to the US. These were certainly the kind of common bonds that could forge a close friendship.

It also occurred to Gregg that Kath was on the rebound from a relationship that she had thought she had had with him. The more that Gregg thought about their affair the more disturbed he seemed to feel. There was also that big animal Stirling who was always giving McGuire a hard time. What if ...? Then it all seemed to fall into place. What if Kevin had decided to take out some insurance, say pass the word around if anything should happen to him? Yes, that's it, and Kathy would be the perfect vehicle for such a message.

Gregg Donoghue could hardly wait to get to Tom Casey's office, although he was dreading what the response would be to these suspicions. His first priority was to phone Roy Stirling in New York. He wanted to check if there was a tape machine in the flat and, if there was, if it had been possible for Kevin to record anything while he was there. As soon as Gregg arrived at Tom Casey's office he explained his suspicions to him, then immediately got on the phone to New York. His worst fears were confirmed. Roy said there was a cassette recorder but that there were no blank tapes, just pre-recorded ones. Gregg knew how easy it was to record over a pre-recorded tape.

'I'm afraid we must assume the worst. We must assume that Kevin got word back to the UK, and act on that premise.'

'Do you know what kind of can of worms you're opening here, Gregg? Do you realise the consequences of what you're saying if it's true?'

'I certainly do. But whatever we decide to do, we'd better move quickly, for that tape went in the post yesterday.'

'Is there no way we can intercept it?' said Tom desperately.

'No. Besides, even trying to trace it would take too long. I guess we'll have to make use of our Irish friends. Perhaps we can arrange to have the house targeted. It shouldn't be too difficult if we have the right contacts. They seem to be killing each other all the time over there, so there's a good chance it would be put down as another sectarian attack.'

Tom Casey picked up his phone and yelled into it, 'Get me Alex Stenton! Get him over here right away.'

That night Tom Casey, Alex Stenton and Gregg Donoghue drew up yet another plan, this time to deal with Kevin's family. Alex got the job of flying over to Ireland that very night to make the relevant contacts. He was also under strict orders not to leave the country until he had confirmation that his mission had been successfully accomplished.

Tom Casey turned to Gregg and said, 'About this girl, the one who posted the package. What's her name?'

'Linda Johnstone.'

'Yes. You realise that you will have to take care of her, don't you?'

81

'She doesn't know anything, Tom.'

'How do you know?' shouted Tom. 'How the hell do you know? She's a danger because she's the only person who can link McGuire to Kathy Conners, and she can be connected to you. As far as I'm concerned, she knows too much. When did Kathy die? We don't know what Kathy told her before she died. No, I'm afraid she'll have to go, Gregg, and I'm leaving that for you to deal with. But wait until Alex returns from Ireland before you act. We'll see how he gets on first, just in case we have another foul-up on our hands. If his mission is a success I'll get him to phone you direct, then you can take it from there. Now remember, it's too late for sentiment: we've got to cover our tracks and there's far too much at stake for us to be taking any more chances.'

10

Meanwhile, at CIA headquarters in Washington, Frank Mariano had received a telex signal from his UK sources. The telex was headed 'AN ATTEMPT TO ASSASSINATE THE LABOUR PARTY LEADER'. The message went on to describe the killing of Rob Paterson, the deputy leader of the Labour party, during a Students' Charity Parade in Edinburgh. The message further described how an abortive attempt had been made on Steve Tulloch, the current leader of the Labour party on the same occasion. 'CHIEF SUSPECTS ARE THE IRA'.

The signal had triggered off a whole series of thoughts in Frank Mariano's head. In particular Frank recalled his discussions with Tom Casey and a wry smile wrinkled across his face. Well, I wonder. What have we here? Frank thought to himself. Could this be Tom Casey in action? Surely the old buzzard wouldn't be that foolish; or would he? He was certainly fired up enough about Steve Tulloch's proposals to remove American installations from the UK.

Frank switched on his intercom and said, 'Get me Tom Casey's file. He's head of CLC Industries. And, while you're at it, give me anything you've got on CLC. In particular, their UK interests over the last five years, together with any current contracts they may be negotiating with the British government.'

Frank made another call, this time direct to his counterpart in MI6, British Intelligence. 'Hi, Bill, what's the latest on your enquiries into the Rob Paterson killing?'

'Oh, they're coming along just fine. What's the CIA interest?'

'Nothing specific. I just got wind of it myself and I wondered if there was anything we could do to help.'

'I think we've got it under control for the moment but we'll sure

83

be in touch if we need you. Thanks for your interest. I'm up to my eyes and ears at the moment. Can I get back to you?'

'Sure,' said Frank and hung up. Cagey bastard! We'll see who needs who, he thought.

Frank's next call was to Jim Hollis. 'Jim, could you come in here a moment. I've got a job for you.'

Jim was one of Frank's senior agents, a very reliable and cautious man of whom Frank thought very highly.

'Well, Jim, I've pulled the file on Tom Casey. It should be with us any moment now. I want you to look into this guy, for I have strong suspicions that he may have something to do with the recent political killing in the UK. Find out who his lieutenants are and trace their movements over the last three months. Let's see if we can build up a profile on what these guys might be up to. Oh, and while I remember, he has a yacht, one of those luxury cruisers that he keeps somewhere off the Florida coast. Where was it now? Oh yes, Apalachee Bay. If it's not there, check Pensacola. See if you can get the coastguard to check out its log book on some pretext. I want to find out where it's been over the last two or three months. I would also like to know who his passengers have been over the same period. I figure old Tom does most of his serious negotiating on that cruiser. Perhaps we won't find out what he was saying, but there's a good chance we'll find out who he was saying it to. Our Mr Casey has some powerful contacts and he's not past using them either.'

Jim Hollis spent three days examining the CLC files and sifting through pages of computer data. He was now in the process of preparing a preliminary report for Frank Mariano. He had discovered that CLC had recently been negotiating a multimillion contract with the British government for updating and maintaining their existing radar and missile installations. Jim Hollis was aware that such a programme was in direct conflict with recent proposals made by the Labour Party, who were at present contesting the current general election in Britain and who, according to all current reports, looked like winning. There had been much publicity in the States over Steve Tulloch's proposals to close down American bases.

The evidence so far examined seemed to suggest that CLC had an excellent motive for interfering with the prospects of the incoming administration. Jim's inquiries into Tom Casey and his team of operatives had revealed that two of his most trusted lieutenants, Alex Stenton and Roy Stirling, were already on file. Alex Stenton was listed as a British undesirable who was dishonourably discharged from the SAS, and Roy Stirling was a Vietnam vet who, at the time of his discharge from the service, was considered to be mentally unstable.

Hollis's next move was to send out a directive to have all three men kept under constant surveillance and for an investigation to be made into their movements over the past three months. Meanwhile he informed Frank Mariano of his findings.

'It looks like your hunch about CLC and Tom Casey is worth further investigation, Frank. Wait until you see my report. This guy Tom Casey certainly has some unsavoury characters working for him.

'How is that report coming along? I'm anxious to see it.'

'It should be ready tomorrow. I'll get it to you as quick as I can.'

'OK. I'll see if I can get an investigation under way at the UK end to see if we can come up with anything over there. I had hoped that our UK friends would have liaised with us but it looks like they're being pretty cagey on this one. Mind you, I suppose we can't blame them. Especially if they suspect that some of our people are behind it. Well, Jim, let me know as soon as your surveillance team reports back. I want to zero in on this job while things are still hot. They failed this time but there's no telling if they'll try again. If they do, I want to be ready for them.'

11

At seven o'clock sharp Kieran McGuire got up and prepared for his 12-mile run, as was his custom on a Saturday morning. This was part of his marathon training, which also involved a 10-mile circuit each weekday. Kieran's total of 62 miles a week had been reached more than halfway through his programme. The target this year was to reach 80 miles a week but that meant going out twice a day. He even gave up karate to accommodate the extra miles.

It was a fabulous morning, not a cloud in sight. Birds were singing and the only other sound to be heard was the trickling of water from a stream as it flowed past the bottom of the garden. Kieran had his bedroom window open and could feel a cool, gentle breeze on his arm. The breeze would be most welcome on a day like this, for it would help keep him cool and stop the sweat from building up. After 4 miles out Kieran would build up a terrible sweat which he had great difficulty keeping out of his eyes. He didn't much like wearing a sweatband because it gave him headaches. Kieran was just tying the final knot on his track shoes when his mother shouted through from her bedroom.

'Is that you off then, Kieran?'

'Yes, Ma, a couple of minutes and I'll be on my way.'

'What about young Richard?' she shouted.

'Oh, just let him sleep it off. I'll see him when I get back.'

Richard was a tourist who Kieran had met in the village pub the evening before and, after a fairly heavy drinking session on pints of Guinness, Richard had left it too late to find room and board, so Kieran had offered him a bed at his house for the night.

'You've got a fine morning for it, but don't you go pushing yourself too hard now, you hear?'

'OK. Well, I'm off. I'll see you in an hour and a half, all going well.'

Kieran, who was feeling really good after having spent half an hour on his warm-up and stretching exercises, thought to himself, I'm gonna make a good time today, I just know it. God willing, I might even break the seven-minute mile. He looked up into the hills and thought they looked particularly inviting this morning. He could hardly wait to get amongst them. Off he went, starting with a slow jog, and gradually worked his way up to a seven-minute-mile pace. He was over the brow of the first hill in no time at all and finally disappeared from view of the house.

Meanwhile, Kieran's mother, Bridie, busied herself getting things ready for the breakfast that morning. There were normally only two of them living in this little country cottage. Kieran's dad had been killed while fighting for the Cause, and his brother Kevin had on two occasions nearly lost his life, before escaping out of the country. They had no idea where Kevin was, or even whether he was still alive, but they both prayed daily for his safe return. Bridie, was determined that she was not going to lose another son to the Cause. She considered that the loss of a husband, and a son who was now a fugitive, was sufficient price to pay for the needs of her country. Bridie did everything in her power to encourage Kieran with his work and his hobbies in an effort to keep his mind off the Troubles.

Kieran, however, had made up his own mind on the subject and certainly had no intentions of taking up arms. Unlike his brother he had a good job as an accountant at the local bank, which he was most reluctant to jeopardise. In his free time he indulged in his marathon running, which was a time-consuming hobby. His only other hobby was chess which he played two nights a week at the local chess club.

Kieran's mother frequently jibed him about the lack of women in his life. 'No wonder I don't see you with a girlfriend,' she would say. 'You haven't left any time to meet one, let alone go out with one.'

Kieran figured that there was plenty time yet to meet a woman.

At 28, he was in no rush to get married. He wanted to get his own life straightened out first.

That morning, an hour after Kieran had left, two men appeared at the top of the hill overlooking the front of the house. One of them lay on his stomach looking through a pair of binoculars while the other, who was carrying a large back pack, stood beside him. What they saw from their vantage point was a post office van arriving at the front of the house, the driver getting out and handing Bridie McGuire a small parcel and some envelopes. Bridie and the postman exchanged a few words before he climbed back into the van and drove off.

The two observers wasted no time as they stealthily made their way towards the house. By the time they reached the front door the post office van was well on its way. The first man, who was armed with a rifle, stood by the door while the other moved towards the window and heaved the large back pack through the glass. He and his companion immediately ran for cover.

Less than a minute later, there was one almighty explosion and the whole place erupted and turned into flames. The two men then headed in the direction that they had come from and made their getaway in a waiting vehicle which took them speedily out of the area.

By this time Kieran McGuire was just a mile away from his house, and homeward bound. He heard the explosion and wondered what it could possibly be. He was extremely concerned, for he knew that his home was the only building in the area for about 5 miles. Perhaps it was a plane crash, he tried to tell himself. Kieran was a very worried man by the time he reached the top of the hill that looked down the valley to his house. Deep down he knew within himself that it had to be his mother's house. There was no other reasonable explanation.

Kieran didn't realise it at the time but he covered the last mile in five and a half minutes, and that was after running 11 miles.

The spectacle that he saw from the top of the hill was exactly what he had dreaded. His home was on fire, engulfed in flames and smoke. Kieran let out a horrified yell and screamed for his mother as he ran the last 100 yards to the house as fast as he could, tears running down his cheeks. He had already told himself that the flames and smoke were not going to stop him. He was by this time feeling immensely strong and the adrenalin throughout his body was in full flow. There was nothing in the world that was going to stop Kieran entering that house to save his mother.

Kieran stormed through the door, coughing and spluttering in the smoke-filled rooms. In between coughs he screamed for his mother, desperately hoping against hope that she might answer his cries. Once in the front room, Kieran quickly dropped to his knees as he realised that most of the smoke was above waist level. It was dark in the room except for the occasional sheet of flame darting in front of him as he crawled his way across the floor. He could hear the crackling of burning timbers and feel the tremendous heat all around him. His eyes were shut and he was feeling his way across the floor, desperately trying to locate his mother. He found her lying face down on the floor.

Kieran grabbed hold of his mother's shoulder and pulled her with all his might, at the same time praying to God that she would be all right. But deep down inside, Kieran knew that his prayers were in vain. He could feel by the weight and limpness of her body that she was already dead.

After a great deal of struggling and dragging, which sapped his remaining strength, he eventually got her outside. Kieran stopped pulling her when he got a safe distance from the fire and slumped down, half on top of his mother's body. He was totally exhausted and drained of any residue of strength. He lay there for several minutes, his body draped across her. Then he remembered Richard, but by this time it was far too late, as Richard's room was by now an inferno and quite beyond Kieran's reach even if he'd had the strength.

Kieran cried and cried, his whole body wracked with sobbing.

After a while, he managed to collect himself and get some control over his emotions. By this time he was strong enough to lift himself up and turn his mother's body over. In her hand, she was still clutching the parcel that the postman had handed to her. He looked at the package and was amazed at how it had survived the flames. Kieran could see that it carried an American stamp. His first thoughts were of his brother Kevin. Yes, it must be from Kevin. He must have managed to escape to the States. Kieran was already wondering how he was going to tell Kevin of this dreadful tragedy.

Kieran looked down at his mother in his arms and thought, Oh God! What could she have possibly have done to deserve this. Hadn't she suffered enough? Kieran lapsed into memories of his father's death, when he was gunned down by soldiers, and how his mother had grieved so bitterly. Why, why? He kept asking himself, who would do such a thing?

Now, dark clouds appeared in the sky, as if from nowhere. It was almost as though someone had ordered the painting of a more appropriate scene, one that was more fitting to the tragedy that had taken place. Small raindrops landed on Kieran's face and mingled with the tears as he sat there stunned by his grief. Rivulets of rain ran down his face, etching a path through his smoke-blackened cheeks.

Then suddenly something seemed to snap inside him. It was as if he had switched to a new mode and undergone some strange metamorphosis. Cold, calculating cunning seemed to take over from caring, rational logic. He stopped crying. Now he had full control of his emotions. He made a vow there and then that he would spend the rest of his life tracking down the people who were responsible for this merciless, brutal killing of his mother. He then reaffirmed his vow, claiming that he personally would kill the people responsible. Kieran now felt that there was nothing left to live for. Life for him was finished, meaningless, now that the most precious being in the world lay dead before him.

He thought about Richard. He knew that Richard must be dead, but he wanted to see the body. Kieran quickly rose to his feet and moved towards the house, where he struggled through the smouldering embers of his home. It had started to rain heavily and the rain dampened the fire. He managed to struggle through to what remained of the bedroom. He was unprepared for the scene that confronted him. Richard's charred body was totally unrecognisable. The face was now a blackened blistering mess and it was almost impossible to distinguish any features. He could hardly believe that so much damage could have taken place in so little time. A sickeningly strong smell of burning flesh was evident, as he silently stood there trying to comprehend the scene before him.

He began to salvage what personal effects he could, putting them into a small haversack, thoughts racing through his head. If he was going to try and hunt down the animals responsible for this, it would be better if he was not hindered by people trying to find him. He was probably meant to be one of the victims, so it would be better all round if they thought that their mission had been successful. Nobody knew that Richard was staying overnight, apart from his mother. He had been passing through and it was a last-minute decision to invite him back to the house. So, as far as the police were concerned, that body in the bedroom was Kieran.

Kieran's next priority was to somehow get into town. Who could he trust? As he scanned his memory trying to identify likely candidates, a name popped into his head. This was odd, inasmuch as it was a name that he hadn't heard for about eight years. Peter! That's it! His Uncle Peter – his father's brother. When Kieran's father was shot eight years ago, Peter had been ready to go on the rampage. He wanted the family to organise a campaign against the British troops. But Bridie wouldn't hear of it. She maintained that there had been enough killing and that it was time for it to end, before the whole family was wiped out. She didn't leave it at that, either. She threatened to turn in any member of the family who went on a revenge campaign. Kieran remembered that his mother and Uncle Peter had a blazing row over that issue right after the funeral, and that his uncle had stormed out of the house and had never spoken to the family since.

Peter had a farm on the outskirts of town and was a man who kept very much to himself. Being a member of the old school, Peter McGuire could still remember the bitterness and hatred that existed before the killing of his only brother, Patrick. He was also a man who didn't forgive easily. Kieran thought Peter's farm would be perfect, the ideal place to hide out. Now if only he could break the ice with his uncle ... but what was he thinking? When he told Peter what had happened to Bridie, he was going to have a hard time holding him back from killing any and every suspect he could think of, such was Peter's hatred and need for revenge. Kieran thought to himself that this revenge thing must run in the family.

Kieran left the house and ran confidently, for now he had a plan, and a specific destination to head for. It took him nearly three hours to reach the outskirts of the town. The first stop was the bank, for he had decided en route that it would be a good idea to transfer all his money into the shared account, and then transfer that account to a different bank in Dublin, under a new name. Kieran was totally exhausted by the time he reached the town but he felt that it would be unwise to hang around in case someone recognised him. He stopped just long enough for a quick drink then headed straight for the bank. After successfully arranging the transfer of his capital to a new Dublin bank account, Kieran made his way to the farm.

As he approached the farmhouse, the door swung open and in the doorway stood a giant of a man in a black polo-necked jumper, wearing jeans tucked into enormous Wellington boots.

Peter McGuire was 6 foot 8 tall and must have weighed 17 stone. His scraggy face sported a large, black, bushy beard that blended into his long, dark, curly hair. He would have looked more at home in some swashbuckling pirate scene than he did on a farm.

Peter was absolutely astounded when he saw Kieran walking up towards him, for he recognised right away who it was. Kieran was a dead ringer for his father, Peter's older brother. Not a word passed between them for a full minute. They just stood there and looked at each other, both of them full of mixed emotions. Then Peter grabbed hold of Kieran and they hugged one another as tears of joy welled in Peter's eyes. Tears that were soon to turn into tears of anger, anguish and sorrow as Kieran told him of the tragedy.

By the time that Kieran had relived the nightmare and related all that had taken place, it was almost midnight. They were now trying to guess who the attackers had been and what on earth this was all about. They both came to the same conclusion: it was likely that Kevin must have been the target. But didn't everybody know that Kevin was out of the country? Or was he? These and many other questions were still being thrashed out by the early hours of the morning. Peter was still ranting and raving, giving voice to all sorts of theories and suspicions, when he suddenly realised that there was no response to his rambling.

He looked over to where Kieran was sitting, only to see that he had fallen fast asleep in his chair. Poor kid, Peter thought to himself. He must be thoroughly exhausted. Why didn't I think of that earlier, instead of keeping him up listening to my ravings after all he's been through? The emotions of both men had been well and truly spent. Peter pulled Kieran over his shoulder and, giving him a fireman's lift, carried him through to one of the bedrooms where he gently laid him down on top of the bed and threw a blanket over him. Kieran had been so tired that he didn't open his eyes during the whole exercise.

As Peter went back through to the living room he noticed a small haversack with its contents half-spilled out onto the floor. It was Kieran's bag of personal effects that he had salvaged from the fire. Peter picked everything up and was about to carry the bag through to Kieran's bedroom when he noticed that there was a package with a US stamp on it. The end of the parcel had been torn, exposing its contents. Peter could see that it was a cassette tape, and right away suspected that it had come from Kevin. Why didn't Kieran mention it? But on second thoughts, given all that had happened, it wasn't surprising that Kieran had forgotten all about it. As they had both decided that Kevin was the likely target for the bomb, Peter thought that the tape could be the key to what this was about. Was this a message, warning Kieran's mother about the possibility of an attack on the house? The more Peter thought about it, the more curious he became until he could restrain himself no longer. He quickly looked out his cassette recorder, set it up and began to play the tape.

Hello, Ma. Hi Kieran! I expect you're both wondering what's happened to me. It seems a long time since I've been in touch. You won't believe how much I miss you both and I'd give anything to turn the clock back so I could be with you again, but I guess it's not to be.

Well, Ma, I know I've been a big disappointment to you. Hey! That's an understatement isn't it? I can hardly remember a time when I wasn't in trouble. Even when I was at school, I was always getting into scrapes. I think most of the time it was my impatience that was responsible, do you remember? I just couldn't wait for anything, I was always looking for short cuts to get what I wanted. I couldn't even wait to grow up. Remember Dad promised to take us all to America? 'The land of plenty' he would say. I used to brag about that to all my schoolmates and I also remember spending a lot of school time day dreaming about what it was going to be like in America, and what I was going to be when I grew up as an American. The possibilities seemed endless then.

Ma, when Dad got killed, my whole life caved in. I was totally and absolutely shattered. I never dreamt that I would lose my father, not ever, because I had such grand plans for him, especially in my day dreams of America. How he was going to be so successful that we would have our own swimming pool. When I think about the things that seemed so important to me then ...! When the soldiers killed my dad, they also killed all my dreams. And I guess I've got a confession to make. When you and Uncle Peter had that big barney after Dad's funeral, I was going to get my own revenge, and that's why I joined the Cause. That's when my troubles really started.

Well, I can't spend too much time on this tape because

somebody could come in at any minute, so I'd better get to the point of why I'm makin' it in the first place. There's no easy way of sayin' what I'm about to say, Ma, so I guess I'll just have to come right out with it. If you are listening to this tape, the chances are that I am dead already. You see, I thought the guys back home were pretty bloodthirsty, but the people out here are real ruthless bastards. They seem prepared to kill at the drop of a hat, and I know they can get away with it, because they're certainly well connected. I figure the way things are going, that it's very likely I'll be their next victim. Especially if the job they've got lined up for me goes wrong. So, I've taken out this little bit of insurance that may give me some bargaining power, should I get the chance to use it. If you take this tape to the authorities, who knows, justice just might be done.

Here's the set-up so far and a list of names of people that I know to be involved. By the way, there's one particularly nasty customer who has given me a hard time since I came over here...

Peter switched off the tape at that point, and leaned over, clasping his head between his massive hands. 'Oh God! When will it end? Please God when will it ever end?' he said in a tearful whisper. 'How much more can that kid endure?'

By the time Kieran got up the next morning, Peter had prepared a large breakfast which they both sat down to in complete silence. Kieran was surprised to find that he still had an appetite considering all that had taken place the day before.

After the meal was over, Peter broke the silence. 'I hope you don't mind, Kieran, but I listened to your tape last night. It's a message from Kevin. But before I say anything, I think you had better hear it for yourself.'

Kieran didn't speak but nodded his head in agreement. Peter then reset the tape and they both settled down to listen, although he by this time was more interested in observing Kieran's reactions. At a point partway through the tape Peter noticed a solitary tear rolling down Kieran's cheek, although his facial expression failed to convey his inner feelings. When the tape finally finished, Peter got up and switched off the recorder, then waited for Kieran to respond, but Kieran said nothing. He seemed to be oblivious to his surroundings and stared blankly into space. Peter was by this time concerned for Kieran's mental state and was determined to force some kind of reaction, if only to prevent him from bottling it up inside.

'Have you thought about what you plan to do next?' asked Peter.

'Yes I have. I know exactly what I'm going to do,' he said in a deceptively calm yet determined voice.

'I see. Do you want to tell me about it?'

'I'm going to America.'

Peter held back his reaction and waited to see if Kieran was going to elaborate, but he didn't enlarge on his statement, for he was too preoccupied with his inner thoughts. Peter then decided to push him still further. 'So you think Kevin didn't make it?'

'I'm almost certain he didn't,' Kieran replied without a trace of emotion in his voice. 'I don't think there would have been an attack on my mother's house otherwise.'

'You'll need quite a lot of money if you're planning on going to America to find the people responsible.'

'I've got my savings and also my mother's money. I'll keep going until I find the bastards or until the money runs out, whichever comes first.'

'If you do find them, what then?' asked Peter.

'I think you know the answer to that one, Pete. I'll do what has to be done. I know what my father would have done. Look, don't try and stop me. My mind's made up. I don't care what it costs or how long it takes. I'm going to find these people.'

'But you must think of your own life, Kieran. Don't throw it away on a revenge trip. You're still a young man with a full life in front of you. Let the authorities deal with it,' said Peter.

'Huh! You've got to be kiddin'. Do you really think that the authorities will do anything? They'll do what they always do in a case like this. They'll write it off as just another sectarian killing. That's probably what these murderers are banking on. You don't honestly think that I could ever live a normal life again knowing that somebody had wiped out my family simply because it was politically expedient, do you?'

Peter could see the determination in Kieran's eyes and remembered the anger and rage that he himself had felt when his brother Patrick was killed, and how he wouldn't listen when Bridie had tried to discourage him from seeking revenge. He could also see the likeness between Kieran and his father and knew that nothing on earth would have prevented Patrick from trying to trace these killers. And why should he expect anything different from Patrick's son?

'I'd like to make a copy of that tape, Pete, so that I can leave one here with you, just in case anything happens to me. Then perhaps you can go to the authorities.'

Kieran stayed with Peter for a further two days, then made his way to Dublin from where he planned to get a flight to the States.

Before he left, Peter gave him a package without disclosing its contents and said, 'This was once your father's, so I suppose it's only right that you should have it now. I only hope that you don't ever have to use it.'

It had taken Alex Stenton only three days to arrange the attack on the McGuire household and to get confirmation back of a successful mission. But he waited until he saw the headlines in the local news before he made plans for his return to the US. Alex's wait for evidence was duly rewarded, when he saw this in the local newspaper: 'An unexplained raid took place on the McGuire household, killing outright a Mrs Bridie McGuire and her son Kieran ... two more victims of sectarian warfare!'

12

Steve Tulloch not only survived the attempt on his life but went on to fight the general election. By this time Labour were winning massive support from the people. Naturally, much of it was sympathy support, but there were also those who thought that if opposing factions were prepared to resort to these tactics they may well be considerably worse than any Labour Party ever was. A great deal of sympathy was gained as a consequence of the funeral of Rob Paterson, which had become a national affair because of the circumstances of his death. The police had been unable to come up with any suspects, which left the field wide open for wild rumours, and speculation. The chief unofficial suspects were the IRA, but they had made no official claim for the deed, something which they had always been quick to do in the past. Then there was the Loyalist paramilitary group. The Libyans and even the South Africans came under suspicion for a while. Rumours that the Conservatives were responsible were quickly scotched by the government. More and more polls were predicting a Labour landslide; it now only seemed a matter of time before a Labour victory was assured.

Meanwhile, police investigations into the Edinburgh Parade killing were continuing. The police had found the gun, the stopwatch and a rope, none of which proved very useful in indicating a suspect. All they could establish was that both the gun and the watch were Belgian makes, but the trail ended there. In response to appeals for information regarding suspicious behaviour in or around the Camera Obscura, the British police received reports of a man who was seen on four occasions at or near the Camera Obscura. His final visit was reported to have been on the day of the explosion.

Police produced an identikit picture of the man from these reports and circulated it throughout the country's police forces. After extensive inquiries, Glasgow police came up with a possible suspect whom they were investigating. It turned out that this man was an ex-army officer known to have extreme right-wing tendencies. A decision was made not to approach the man until his business interests had been fully investigated. So far, they had established that his company was a subsidiary of a larger organisation, which in turn appeared to be owned by CLC Industries.

Back in Washington, Tom Casey had received Alex Stenton's report confirming that his mission to organise a hit on McGuire family had been successfully completed. Tom was now feeling secure in the knowledge that he had taken care of all the risk areas of his first attempt at sabotaging the British economy. He was now contriving to deal with this situation from an entirely different approach. This time he had enlisted the aid of a few very influential business contacts, all of whom had large industrial commitments in the UK. Tom had managed to convince them of the many dangers to their business interests if a Labour government was allowed to flourish. This consortium of business associates, which included at least two heads of multinational corporations, was getting together to launch a new project called AROE, which simply meant the Accelerated Readjustment of an Economy.

This unsavoury alliance had a lot of financial clout to wield against any economy that it considered to be a threat to their interests. The aim was to organise and control a labour force of such proportions that it would have a significant effect on the economy of the victim country. The target was 1 million employees. The plan was to create a dependency situation, whereby small industries and their suppliers would be almost entirely dependent on one major core industry. This would create an extremely fragile structure, not unlike a house of cards, so that by pulling out key cards, it would fall. There were already many examples in existence of such structures, for example the motor industry. This industry, despite its automation, was still highly labour intensive. It was also supported by a large amount of peripheral industries such as suppliers of gear boxes, braking systems etcetera. These companies in turn depended on a whole army of suppliers for component parts. Collectively, it's likely that a million jobs are dependent both directly and indirectly on this particular core industry. Should the financial base that supported that core industry be removed, then the whole structure would undoubtedly fall.

The intention of Tom Casey and his associates was to create such a pyramid, to have a million people at their disposal, so that they would be in position to pull the plug when the time was right. At a prearranged date they would withdraw all their finances and other resources so swiftly that massive unemployment would be created practically overnight. The dole queues would be swamped. Investors would be quick to withdraw their funds and this, in turn, would create a domino effect throughout the whole British economy, leading to a run on the stock market. The fact that Tom Casey and his confederates were manipulating the whole situation would mean that they were in the best position to predict how the market would respond. This would then allow them to make the best investments. With such advanced knowledge they could make a killing on the stock exchange. Such a situation would be catastrophic financially to a British economy already swamped with unemployment and would inevitably lead to a public outcry.

Such a government would lose so much credibility that Parliament would be forced into a vote of no confidence, leading to a call for another general election with the Conservatives returning to power. The irony of this whole situation was that the consortium that instigated such a destabilisation would be in a position to make substantial profits on all fronts.

The economy, under a Labour government, would be rife for such a scenario simply because among the party's major pledges was, first and foremost, to reduce unemployment. Their manifesto clearly stated that they intended to invest in a massive drive to create employment. First of all, they would invest a considerable amount of money into a building and works programme consisting of roads, houses, bridges and projects such as the Channel Tunnel, which had originally been in private hands. The Labour government intended to buy enough shares in the project to stimulate sufficient interest to get it started, because private industry had been dragging its feet. Their next major step in creating employment would be to give incentives to foreign industries willing to start up factories in the UK, offering potential foreign investors factories on rent-free land for the first year of operation. They would also be offered major tax concessions for the first four years of operation, thus giving them an excellent opportunity to get into a quick profit-making situation. These concessions would be paid for by the money saved on unemployment benefit. Also, when these people who had been previously unemployed started work, they would become taxpayers again, and this new source of revenue would more than pay for the cost of the incentives given to foreign industries. A further incentive that had recently been proposed by the unions was strike-free contracts. Such proposals would prove irresistible to foreign investors and these were precisely the conditions that the Casey consortium would target in the AROE project.

The consortium would exploit such a situation in the following way. First, they would move their capital equipment into these brand new factories. This equipment would be transferred from Third World countries which were no longer so competitive because of their demands for higher wages. The exercise would amount to killing two birds with one stone: punishing the Third World countries for their new demands by pulling the plug on them, whilst at the same time making the UK more dependent on the consortium. Once the set-up was established, real profits could be made over the first year of operation, due to the benefits offered by the government. The consortium's next move would be to withdraw these profits at an appropriate appointed time. By the end of the first year major peripheral industries would have accumulated around the core industries. When enough dependent ancillary industry had accumulated, the time would be right to pull the plug.

This was the essence of the AROE project which the consortium was putting together. They had even considered a follow-up situation whereby the Third World countries would now be willing to make major concessions for the return and reinvestment of the same industry. It would then be quite a simple matter to transfer their capital equipment back to the Third World countries. The only major expense accrued by this time would be the transfer of capital equipment, but this should be more than offset by the profits made during that period.

As predicted, the Labour Party was duly elected with a landslide victory, which gave them an overall majority in the house. Their first policy implementation was to start up a Building and Works Programme in an attempt to combat unemployment. They also set up a committee to investigate new ways of attracting foreign industry to the country.

Tom Casey, who was representing the consortium, sent an envoy over to promote American interest in a major investment programme in the UK, which would be particularly interested in any incentives that the new Labour Government were offering. Delegates of the new government were only too happy to have talks with these representatives from the consortium and to discuss concessions to the right kind of investors. After a week of exploratory talks, serious negotiations got under way. It wasn't long before likely sites were being proposed for the new industry. The unions involved in these talks were proposing to negotiate non-strike agreements as a further incentive in exchange for a reasonable pay structure that would be allowed to grow in proportion with profits. Tom Casey and his associates were delighted. They couldn't be more pleased with the way things were going. They were now planning ways of accelerating the proposed programme.

13

Kieran McGuire arrived in Washington on 12th July. By the time the plane landed at Dulles airport the temperature in Washington had reached 100 degrees and record levels of humidity were being reported. Kieran had never experienced such heat before. He was sweating profusely and his clothes were sticking to him, causing him a great deal of discomfort. Fortunately, there were no hold-ups at customs and he didn't have to wait long for a cab to take him to his hotel.

By the time Kieran got to his room he was shattered. After unpacking his bags he lay down on the bed and tried to rest whilst collecting his thoughts. He had to remind himself why he was there and why he should be putting up with all this discomfort. Kieran forced himself to think back on recent events and follow them through step by step, not because he was some kind of masochist, but purely as a means of getting things back into perspective. He was trying hard to combat the confused mental state that he found himself in.

Of course, all that was wrong with him was that he was suffering from jet lag together with a mild case of heat exhaustion. Within minutes he was fast asleep. He was so exhausted that he slept through the rest of that afternoon and most of the evening. It was 8.30 pm when he first stirred, but only long enough to get out of his clothes and back into bed again.

The following morning Kieran awoke somewhat refreshed from his long sleep. After a quick shower he donned his summer gear then made for the hotel restaurant. As it was almost 24 hours since he had last eaten he was very hungry and could hardly wait to sample one of those large American breakfasts that he had heard so much about. Kieran was not disappointed at the enormous meal that was laid before him. Now that he was well fortified he felt ready to explore Washington city, allowing himself time to adjust to this new environment.

Kieran decided to take advantage of the bus tour which the hotel had laid on for its patrons. This was a two and a half hour sightseeing trip round the regular tourist attractions, starting with the Jefferson Memorial. Kieran was impressed by this magnificent structure overlooking the Tidal Basin, a vast expanse of blue water surrounded by an abundance of brilliantly coloured cherry trees which were a gift from Tokyo City. From there the bus travelled along West Basin Drive and through the park to the Lincoln Memorial, an enormous monument in white marble to the man of wisdom. The statue is situated in the centre of the monument which contained 36 Doric columns representing the states in the Union at the time of Jefferson's death. The coach then travelled east along the central tour route where it made a brief stop at the National Science Foundation, after which it continued past the Washington Monument on its way to the Smithsonian Institute. This was certainly the highlight of the tour. The Smithsonian is a museum of history and technology, featuring everything from the largest African bush elephant to the *Apollo II* Command Module which carried Armstrong, Collins and Aldrin to the moon and back. By the time the tour was over Kieran was feeling a bit more acclimatised to his surroundings, but his head was buzzing with the facts and figures that had been fired at him by the tour guide.

When he got back to the hotel, Kieran was ready to eat again. During his meal he consulted a city map, looking for Ward Place, which he had been told was just north of Washington Circle. This was Kathy Conner's address, which he had obtained from the tape. After lunch it took Kieran two hours to find the place, only to be told by neighbours that she hadn't been seen around the neighbourhood for about a month. Kieran was feeling a bit frustrated, but he told himself that he hadn't come all this way for nothing. He was prepared to knock on every door in the block until he found someone who knew where she might be.

Kieran's luck took a turn for the better, because the fourth door that he tried was opened by an elderly lady who said that Kathy worked in a department store called Styles at the local mall. Kieran looked at his watch. It was now four o'clock. Good, he thought to himself. Unless today is a public holiday there's a good chance that it would still be open. Having obtained some directions from the helpful old lady, Kieran made for the local mall.

On arrival at the shopping centre he had no difficulty locating the store, for it turned out to be the biggest and most popular one in the mall. Styles turned out to be a massive complex on four levels. The sheer size of the place was going to make his task more difficult than he expected. After a few inquiries at the ground level, Kieran was able to establish the department and floor where Kathy worked. At last, he thought. Now I'm getting somewhere.

On arrival at the correct floor, Kieran asked the first uniformed assistant that he came across if she could help him locate Kathy Conners. It happened that he was talking to Linda Johnstone, who was astounded to find someone inquiring about Kathy at the store, but she recognised the Irish accent and suspected that he might be one of Kathy's relatives. However, before she was prepared to answer any questions about Kathy, she wanted to know who was making the enquiry.

'My name's Kieran McGuire,' he said. At this stage, Kieran didn't see any need for deception. After all, if Kathy Conners had sent the tape, she must be an ally.

'Oh!' said Linda, 'You must be Kathy's cousin from Ireland.' This was an assumption that Linda had made when she saw the name on the package that she had posted for Kath.

'More a friend than an actual cousin,' said Kieran. 'Could you tell me where I might find her, please? It's really very important and I have come a long way to see her.'

Linda, having established what she thought was a legitimate link between Kathy and Kieran, namely the parcel, became less guarded. Her reservations with regard to answering questions about Kathy stemmed from some recent newspaper and police inquiries about her. There had been an unfavourable news report on Kath and the circumstances surrounding her hospitalisation.

'Well, Mr McGuire, I'm afraid I've got some very bad news for you.'

'What do you mean?' exclaimed Kieran, fearing once more that his journey might have been for nothing.

'Kathy was taken into hospital four weeks ago suffering from pneumonia and her condition steadily deteriorated. I'm afraid she passed away just ten days ago.'

Kieran was stunned. His face turned chalk white as he struggled to deal with this unexpected information. It seemed that just about everybody he had been in contact with during the last month had died or been killed. His confused mind was desperately searching for explanations. He even started to think that somehow he was responsible. Linda mistook the look of shock and confusion on Kieran's face for grief, and was anxious to console him.

'Kathy was my best friend,' said Linda. 'I know how you must feel. Look, have you just arrived in Washington?'

'Er, em . . . yes,' said Kieran, still struggling to sort out the confusion that was going on in his head. 'Yes, I just arrived in Washington a few hours ago, though I have booked into a hotel.'

'I see,' said Linda. 'I know, why don't you come home with me before you go back to your hotel? You could have a meal at our place and you can tell me how you came to know Kathy. We can't leave you on your own under these circumstances,' she said compassionately, 'especially on your first day in America.'

'Hey, that's awfully good of you to be so kind, Miss . . . ?'

'Oh, I'm sorry. I haven't introduced myself. My name is Linda Johnstone. Kathy was a very close friend of mine.'

'I don't know if I should take advantage . . .'

'Oh don't be silly,' said Linda before he could finish. 'I won't hear of any objections. Look, I'll have finished work in about fifteen minutes. Why don't you go and grab a cup of coffee and I'll join you in the cafeteria when I get cleared up in here.'

* * *

Kieran got a grand welcome at the Johnstone household, for Linda had taken the trouble to phone in advance to tell them of Kieran's predicament and that she had invited him home for a meal. Kieran felt good to be amongst family people again and his first impression of the Johnstones was a favourable one. They were a close-knit family and he could tell by their mutual respect for each other that they were Christian people.

After the meal they gathered together in the lounge for a drink. George Johnstone was very interested in knowing how things were, back in the UK. He asked Kieran if the British government were really serious about closing down American bases or whether he thought this was some kind of vote-catching electioneering. Kieran, up until this point in his life, had been completely non-political. He had hardly ever looked at a news bulletin so he was unable to give George an informed opinion of the situation. George was a bit disappointed by Kieran's response, for he had been looking forward to a bit of friendly political banter and had anticipated some trading of views on the subject.

About ten o'clock the Johnstones declared that it was time for them to turn in. They had sensed that the young couple wanted some time alone, so they retired to bed early, leaving them the rest of the evening to themselves. Linda was aware of their tact, but she found herself feeling embarrassed by it, for she didn't realise that she had been giving off such obvious signals. Linda was usually very careful about showing her innermost feelings. She had certainly taken a shine to the young athletic Irishman and had found his conversation stimulating and his candour refreshing.

She also sensed, though, that underneath all that Irish charm there lurked a darker side to Kieran McGuire, a darker side that occasionally showed through, especially when the subject of families arose. She found Kieran on these occasions to be very evasive and almost argumentative if he was pressed in any way about his family. She had also noticed that he was uneasy with the way he handled such situations and his attempts to change the subject were clumsy and far from subtle. Linda sensed from Kieran's behaviour that he had recently experienced some major family trauma and was obviously reluctant to talk about it. Her powers of observation had been developed when she was a young girl in Edinburgh and were a consequence of her being deprived of companionship. She had often, therefore, found herself in the position of observer rather than participant in relationships. It was not surprising that she had developed skills in this area.

For Kieran's part, he felt quite relieved when the Johnstones retired to bed, purely because their questions, innocent though they were, seemed to be getting closer to areas of his recent past that he wasn't yet ready to discuss. He was also thankful for the opportunity to be alone with Linda, for he found himself becoming more and more attracted to her. This wasn't too surprising, considering that she had good looks together with a very pleasing figure. Kieran also found himself attracted to her soft voice, her caring concern for others, and her willingness to put herself out for a complete stranger. She had also shown a great depth of understanding. Kieran found that he had to fight the urge to confide in her because her manner was so disarming.

Their obvious attraction to each other was evident in the way they conducted themselves for the rest of that evening. They exchanged niceties and restricted their comments to polite conversation, paying particular attention to each other's signals so as not to offend in any way that might upset the rapport that they had already built between them. It was midnight before they decided to call an end to their evening. It had already been agreed by the Johnstone family that Kieran would stay overnight.

By the time he got to his room he was feeling exhausted. This time it was mental fatigue, for most of the early part of the evening had been spent trying to parry Mr Johnstone's searching questions. His feeling of exhaustion was, however, balanced by the pleasant glow that he felt following his captivating tête-a-tête with Linda. When Kieran got into bed he realised that his mind had drifted into an almost trance-like state. He forced himself to snap out of it.

Once again he forced his mind to recall all the recent traumatic events that had taken place, for he had to remind himself why he was really in Washington. Kieran had allowed himself to be seduced by the friendliness of these people and the cosy environment they had provided for him. Before going to sleep he made up his mind that something should be done to redress the situation, that he must put things back into perspective. If things turned out the way he expected them to, then he was going to be a man on the run, for Kieran's objective was to search for and destroy the people who had systematically wiped out his whole family. He felt that he mustn't let anything get in the way of that goal. He reconciled himself to the fact that there was no longer a future for him, so there was no point in cultivating a new relationship as he was unlikely to be around long enough to enjoy it, especially if the authorities caught up with him.

Linda went to bed feeling a warm glow inside, and wondered what she could do to prolong Kieran's stay, so that their relationship would have a chance to develop. The more she thought about him the more she liked him, but these thoughts were punctuated by feelings of concern. It was obvious to Linda that Kieran was a deeply disturbed young man, no matter how hard he tried to hide it. She was very aware that there was something amiss and speculated over some possibilities that might explain his behaviour. Linda tried to analyse the information that she already had about Kieran. He had never made it clear why he had come all this way to see Kathy. There obviously wasn't any romantic connection between them, for Kathy, secretive though she was, had never ever intimated that there was someone she cared for in Ireland, and she had always shown a keen interest in Gregg Donoghue. Why did Kathy contact Kieran? What was the message about? Linda fell asleep that night with a head full of unanswered questions.

The next morning Kieran didn't waken until nine o'clock. It was the best sleep that he had had in weeks. After breakfast Linda offered to drive him back to his hotel. In the car she tentatively quizzed him about how long he intended staying in Washington, and if he had any other business to attend to while he was here. Kieran told her that he was now going to try and locate a certain Gregg Donoghue, who also happened to be a close friend of Kathy's.

'Oh, Gregg!' exclaimed Linda. 'I know Gregg Donoghue.'

'You do?' asked Kieran.

'Why yes. Gregg would often phone me when he was looking for Kathy. You see, Kathy and I used to spend a lot of time together.'

'Perhaps you can tell me where I might find him then?' inquired Kieran.

'Aah...' she said. 'That's a difficult one. You see Gregg tended to be a bit secretive about where he stayed when he was in Washington. I don't think even Kathy knew where, although some of the time he stayed at her place. As far as I could make out, Gregg never stayed in one place long enough to set up house.'

'Oh, is that right?' said Kieran thoughtfully. 'Perhaps he's a travelling salesman, then?' Kieran was trying to establish just how much Linda knew about Gregg.

'Oh no. I shouldn't think so. Kathy suspected that he worked with the FBI, although she never explained why she thought so. That could certainly be one possible explanation for his nomadic behaviour.'

'Yes, perhaps you're right,' replied Kieran. 'Have you any idea how I might find him then?'

'I guess not, and I shouldn't think he's likely to phone me now that Kathy's gone. If he does, though, shall I tell him that you're looking for him?'

'Oh yes, please do.'

'Will you be staying in Washington long, Kieran?'

'I don't know exactly how long I'll be staying,' he said.

'Well, will I see you again?'

'I certainly hope so,' replied Kieran. 'Can I take you out for a meal somewhere? Perhaps you could show me a bit of Washington.'

'Oh yes!' exclaimed Linda. 'That would be wonderful.'

'Good, then I'll pick you up around seven o'clock tomorrow, all right?'

'OK. That's fine. I'll see you then.'

This was a timely end to their conversation, as they were just arriving at the hotel.

When Kieran got to his room he tried to figure out his next move, knowing that he had no alternative but to stay on in Washington for a while and see if Donoghue turned up. He hadn't figured on quite so many complications and had thought that, once he located Kathy, a chain reaction might take place leading him to all the parties concerned.

He took out a copy of his brother's tape and played it on the hand-set that he had picked up at the airport. He figured that there just had to be another line of investigation. He couldn't see himself just waiting around a hotel room indefinitely. Listening attentively to the tape, he heard Kevin's voice referring to the airline with which he was to travel to London.

'Atlantic Air. Yes! That's it!' shouted Kieran, switching off the tape. Kevin was to travel to London disguised as a crew member on one of their regular flights. Why didn't he think of this before? It should be much easier to find an airline company than an individual. Now what other names did Kevin mention on his tape? Kieran moved the tape controls to fast forward and stopped intermittently, until he came to the part of the tape where he remembered names being mentioned. The next name he heard was that of Roy Stirling. Now then, what do we know about this guy? he thought as he rewound the tape and lay back on his bed, prepared to listen to the whole tape over again. This was to be his standby target.

14

Kieran McGuire had hired a car that evening and was on his way to pick up Linda Johnstone at her home. For the first time in weeks he was feeling good about himself and was looking forward to his date with her. It had been years since he had been out with a girl and he was feeling quite excited about the prospect. As he arrived at Linda's house he could see her standing in the driveway waiting to meet him. She looked stunning in black velvet trousers and a white fur jacket.

'All ready for the high life?' said Kieran as he opened the car door for her to enter. 'Where are we off to, then? Since this is your territory, you'd better decide.'

'Well, I know a great restaurant to start with,' said Linda.

As Kieran and Linda set off towards the city they were too wrapped up in each other to notice the dark green station wagon following them. It wasn't until Kieran opened up the throttle and started speeding up the freeway in an attempt to impress Linda that he noticed the car in his rearview mirror, weaving in and out of the traffic, following his every manoeuvre. Meanwhile Linda, who was not in the least impressed by his speeding, asked him to slow down before he got them both killed. Kieran reluctantly conceded the point and slowed down to a regular 55 mph. As he did, he observed that the car behind had also reduced speed to match his own. Now he was convinced that they were being followed, but by whom?

Kieran figured that it was unlikely to be the police, for surely they would have pulled him over when he was speeding, unless they intended to stop him at a more appropriate part of the freeway. By this time Linda had noticed Kieran's preoccupation with the rearview mirror.

'What's wrong, Kieran?'

'I think someone's following us,' he said. 'Can you think why anyone would want to?'

'It's the police,' said Linda. 'It's got to be. Who else could it be?' she said in a slightly agitated voice.

'Take it easy. I haven't figured it out yet. Look, I'm gonna slow right down, at the next junction. If that's the police then they're gonna have to stop me or overtake.'

At this point, Kieran's mind was working overtime trying to figure out the possibilities. After all he had been through, anything was possible. As they approached the junction, their speed had reduced to 28 mph. The green car had started to close in on them and gradually pulled out to the side as if to overtake. Kieran by this time could clearly make out the occupants of the car. He could see the driver repeatedly looking back over his shoulder towards the rear seat as the gap between the two cars lessened. Then, quite suddenly, the rear passenger came into view. Kieran could see that he was starting to lean forward as their car was just about to pull level. Kieran's heart pounded as he sensed the imminent danger.

Instinctively, he slammed his foot hard on the accelerator and pulled the steering wheel hard over to the right. There was a major collision between the two cars as Kieran's headlamp and front wing smashed into the side of the other vehicle, causing it to swerve violently. He could see the rear seat passenger being thrown to the far side of the interior and a gun fall from his hand as he reeled back. There was nothing for it now but to get out of there as fast as he possibly could. Kieran's car shot across the front of the stationwagon at high speed and, within seconds, opened up a considerable gap between the two cars.

Linda had not seen what Kieran was reacting to and she thought her companion had quite suddenly gone mad. She screamed and yelled at Kieran, her hands flailing and hammering into his side. Kieran was not far from panic-stricken himself, and was fighting desperately to keep a clear head. Until now he had reacted spontaneously to the situation, as there hadn't been time to think, but all his instincts were to get as far as possible from his pursuers.

Linda's was making frantic efforts to relieve him of the wheel, and again Kieran reacted swiftly. It was almost a reflex action as he suddenly released his right hand from the wheel just long enough to deliver a tremendous blow to the side of her face. It was the only way he could control her. Linda went reeling back into her seat only to be propelled forward again by the momentum of the car. She came to rest slumped over her seatbelt in a crumpled, motionless heap. She was out cold.

Kieran's speed was being impeded by the build-up of traffic in front of him. He looked again into his rearview mirror and could see that the station wagon was once more gaining on him. In anticipation of being fired upon by his pursuers, he swerved the car from side to side. A bullet smashed through the rear window, shattering glass all over the rear seat. Thank God Linda was unconscious. Another loud pinging noise was heard as a bullet ricocheted off the nearside wing of his car.

Kieran decided that they were getting too close for comfort, and that it was time to substitute guile for speed. He glanced out of his side window and was quick to register a gap in the traffic travelling in the other direction. Aware that he might never get another chance like this, he instantly made a hard, sharp turn to the left. This manoeuvre was so fierce that the whole car lurched over to one side, causing severe tension on its suspension system. Kieran's car shot across the central reservation and onto the south-bound lane, where he completed his U-turn just seconds before the oncoming traffic caught up with him. This caused sheer chaos on both sides of the freeway as cars swerved and braked in an effort to avoid collision. There was the sound of screeching brakes and horns blasting.

The pursuing vehicle was quick to follow Kieran's stratagem and it too crossed over the central reservation, only to be brought to a sudden terminal halt as two vehicles collided with it, causing an enormous explosion and a burst of flames as the station wagon's petrol tank ignited.

Kieran was less than 100 yards down the freeway when he heard the explosion and looked in his rearview mirror. He could just make out the tail section of the green vehicle jutting out from the wreckage of twisted metal and the billowing black smoke. Oh my God! Not more deaths. Jesus, when will it all end? Why me? Why am I the centre of so much death and destruction? He slowed the car down to a normal 55 mph as there was no longer any need for escape.

Just then, Linda started to recover. The explosion and the sharp movements of the car had brought her back to consciousness. Kieran heard Linda groan as she stirred and looked over towards her, just in time to see her eyes open.

'How are you feeling Linda?' She was still groggy from the blow to her face and hadn't quite come to her senses, so was unable to respond. 'Hold on, Linda. A few minutes longer and we'll be leaving the freeway at the next junction, then I'll pull over at the first opportunity.'

Linda lifted her hand to her face and stroked her cheek. She could still feel the pain, and a lump where a swelling had appeared. It was all coming back to her now. Kieran was driving like a madman and she had tried to get control of the wheel, then he had hit her. Yes! That's it.

'You hit me!' said Linda out loud. 'You bloody hit me.'

'Now hold on, Linda. I can explain if you just hold fire. Everything is under control. See that junction up ahead? That's where we'll leave the freeway and we're gonna find someplace where we can stop and talk.'

Linda sat there in stunned silence as the car veered off to the left and started down the slip road. She was still confused and was trying to get her head straightened out. She had been thinking that Kieran's behaviour was completely out of character ... but was it? She hadn't known this man long enough to make such an assessment.

Kieran pulled into the first drive-in restaurant they came to. 'This will do nicely,' he said.

'Not exactly what I had in mind,' said Linda sardonically. 'It's hardly the place for fur coat and velvet trousers now is it?'

'Listen lass,' said Kieran impatiently. 'You're not fully aware of the situation we're in. We've got far more important things to worry about than your fur coat. Have you looked at the rear window yet?'

'You don't mean that pile of broken glass on the back seat do you? No doubt the result of your crazy driving! Just where on earth did you learn to drive anyway?'

Kieran was getting just a bit exasperated by this time and jumped out of the car, slamming the door behind him. He walked over to the crumpled wing.

'Do you see that?' he shouted, pointing to a small round hole at the side of the wing. 'That's a bloody bullet hole! The first bullet smashed the rear window! If it wasn't for my crazy driving, neither you nor I would be here to tell the tale.'

Linda was astounded. She just couldn't bring herself to believe what she was hearing. Her impressions of what had taken place were hard enough to cope with, but this was another matter. This was bordering on sheer fantasy. Who would want to kill me or Kieran for that matter? He only arrived yesterday, or was it the day before? So much had happened in such a short space of time that Linda had lost track of what day it was. She got out of the car to have a look at the hole that Kieran was pointing to.

After examining the bullet hole in the wing she looked up at Kieran and tears welled up in her eyes. 'What on earth is going on?' she said tearfully.

Kieran grabbed hold of her and put his arms around her. 'Take it easy,' he said. 'Just take it easy, we're going to get to the bottom of this, believe me.'

They got back into the car and Kieran said, 'I think it's time I told you exactly why I came over here. But first I think we'd better get this car off the road. It's far too conspicuous. Oh wait a minute, we haven't eaten yet. What do you want, Linda?'

'I'm not hungry any more. There's no way I could eat now.'

'Well look, I'll tell you what we'll do. If I drop you off at that hotel we just passed, you can stay there until I find someplace to dump this car and then when I get back we can discuss the situation more fully.'

After dropping Linda at the hotel Kieran drove the car for a few miles up a nearby dirt track until he came upon a large area of open countryside. He then drove into the middle of a field, making sure that he was well clear of the road. He got out of the car, removed the petrol cap, then took off his tie and lowered one end of it into the petrol tank and waited until it was soaked through with fuel. He then left approximately 10 inches of petrol-soaked material hanging from the tank, thus creating a fuse. Kieran went back into the car and ignited the dashboard cigar lighter, which he used to set the tie alight. As soon as it burst into flames Kieran ran as fast as he could, putting as much ground as possible between himself and the car. He cleared a considerable distance before the tank exploded, then stopped for a moment and watched as the flames spread throughout the rest of the vehicle.

Kieran had walked for about a mile down the dirt road when a passing pick-up truck stopped and the driver offered him a lift. Another 15 minutes later he was back at the hotel. Linda was furious.

'Where on earth have you been? At least two men have tried to pick me up. I've never been so embarrassed! How could you leave me sitting alone in a hotel lobby all this time?'

'I'm sorry, Linda. I guess it took a bit longer than I expected.'

'And where is your tie, for heaven's sake?' she said impatiently.

'Never mind my tie. We've got far more important things to talk about. Let's go into the lounge and have a drink while we discuss this. I don't know about you, but I sure need one.'

Kieran related what he had experienced over the last two weeks. He described to Linda, as dispassionately as he could, the calamitous events that had overtaken and transformed his life. He also gave her a brief history of his father's involvement in the IRA and how Kevin had run away to America.

Linda was utterly appalled at what she was hearing. Although she had heard about the sectarian killings in Ireland, she had always found it difficult to relate to them. The British media used to give almost daily reports on the troubles in Ireland until people became quite saturated with such news. This overexposure to unpleasant events had led many people to switch off.

'Oh, Kieran,' Linda said as she reached out to put her hand on his arm. 'I had no idea you had been through so much. Please forgive me for my impatience. It's not until you actually meet the victims of such tragedies that you are able to get some insight into the horror of it all.' Linda's heart was stirred and filled with hurt and compassion for Kieran.

Kieran, concerned that Linda was about to break into a tearful outburst, quickly continued with his story. 'I haven't yet told you why I came over to America in the first place, and why I was trying to locate Kathy Conners. You see, shortly before my mother died, the postman had delivered a parcel. She was still holding that parcel when I dragged her body from the fire. This package contained a cassette that Kevin sent to us from New York. It seems that he'd got himself in yet another corner, and this time he figured there was a good chance that he might not get out alive. Kevin had made a tape recording telling us what he had been pressured into doing. Now before I go on, Linda, don't get me wrong: my brother Kevin was no saint. He had done a few bad things in his life but as far as he was concerned he was fighting for Ireland, the same as our father had done before him. Anyway, it seems that some extremely influential organisation over here was trying to pressurise Kevin into taking part in an assassination attempt on a prospective government head.'

'What?' said Linda incredulously. 'An assassination! Do you realise what you're saying?'

'Yes, I realise only too well what I'm saying. It's my firm belief that I've lost all that remained of my family because the perpetrators of this crime were trying to cover their tracks. So you'd better let me finish, for your own life may very well depend on it.'

'I'm sorry, Kieran, believe me. I won't interrupt again. It's just that this whole situation seems so incredible. It's like something out of a Bond movie.'

'Anyway, as I was saying. Kevin's tape not only told us about the conspiracy but also revealed the names of at least two of the participants. One of them was keeping him prisoner in a house in New York, and I'm gonna take particular pleasure in sorting him out,' said Kieran with measured anger in his voice. 'And the other one so happens to be that FBI friend of yours, Gregg Donoghue.'

'Oh no! Not Gregg! Surely not him,' said Linda.

'I'm afraid so,' said Kieran gravely. 'Kathy Conners's friend. His name is on the tape.'

'Just a minute,' said Linda as a thought suddenly dawned on her. 'This tape you're referring to ... I wonder. Could this have been the package that I posted?'

'You posted it?' said Kieran in surprise.

'Yes. Shortly before Kathy passed away, she asked me to post a small brown package for her. That's where I saw your name. The parcel was addressed to a Mrs B. McGuire. Yes, I remember, because Gregg was with me when I posted it and he seemed to be very interested in who it was going to. He certainly registered that the name on the package was McGuire.' Linda's mind was just starting to tune in to all the implications.

'Does this mean, then, that Kathy was posting this package for Kevin? It's all starting to fit into place now. But wait a minute, if Gregg Donoghue works for the FBI ... You're not saying that the agency is also involved in all this, are you?'

'I don't know,' said Kieran. 'But all the indications seem to point that way. So let's try and summarise. My guess is that Gregg suspected the package you posted was from Kevin. He must have decided that it could be some kind of insurance Kevin was taking out, by letting his family back home know what was going on, which is exactly what it was. The only snag is that Kevin said on the tape that, should we receive the message, then it meant that he was probably already dead.'

'This must mean that Kathy knew Kevin was dead!' interjected Linda.

'Yes. But we don't know what Kathy's involvement was in this affair.'

'I'm afraid I have no idea,' said Linda. 'Kathy never mentioned Kevin to me. The first I heard about him was when you arrived. I always thought she was pretty close to Gregg. But mind you, as it turned out, there was a lot about Kathy that I didn't know.'

'If Gregg did figure it the way I suggested,' said Kieran, 'then that may well explain the attack on my mother, which was probably intended to kill me as well. Let's face it, if these people were prepared to assassinate Steve Tulloch and his running mate Rob Paterson, then killing my family was going to be no major obstacle to them. It may also explain where you come into all this.'

'So where do I fit into all this? And what's all this got to do with a car following us and all that shooting? And how did you get away from that car?'

'I didn't,' said Kieran. 'They were involved in a collision on the freeway.'

'Oh! No! Surely not more deaths,' she said.

'I don't know what happened,' said Kieran. 'But I wasn't hanging around to find out. Look, Linda, your part in all this is a very significant one, I'm afraid.'

'How do you mean?' said Linda in an almost inaudible whisper.

'It looks to me as if you're the one they're after, since you're Kathy's best friend. And didn't Gregg Donoghue know that? They wouldn't know how much Kathy had told you, or if indeed she had told you anything. But one thing's for sure, it looks like they just don't want to take any chances.'

'But how do we know that it's not you they're looking for?'

'That's easy because there's no way they could have known that I was still alive. After the attack on my mother's house, the local papers reported that we were both killed.'

'But surely there would have been some evidence of two people being in the house at the time of the fire? They would hardly just assume that you were there.'

'Yes, you're right. There was another person in the house at the time.'

'Who was it?'

'I don't want to go into that just now. It's a long story and I'd rather not discuss it at the moment. Anyway, it looks like I'm not going to remain anonymous for much longer.'

'Why's that?'

'Well, once the FBI traced the registration number of that hired car, they're going to find out who I am, and that my name's McGuire. Then things will really hit the fan, especially now that they've linked you to me.'

'But I know nothing!' said Linda.

'It's not what you know that counts! It's what they think you know. And there's too much at stake for them to take the risk. It won't take them long to trace my hotel from the car hire company, so when they finally get round to searching my room, they're sure to find Kevin's tape. I'm afraid it looks very bad, Linda. I don't mean to scare you but it looks like we're in it up to our necks. Until now we have assumed that Gregg Donoghue was working for the FBI, which means we're gonna have the whole organisation after us. But there is a chance that Gregg's just a rotten apple working for an outside organisation. Let's hope that the latter is the case, but we'll have to work on the assumption that we're up against the FBI, at least until we know better. You realise that you won't be able to go home for a while: they're almost certain to be waiting for you.'

'But, what about my family? How are they to know what's going on? Oh Kieran, what are we going to do?'

'We're gonna survive, that's what we're gonna do. Meanwhile, we'll stop over here for the night, after we get something to eat that is. I'm starving.'

'Oh, how could you even think of food at a time like this. Aren't you scared?'

'I'm as scared as you are, but we've still got to eat. Now, let's see what they've got in the restaurant.'

15

'There's an outside call for you, Mr Donoghue. It's from the Columbia Hospital. Are you free to take it?'

'Who is it, Ann?'

'He won't say, sir. Shall I put him through?'

'Yes put him on.'

'Donoghue here, what can I do for you? ... Who? ... What the hell are you doing in the Columbia? What on earth happened?'

Gregg's call was from the driver of the car which had been following Linda and Kieran. His partner had been killed instantly in the multi-car collision when they made chase across the central reservation of the freeway. The survivor was miraculously thrown clear, and ended up with a broken collar bone, a broken arm and a compound leg fracture.

'We got a make on the car. It was a hired car from the Morgan Car Hire Agency but I haven't been able to follow that one up. That's why I'm phoning you now. It looks like I'm gonna be in dock for quite a while.'

Gregg was fuming. He knew that Tom Casey was going to accuse him of being responsible for yet another foul up.

'When and where did all this take place?' he asked sternly.

'I reckon it was about three hours ago on the...'

'Three hours ago!' interrupted Gregg.

'Look! You're bloody lucky to be gettin' any report at all! My partner never made it. You know what I mean? He's dead, bloody dead. Got it?'

'OK, OK I got the message,' said Gregg. 'Keep your hair on. Look I'm sorry about your buddy. Which way were they headin'?'

'They were heading north on route 95.'

'OK, thanks for reporting in when you did. Look, I'm sorry if I was a bit insensitive, it's just that...'

Gregg heard a sudden heavy click on the other end of the line. His operative was obviously not buying his untimely apology.

Gregg had been so fired up about his two operatives losing Linda that he forgot to ask for a description of the person who was travelling with Linda. There was obviously no point in phoning him back as the guy was certainly in no mood to cooperate. Gregg decided to send somebody down to the hospital to interview the irate agent and to see if he could get a description of the other occupant of the car.

So now there are two of them, thought Gregg. Who the hell can the other person be? This is sure turning into one big headache! Well, if it was a hired car it's unlikely to be Linda Johnstone who was driving it, as she had a car of her own. Whoever was driving certainly knew what they were doing if they were able to get clear away from two experienced agents. Gregg sent an immediate signal to all the agencies in the surrounding states, giving the registration and description of the vehicle. Their orders were to stop the car on sight and to apprehend the occupants. He also assigned another two agents to take over the chase.

Gregg was getting more agitated the more he thought about the other occupant of the car. We've gotta pin this one down now, he thought, switching on his intercom. 'Listen Ann. Send somebody down to the Morgan Car Hire Agency. You'll find the address in the book. Oh, and make sure that they're a badge holder. I want them to pick up an application form that was filled in by the hirer of a blue Ford. The registration is...' Gregg reckoned he would at least get a name and an address from this inquiry and that would be a major start.

Within the hour Gregg had the name and the address of Linda's companion on his desk. He looked at it for a full minute in stunned silence and extreme consternation. The message before him read: 'Kieran McGuire, Parkview Hotel, Washington'. What had started off as a major headache was now turning into a full-blown nightmare.

Gregg got back on to his secretary. 'Listen. I want you to hold all further incoming calls until you get hold of Alex Stenton. You'll have the number in your desk diary and, Ann, this is top priority. If you can't locate him at his office, find out where he is and get him to get in touch with me right away.'

Fifteen minutes later Alex Stenton was on the phone. 'Hi, Gregg, what's all the panic about? What's all this about top priority?'

'Alex! I'm afraid I've got some bad news for you. There's a guy called Kieran McGuire.'

'He's been staying at the Parkview Hotel in Washington. I don't know how long he's been staying there, not yet anyway.'

'OK, what's the connection? There's gotta be a few thousand McGuires living in this part of the world, you know that. That's why they have a St Patrick's Day parade here in New York every year.'

'Alex, this one is at the moment on the run with Linda Johnstone. Now, need I say more? Or do you figure that's just another coincidence?'

There was silence on the other end of the line.

'Hey! Alex. Are you still there?'

'Yea, I'm still here. Have you told Tom Casey about this?'

'Are you kidding?' came back Gregg with thinly disguised astonishment. 'I'm in enough trouble as it is without asking for more.'

'Look, why don't you and I get together on this and see if we can sort it out between us?'

'I'm all for that. That's why I called you in the first place. I'm planning on searching McGuire's hotel room this evening. Do you want me to wait until you come over or shall I go ahead without you?'

'I don't know how soon I can get over there but you can bet your bottom dollar I'll be there as soon as I can. You go ahead and search his room. You know what you're looking for. I'll have to go now. See you later.'

That night Gregg went to Kieran's hotel and searched his room. There wasn't much luggage, just a holdall and a small briefcase. The holdall hadn't been unpacked and, going by the amount of clothes that it contained, the owner hadn't intended being around for long. In the briefcase was an assortment of US road maps, some tourist paraphernalia and a shaving kit. In the side pocket Gregg found a World War II German Luger with two cartridge magazines. Now this is much more interesting, thought Gregg. I wonder what the lab boys will make of this little baby.

The room showed few signs of disturbance, although the washbasin looked as if it had been used recently. There were the usual toothpaste stains, a wet soap and damp face cloth. He turned to the bed and, although it had been made, the top cover was considerably wrinkled as if someone had lain on it. There was an indentation in the underside of the pillow, and there he found Kieran's tape recorder. He smiled in anticipation.

'Well, I wonder?' he whispered to himself as he sat down on the bed and pressed the 'Play' button. It was eerie listening to Kevin's voice again, like being haunted by the dead. But now he was certain. Gregg could picture him in his mind, lying on the bed playing the tape over and over again, working up hate. We'd better get to this guy in a hurry, before he gets to us, he thought to himself. Gregg slipped the recorder into the briefcase which he took with him as he left the room.

Alex Stenton arrived in Washington the next day. He hadn't slept the night before and was feeling decidedly ragged. By the time he got to Gregg's office his concern was outwardly apparent. He really looked quite anxious. It was the first time that Gregg had seen Alex lose his cool. He always had Stenton figured as a cold-blooded character who never showed signs of emotion.

'Hello, Gregg. Did you find anything at this guy McGuire's place?'

'You won't believe what I found, Alex. It could hardly be much worse, believe me.'

'What! What do you mean?'

'I've got the tape, yes the tape that Linda Johnstone sent to Kevin's family.'

'No! No, you can't have. That's impossible! They're dead, they're all dead. I saw the reports in the local paper: mother and son both killed outright.'

'Don't ask me to explain it. I'll let you hear the tape and you can make up your own mind.'

Alex settled down to listen to it. 'OK, I've heard enough. Are there any more names on there, other than yours and Roy's?'

'No. As far as he was concerned, we were it.'

'Thank goodness for that,' said Alex. 'How on earth did he get hold of a bloody tape recorder anyway?' he said angrily.

'There's no point in going into that now,' replied Gregg. 'What's done is done. What's important now is how we're gonna find them.'

'We've got to find them, and soon. Wait a minute,' Alex said thoughtfully. 'He's only got two names to work with so perhaps we can use this to our advantage.'

'What do you mean?'

'Well, think about it. This guy's obviously over here on a personal revenge mission. He wants to settle the score himself, otherwise he would have taken the tape straight to the police. Perhaps we can use you and Roy as bait to flush him out. That just might be quicker than chasing him all over the country. My bet is that he doesn't plan to leave the country until he's settled the score.'

'It sounds a bit risky to me,' said Gregg.

'Tough!' replied Alex. 'If you had been a bit more careful in the first place, we wouldn't be in this mess.'

'Listen, Alex, before you go passing the buck, you were supposed to take care of the Irish end personally. If you had done your job right there wouldn't be a Kieran McGuire to worry about, now would there?'

'OK, OK, there's no point in us fighting over whose fault it is. Let's kill that one right now. What's the latest on your search programme?'

'Zilch, I'm afraid. There's been no sign of that car anywhere in the last twenty-four hours. Either they've been moving bloody fast or they've decided to lie low for a while.'

'I want to get back to this bait idea,' said Alex. 'I think we should run a news item on Roy Stirling. It seems that he gave McGuire a rough time, according to this tape. I reckon that our new adversary would be only too glad to meet up with our Mr Stirling. What say we make this a more likely prospect?'

'Are we gonna tell Roy about this?' asked Gregg.

'No, I don't think so. We'll keep a look out for him, won't we?'

'What exactly do you have in mind?'

'Well, I was thinking...'

At the Buckridge Hotel, where Kieran and Linda spent the night, Kieran made a point of getting up early the next morning. He got a lift into Elkridge, where he was able to buy a secondhand car. He also picked up some casual clothes for Linda and himself. By the time he got back to the hotel Linda was already down for breakfast, so he joined her at the table.

'Where have you been, Kieran? I wish you wouldn't go off like that without telling me where you're going.'

Kieran decided to ignore her rebuke and asked her if she had seen the morning papers yet.

'No,' said Linda.

'I picked one up when I was in town,' said Kieran. 'The car that was following us was in a collision with two other vehicles. There was only one person killed and that was the passenger in the station wagon. That's the guy with the gun, I might add. The driver survived. It might have been better for us if they'd both died.'

'Kieran, how can you say such a thing?' said Linda sharply.

'Don't get me wrong. I don't mean to sound callous, but the fact that one survived means that they probably have a good description of me by now and that's gonna make it all the harder to remain undetected for long. I managed to pick up a secondhand car in Elkridge. It's an old Buick, but beggars can't be choosers I guess. Oh, and I also got us some casual clothes to change into.'

'How did you know my size?' asked Linda.

'I didn't. I just guessed. I figured size wasn't too critical when it

comes to jeans and sweatshirts. Well, I've been up most of the night
thinking about our situation and trying to draw up some plan of
action. There's no point in just running all over the country hoping
that they won't find us. It's better if we have a direction to aim for,
some place where we can lie low for a while and see if we can think
of a way to redress the situation. Now, all things considered, if the
FBI is involved, and I mean the whole organisation, then we haven't
a chance in the US. It's just too big an outfit with vast resources
to draw upon. So I figure our best chance is to head for the Canadian
border. At least that way the FBI will have a harder time keeping
track of us and, hopefully, less influence.'

'Canada! Oh, Kieran. This is all happening far too fast for me.
I haven't had time to think. You say you were up all night thinking
about this. Why, when my head hit the pillow, I was out like a
light! I guess I was just too shattered to think about all that's
happened. And now, now you're talking about going to Canada.
What about my family? How am I going to get in touch with them?
And when I do, what on earth will I tell them?'

'Listen, I know how you must feel, but you'll have to remember
that your life is at stake – yours and mine. From now on we'll both
have to be very, very careful in everything we say and do. I don't
think it would be wise to just pick up the phone and speak to your
folks. Believe me, Linda, despite my IRA affiliations, I don't know
all the moves and I certainly don't know if we will be able to keep
one step ahead of the FBI, for I haven't a clue how they operate.
I'm just playing it all by ear and trying to stay alive.'

'Can't we just report them to the proper authorities?' asked Linda
almost tearfully.

'But who are the proper authorities? If the bloody FBI are in on
this then there's a good chance that the US government's also involved,
and who are we gonna expose them to?'

'Do you have to make our position sound so desperate?'

'I'm sorry, Linda, but this is the real thing and I figure that you'll
function much better if you know just what we're up against. However,
I've got a feeling that there is something we may be able to do, but

I just haven't had enough time to think it all through. Believe me, the situation is not hopeless.'

'What about my folks, Kieran? Isn't there anything we can do? They'll be worried sick already, even if I could just get one message to them so that I can put their minds at rest. They've been so good to me. I just can't torture them this way.'

'Well, you realise that the agency will almost certainly have tapped your home phone by now. As soon as you make that call you could be giving our position away.'

'But doesn't it take time to trace a call? If we keep it short then they won't have time to trace it.'

'All right then,' said Kieran. 'Here's what we'll do. We'll save more time in the long run if you prepare what you want to say beforehand, so I want you to go up to your room and write it all down. Now remember, keep it brief, no more than ninety seconds. OK, you get started on that and I'll see you later. Oh, wait a minute. Mind and let me see what you've written before you call. In the meantime I'll pick up some supplies for our journey. I'll see you in the lobby in half an hour.'

Linda sat in her room, desperately trying to think of a way to tell her family what was going on and why she hadn't come home. How could she explain to them that she wouldn't be coming home for a while? She picked up a pen and started scribbling on a notepad, trying to force her mind to resolve the dilemma confronting her, but the sheer frustration of her constraints was inhibiting her ability to think clearly. She suddenly stopped writing, threw down the pen and said to herself, 'This is silly.' She tore off the top sheet of paper, scrunched it up in her hand and threw it into the waste paper basket, then picked up the phone and dialled her home number.

Mrs Johnstone answered and recognised Linda's voice immediately. 'Oh, Linda, where have you been? We've all been frantic with worry. Are you all right? When are you coming home?'

Linda jumped in and said, 'Aunt Mary. I'm so sorry to have caused you all this worry and concern. Please forgive me. You know that I would never do anything to hurt you.'

'But Linda, what's wrong?' interrupted Mrs Johnstone.

'I haven't got time to explain to you in any detail, but I'm phoning to tell you that I'm going away for a while. I don't know how long exactly, but I'll be in touch as often as I can. Please don't worry about me. I'll be fine. I love you all very much. I really must go now, Aunt Mary, so please don't make it any harder than it is. Goodbye for now.'

Linda hung up the phone and burst into tears, wondering if she would ever see her family again. She looked at her watch. The call had lasted no more than 45 seconds, well within the time limit given by Kieran.

She changed into the clothes that he had bought her, before meeting Kieran in the hotel lobby as arranged.

He was waiting for her and looking a bit anxious. 'Have you prepared something for the phone?'

'It's done,' she said haughtily.

'What do you mean, it's done? I thought we had agreed to...'

'I didn't agree to anything. It was your idea, not mine. But I'm not a child, you know. I'm perfectly capable of handling this in my own way.'

'I'm sorry,' said Kieran. 'I guess I was perhaps being hyper-cautious.'

'Kieran, you'll have to trust me to make my own decisions. If we're going to be in this together we're going to have to work together.'

16

Frank Mariano picked up his Tuesday morning *Washington Post* and was surprised to see one of the headlines referring to Atlantic Air. He remembered that this was a subsidiary of CLC, the corporation that he was currently investigating. The article read as follows:

Atlantic Air, who are celebrating their silver jubilee year, have decided to mark the occasion by giving their Head of Security, Roy Stirling, an award for a good safety record ... in twenty-five years of flying there have been no fatalities with this airline.

Frank called Jim Hollis to his office. 'Jim, have you seen this article?'

'Not yet. I haven't had time to look at my paper this morning.'

'Well, have a look at mine,' said Frank.

Jim took the paper to read the article. 'Just a minute there's something wrong here.'

'Yes, that's what I thought. Didn't your report say that Alex Stenton was head of security for Atlantic Air?'

'Yes, you're right. This guy Stirling is certainly a chief of security, but he works for CLC. He also acts as a personal secretary to your old friend Tom Casey.'

'I thought I knew the name. Now why would they just kinda switch roles like that? What do you think?'

'There could be quite a simple explanation for it. Perhaps Alex Stenton was just not available that day and Roy Stirling was merely standing in for him. After all, the whole point of the award is probably just safety hype. You know, letting the public know that it has always been safe to fly Atlantic Air. So it really doesn't matter who accepts the award, I suppose.'

'Umm, you could be right, but I think you'd better check on it. Somehow I get the feeling that Tom Casey wouldn't want to put any of his heads of security in the limelight unless he had a very good reason for it. Tom Casey may be an old scoundrel but he's certainly nobody's fool. Yes, the more I think about it, the more suspicious I become. I want you to get a man down there for the celebrations and get him to nose around a bit and see what he comes up with. By the way, how's our surveillance team coming along? Have they found anything interesting yet?'

'Well, Roy Stirling seems to have made quite a few trips between New York and Washington, but we're not too surprised about that. His function as security chief would account for this kind of commuting. Alex Stenton, though, had quite an interesting trip recently, but I was saving that for my report.'

'Oh! What's that then? Come on, let's have it.'

'Well, it looks like our Mr Stenton spent three days in Ireland recently.'

'Ireland eh? That is interesting. What on earth was the head of security for Atlantic Air doing in Ireland? They don't have a scheduled flight there do they?'

'No, they don't. London's Heathrow is the only British Isles airport they use.'

'Was he on leave, then?'

'I don't know, but three days is hardly a vacation.'

'But he must have had some reason for being over there. What else have you found out?'

'Not much more, not yet anyway. His secretary let it slip that he had been out of the country. She was speaking to some irate customer who was complaining that this was the second time that his appointment to see Mr Stenton had been cancelled. Our man, who was in the office at the time, overheard this and wangled out of her, that she had made a reservation on a flight to Ireland for him.'

'What about the other end?'

'You mean Ireland?'

'Yes, have you managed to follow it up yet?'

'We're still in the process of doing that, but if you leave it with me I'll get back to you with that report just as soon as I can.'

'Before you go, Jim, what's the old man himself up to at the moment?'

'You mean Tom Casey?'

'Yes, that's the one.'

'Mr Casey has been keeping himself exceedingly busy over the last few weeks but it all appears to be quite legitimate and above board; he's been holding meetings with a lot of high-powered people lately.'

'Who do you mean? Anybody I know?'

'Well, he's had meetings with the heads of two multinationals and they've been collectively negotiating contracts in Britain, with the new Labour government.'

'Is that so?' said Frank, savouring this new information. 'This is certainly starting to look very interesting. Listen, I'm now convinced that he's up to something, for if there's one thing that I'm absolutely certain of, it's that Tom Casey definitely has no love for the Labour Party. Keep these inquiries going. I think we're starting to get somewhere.'

By this time Tom Casey's consortium had already won agreements with the new British administration and steps were now under way to implement the programme. Three sites had been selected. One in Liverpool, one in Newcastle and the other was expected to be in Glasgow. In Liverpool a newspaper report declared:

A 100,000 sq. ft. factory is being redesigned to accommodate today's technology and become one of the world's most advanced microchip factories. Its aim is to make Britain one of the world leaders in silicon chip technology. The factory is expected to employ a workforce of 500, rising to 1000 within a year of completion. This plant is expected to supply the needs of British electronic engineering, thus putting Britain once again in the forefront of microchip technology.

In fact, this was a ready-built factory which had been paid for by the government and was to be fitted out with capital equipment shipped in from Korea, which had previously been the host country for this supposedly super-advanced technology. The Korean factories were being closed down because the high-powered magnifying equipment being used to assemble these components was seriously damaging the eyes of the Korean workforce who were now starting to demand compensation. Prior to this, employees whose eyes had so deteriorated that they were no longer capable of coping with the work, were simply paid off and replaced by new workers. The costs of compensation, together with the demands for higher wages, meant that Korea was no longer a viable economic proposition. Apart from this, new photographic techniques had been developed that had made the use of high-powered magnifying equipment obsolete.

At the Newcastle site, a major new car industry was to be developed that would launch a new luxury car on the market. This plant had previously been in operation in Brazil, but had been the victim of a corrupt administration. It was decided that the plant would be better placed in Britain, as the new design had been modified to accommodate the European market. The British government had been given substantial assurances that the company was to be controlled by a new management team, and would have the backing of a major multinational company.

This site was to occupy 5 acres and employ approximately 8,000 people to begin with. The factory was to be the core activity that would support a substantial amount of ancillary industry which was expected to boost the employment figures in the area to around 20,000. Depending on the success of the new car, these figures could probably increase by 30 per cent.

The Scottish site was at present being disputed by the Glasgow council who, although desperately anxious to accept the new industry into the area, were dubious about the amount of concessions being asked for by the company. They were currently in the process of trying to negotiate a better deal.

All things considered, Tom Casey couldn't be more pleased with the way things were moving. His consortium now had a firm foothold in key employment areas in Britain. Phase II was about to be completed and, once the Scottish plant was established, they would be ready for phase III.

Back in Washington, Tom Casey sat back in his chair and pushed a button on his TV remote control. A picture flickered on the screen in front of him. It was the six o'clock news and the newscaster was doing a street interview. He had just announced that Senator Brian Mitchell, who was standing again for re-election, had interrupted his campaigning to make a special visit to Washington.

'Well, Senator, what's the current situation in South Carolina? How's the election coming along?'

'Oh, there's a long way to go yet. It's too early to say.'

'Care to tell us why you're in Washington this week, Senator, right in the middle of your campaign? Are you here to raise funds for your campaign perhaps?'

'Funny man, eh? Have you guys got nothing better to do than waste my time? No, I'm not here to raise funds, but I am still a working senator until my term of office is over. So why don't you let me get on with my business?'

'Understand you were called to Washington by the President. Would you care to comment on that?'

'Nope! No comment. Now, can I get on with my business?'

Tom Casey switched off his TV at that point and was wondering what Brian Mitchell was up to. He always was pretty close to the President. Perhaps it's time they had another get-together. He leant over to his intercom and pushed a button,

'Lena, do you know if my yacht is ready for a weekend trip?'

'Yes, sir, but it's still down at North Shore.'

'Right, I'd like you to send out an invitation to Senator Brian Mitchell. We took him on a trip a few months back, so you'll find his number in your diary. After that get in touch with the skipper and ask him to have her ready for this weekend. Then you can go home, Lena. I shan't need you again this evening. Thank you for staying back.'

* * *

Linda and Kieran were by now on their way to Canada and were continuing on route 95, heading towards New York.

'Why are we going this way, Kieran? It isn't exactly the quickest way to Canada you know.'

'Yes, I know,' said Kieran. 'But I figure that whoever picks up our trail will be expecting us to put as much distance between Washington and ourselves as possible. When you look at the map there are two obvious routes to take. One is to head south towards Florida, where they might expect us to try and ship out from the coast somewhere. The other is to head north-west across country to Canada. That would be the quickest way out of the States, but I figure we should stay where the population is thickest, where we can lose ourselves amongst people. So you see, we're gonna stay on route 95 and head straight for New York. From there, we can cut across to Montreal via route 87.'

'Quite a devious character Mr McGuire, aren't you?'

'We're gonna have to be. The kind of people who are looking for us are professionals.'

'I was just thinking,' said Linda in bemused way, 'if we're going to be running away to Canada together, perhaps it would be a good idea if we got to know each other a bit better, don't you think? So, why don't you tell me about yourself?'

'OK. What do you want to know? How many back teeth have I got? How tall I am? Is that the sort of thing you have in mind?' said Kieran teasingly.

'No. Of course not. You know fine what I mean. Tell me about Ireland. What did you do for a living? And tell me about your family ... Oh, Kieran. I'm very sorry. It slipped my mind for the moment.'

'Don't worry about it,' said Kieran, trying to spare her further anguish. 'I'm not afraid to talk about them. We were a very close family despite our differences. They'll always be alive in my mind. And anyway, don't spoil the mood. It's really good to see you smile again.

I was beginning to wonder if I ever would. Now, let me see, what do I do for a living? Well that's easy. I was an accountant and I worked for a local bank. Really boring, isn't it? Never mind, what about my family. Well, my dad was a right tearaway when he was young, a real, hot-blooded Irishman. I think that's what most attracted my mother to him. He always spoke his mind and he didn't care who heard it. I guess that just might have been the start of his trouble.'

'Oh, I know what you mean,' interrupted Linda. 'My dad was just like that and it landed him in a whole heap of trouble. Oh, I'm sorry. I've interrupted your story.'

'It's all right. Yes, as I was saying, when a person has strong views about a subject it's not always wise to voice them, especially if you live in a place like Ireland. It's only a matter of time before you are forced into a polarised position. That's when you have to make a stand and declare your loyalties, then there's no turning back. My father joined the IRA shortly after he got married. I'm afraid marriage didn't do a lot to mellow him. If anything, it made him all the more bitter when he couldn't get a job because of his religion, but that sort of thing happened on both sides of the fence, and I don't want to open that can of worms.'

'How come Kevin followed in your dad's footsteps and you didn't?'

'Kevin was the impatient one. He always was. That's why he didn't do too well at school, not because he didn't have it in him, he was just too bloody impatient to study. Kevin acted like the Irish solution was just around the corner. He figured that Ireland had waited long enough and he, for one, wasn't prepared to wait much longer. Kevin always did ask a lot out of life. Life to him was nothing but a big gamble anyway, so why wait for what you want? That seemed to be his philosophy when he was younger. I used to tease him about his height. Even when he was twenty-one there was four inches difference between us. I used to say, "When are you ever going to grow up Kevin? Are you always gonna be a wee fella?" But he was never stuck for an answer. He used to say that he was smaller because at school the teacher kept patting him on the head saying, "Good boy! Good boy!" He claimed that's what stunted his growth.'

Linda laughed. 'That's a good one. He seemed to have a good sense of humour anyway and a touch of the old Irish, eh?'

'Oh, he had that all right.'

'What about your mother? Are you ready to talk about her yet?'

'Nope. I'm afraid I'm still hurting from that experience. I'd rather not.'

'I understand. It must have been dreadful for you.'

'Anyway, that's enough about me. Why don't you tell me something about yourself, Linda?'

'OK, let me see now...'

Linda spent the next hour telling Kieran about life back in Scotland and how she had first come to America. By this time they had been travelling for about five hours with only one stop for something to eat. It was beginning to get dark and Kieran decided that it was time they pulled in somewhere and settled down for the night. He had noticed a couple of signs for a place called Clifton and asked Linda to look it up on the map.

Clifton is an industrial town in New Jersey, just west of the Hudson River and north-west of New York City. They both agreed that Clifton should be their next stop-over.

'By the way,' said Kieran. 'I don't quite know how I'm gonna put this. Em, let me see now...' he said hesitantly.

'Come on, Kieran. What's on your mind? Are you thinking about our sleeping arrangements?'

'Well, yes. You've got it in one.'

'I thought so,' said Linda knowingly.

'You see, I don't mean to be pushy, but it's sure gonna be double the expense getting separate rooms wherever we go. Quite apart from drawing attention to ourselves, it's gonna be awful inconvenient, you know what I mean.'

Linda didn't answer immediately. She decided to let him stew for a while. 'Well, I don't mind sharing a room, as long as there are separate beds.'

'OK. I get the message.'

'Look, don't take this personally, but I'm one of those old-fashioned girls who's waiting until she gets married, so perhaps you should get used to the idea of separate sleeping arrangements now. That way it won't be a problem later.'

Perhaps Kieran was tired, or maybe it was the way that Linda had made her last remarks. Whatever, Linda's explanation certainly turned out to be a classic conversation-stopper because no further talking took place until they arrived in Clifton.

Kieran decided to avoid the motels on the outskirts of town and drove right into the centre, where they booked into one of the major hotels, his logic being that keeping to high profile hotels might possibly mislead pursuers as they wouldn't expect people on the run to stay in the bigger hotels.

Linda was weary after sitting all afternoon and was anxious to get out and stretch her legs, so after their meal she decided to do some late-night shopping. She was dying to buy some new clothes, for the ones that Kieran had provided were ill-fitting and were certainly not her idea of casual wear, so they both went their separate ways.

Kieran picked up a copy of the *Washington Post* at the hotel foyer and took it to their room. As he scanned the headlines his eyes suddenly caught a reference to Atlantic Air alongside a picture headed 'Chief of Security'. He looked at the caption below the picture and was astonished to see Roy Stirling's name. So that's the bastard who gave Kevin a hard time. Maybe it's time you got a taste of your own medicine my friend, thought Kieran. He quickly read through the rest of the article, absorbing every relevant detail. He could hardly believe his luck, for he not only had a picture of the man he most wanted to take revenge on, but he also had a time and location for meeting with him. Kieran abandoned any idea of leaving the country. His mind was now almost totally preoccupied with thoughts of revenge and how this could best be achieved.

The Atlantic Air celebrations were to take place in one of Washington's most prestigious hotels, the Sheraton, and the proceedings were scheduled to begin at 7 pm the next day. Kieran knew he might never get another opportunity like this, and that he'd be a fool to let it pass. But, Linda. My God, there's no way he could risk taking Linda back to Washington. He obtained a railway timetable from the hotel reception desk. He had already decided to leave the car with Linda.

He was still trying to think of a way of telling Linda, when she quite suddenly and dramatically burst into the room carrying an enormous bundle of packages. Linda was bubbling with enthusiasm about all the clothes she had bought. She had even bought some shirts and a jacket for Kieran.

'Just you wait and see what I got for you. I couldn't resist it,' she said, unwrapping the box containing the jacket.

'And might I ask how you knew my size?' inquired Kieran in mock smugness.

'That's easy,' she said. 'I just looked at the label of your jacket on the back seat of the car.'

'Oh! A real smarty, eh!'

'Well! What do you think?' said Linda holding the jacket up in front of him.

'Wow! How did you know I was into tweed jackets? It's a beauty,' replied Kieran as he took it from her and tried it on. 'But don't you think it's a bit ... American?' he said. 'I notice that they wear their clothes a bit on the big side over here.'

'Precisely!' said Linda emphatically. 'That's just what you need. Back home in the UK, the men tend to wear their clothes too close fitting. That's why they look all stiff and encumbered by their clothes. It's time you learned to hang loose. I think you'll look very smart. Besides, if you're trying to hide in America, don't you think it's a good idea to look American?'

'You've got a point there,' he said with a smile.

'Yes, and I also notice that you seem to be picking up the accent quite well,' said Linda.

'Oh, that. Yes, it's quite easy to slip into. I didn't realise I had, until you pointed it out to me.'

'Don't worry,' said Linda. 'I'm just teasing. It's not that evident. Anyway, it'll be a useful addition to your disguise.'

'I notice you don't seem to have lost your Scottish accent. I can still detect it on occasion. How come?'

'I'm not sure,' she said. 'Perhaps it's because my Uncle George that I live with didn't lose his. He reckoned a Scottish accent was a bonus out here. People seemed to like it and, also, my best friend Kathy was Irish and she didn't speak with an American accent either. Perhaps that had something to do with it as well.'

Kieran decided to take advantage of Linda's apparent good humour and disclosed his intention of going back to Washington. But he had completely misjudged her response: Linda was furious.

'What on earth do you want to go back there for? Are you mad? Didn't you tell me that they would probably have searched your hotel room by now and would know who you are and why you're over here?'

'Look, Linda. Look at this report in today's paper. The very guy I came over here to find, and probably the one who killed my brother! He's due to be at the Sheraton in Washington tomorrow. I may never get another shot at this.'

'Another shot at what?' said Linda angrily. 'Getting killed? What on earth are you thinking about? What exactly are you planning to do?'

'I'm not sure. I'm not sure, but I've got to go. I've got to find out what this is all about. I know for sure that this guy Stirling can tell me. Besides, perhaps the American Government is not involved. This may well be a renegade group acting on its own initiative. If that's the case then there's a chance we can draw the attention of the proper authorities to their activities which, at the very least, might take the heat away from us.'

'Kieran! Oh Kieran! I'm so afraid for you. What can you do? You're only one man against who knows how many. Perhaps even against the FBI.'

'Trust me, Linda. I just want to have one crack at it and, believe me, if this fails I promise you I won't ever try again.'

'What do you mean, if this fails? You could get yourself killed, and what will that prove?' exclaimed Linda, with tears welling in her eyes.

Kieran took her in his arms and cradled her head on his shoulder as he tried to comfort her.

'Please believe me, my concern is also for you. I don't want to be on the run for ever and this may well be the only chance we'll get to turn this thing around. I've been looking at the map again and I see that there's an alternative route to Canada from here. I think it may even be quicker.'

'I thought you said speed wasn't the most important thing to consider,' remonstrated Linda.

'Don't get awkward with me, Linda. Please, not now. We're in this together and we'll get out of it together, just you wait and see. Listen, I want you to take the car and drive over to Buffalo tomorrow evening. I've been reading the brochures, and it seems that Buffalo is a regular tourist attraction for visitors wanting to see Niagara Falls.'

'Yes I know,' said Linda. 'I've been there.'

'You have? Great, then you'll know about the bridge.'

'Do you mean the one that takes you into Canada?'

'Yes, that's the one, the Border Bridge. Look, if you book into a hotel and wait for me, I shouldn't think I'll be gone any more than three days.'

'And what if you are? Or worse still, what if you don't return at all?' replied Linda.

'Let's think positively now,' said Kieran. 'All this negative thinking is getting us nowhere.' There was a short pause. 'Listen, we're gonna have to make some arrangements so that we can meet up again. How about when I arrive in Buffalo, I make for this Border Bridge. It shouldn't be too difficult to find and if I make a point of getting there for midday all you have to do is see that you're there between twelve and one every day for the three days. Come on, Linda. What do you say?'

Linda could see that Kieran was determined to go through with this and that any further argument on her part would be futile. On the contrary, it would be liable to make him all the more determined, so she decided that her only alternative was to relent.

17

The next morning Kieran McGuire was on a train heading back to Washington. Because there were few passengers on board he had managed to find an empty compartment where the solitude gave him the quiet that he needed to think and take stock of his situation. He allowed the tranquility of his new environment to take over for a spell, as he indulged in some long overdue relaxation. For a few minutes he simply sat there listening to the soothing clickety-clack of the train as it sped towards its destination. Kieran was thinking how lucky he was to have got hold of this information when he did. A day later and he would have completely missed the opportunity. He looked again at the previous day's *Washington Post*. He studied the picture of Roy Stirling, making sure that he would recognise him when they met.

However, the more he thought about his good fortune, the more suspicious he became. For the first time there were seeds of doubt in his mind. He considered it to be a strange coincidence indeed that the very man he was looking for should be receiving all this publicity, when you might think that such a person would avoid news coverage and would be more inclined to keep a low profile. I wonder, he thought to himself. Could this possibly be a ploy to draw me into the open? Let's face it, they're bound to have Kevin's tape by now and it wouldn't take a genius to work out who I was looking for. What better way to attract my attention than by advertising his picture in the local press. Aw, come on Kieran, maybe you're getting just a wee bit paranoid here.

But all the pieces seemed to fit. No matter how hard he tried, he just couldn't get away from the idea that he was heading into a trap. Kieran, who had previously been intent on pursuing his target regardless of the odds, now realised that he would have to exercise extreme caution if he was to have any chance of success. The thought that they might be waiting for him now became the focus of his attention. He had never had a proper plan of action. Revenge had been his driving force, that is until the tables were turned on him, then survival took precedence. But now, for the first time, he had a specific goal to aim for, a target to zero in on. All his feelings of hate and revenge were being rekindled and were driving him with ever increasing determination. Even if it was a trap, turning back was out of the question, for now he was fully committed.

Kieran looked at his watch. He had two hours and 45 minutes before the train was due in Washington DC. He was going to need all of that time to come up with some way of getting to Roy Stirling, and a way that took into account the possibility of a trap.

In Washington, meanwhile, Alex Stenton and Gregg Donoghue were preparing a reception for Kieran in the hope that he would take the bait and come after Roy Stirling.

'Have you got the hotel covered, Gregg?' asked Alex.

'Yes, I've got two men out front in the car park and another two around the back. Your own security people have been alerted and they'll take care of the inside.'

'Nice work. All we need now is for our Mr McGuire to appear.'

'Do you really think he'll come?' said Gregg.

'No doubt about it. He'll be here all right. You don't think he came all the way from Ireland just to pay his respects, do you? Put yourself in his shoes. What would you do if somebody had just killed your brother and then wiped out what was left of your family? Believe me, this guy is not only going to be here, he's on a revenge trip and he's not stoppin' until he gets some kind of satisfaction, or until we stop him first. We just better make sure that we're ready for him. Where's Roy?'

'He's at head office right now. The boys have planned a little in-house celebration for him before he leaves for the main event at the

Sheraton. Hey, Alex, that sure was a good move g'tting' Roy to stand in for you as head of security. How did you manage to square that one with Tom Casey?'

'I didn't. Tom's out of town at the moment. He's got business in New York with the syndicate.'

'But won't he find out when he reads the *Post*?' asked Gregg.

'Just you leave that one to me, I'll worry about Mr Casey.'

'Do you want me to stay close to Roy?'

'No, I certainly don't. If McGuire does manage to get near enough, he might just figure out who you are and we don't want to give him two targets now do we? Besides, you're too valuable a man to lose at this stage.'

'Don't go figurin' on using me for the second bait if this one fails. I'm not planning on being anyone's patsy.'

'Why not, you got a problem with that? Frightened, are we? Then maybe you'd better make sure that we get McGuire when he shows up this time, OK.'

'You're a callous bastard, Stenton. I can see I'm gonna have to watch my back when you're around.'

By the time Kieran arrived in Washington, he had prepared a list of equipment that he intended buying. As he no longer had his gun and there was little opportunity to acquire another at such short notice, it was time to improvise. His first stop after leaving the station was at a local garden centre where he purchased a can of weed killer. He then headed for a grocer's shop on the other side of the street where he bought two packs of sugar. All that remained now was to locate a hardware store for his final purchases. He was in luck, for the grocer was able to direct him to one that was only two blocks away. In the hardware store, Kieran bought three lengths of steel pipe of various diameters. He also purchased a reel of lacing cord and a can of kerosene.

Armed with all this equipment, which he stuffed into a holdall, Kieran set off to look for a hotel in the downtown district. As

Washington is a major tourist attraction, it is well provided for with hotel accommodation, so it didn't take him long to locate one. It was a quite respectable hotel in a large Georgian-style building. Kieran had chosen the downtown area because it was a reasonably distance from both the Sheraton and the Atlantic Air building which he had investigated when he first arrived in America.

Once settled into his room, Kieran located the hotel janitor who was only too willing to accept 20 bucks for the use of his workshop for an hour. Kieran wasted no time in getting organised. He immediately moved into the workshop and prepared his equipment. His intention was to construct two pipe bombs. He had learned to do this when he was still at school in Ireland. The kids back home were only too aware of explosives during the disturbances, so it was not surprising therefore that some of them would get together and experiment amongst themselves. So Kieran had learned how to make a pipe bomb using ordinary domestic ingredients. In school, he had learned about the explosive properties of sodium chlorate when mixed with sugar. It was only a matter of time before the kids identified a certain type of weed killer as a useful source of sodium chlorate.

The first thing he had to do was to make up a solution of sodium chlorate and sugar mixed in water. He then cut several lengths of lacing cord which he allowed to soak in the solution for several minutes before hanging them up to dry. These were to be used as fuses for the bombs. His next task was to prepare a dry mix of sodium chlorate and sugar which was to be used as the actual explosive.

It was now time to prepare the steel pipe and make it into a suitable container for his explosive mix. He placed one end of the largest pipe into a vice and crimped it by closing the vice, thus sealing off the end. As an added precaution, he placed a cotton wad inside the pipe, pushing it all the way to the bottom. He then poured in a quantity of the explosive mixture until the cavity was three-quarters full, finally placing a length of lacing cord into the open end of the tube, followed by another cotton wad. He very carefully sealed this other end of the pipe in precisely the same way as before, this time taking extra care that there were no particles of the explosive mix near the part of the pipe that was to be crimped. Failure to take this precaution could have been fatal, as the presence of even a few particles would be sufficient to ignite the device. Kieran then repeated the exercise with the smaller tube, thus giving him two pipe bombs. The third length of steel was strapped to a small block of wood that Kieran found in the workshop. This was to be used as a dummy gun should he get close enough to surprise his target.

He was now ready for the second stage, which was to set off an explosion in the Atlantic Air building just big enough and loud enough to draw plenty of attention to the area. Kieran figured that if he couldn't get to Roy Stirling he would just have to bring Stirling to him. He was working on the premise that, if an explosion was reported in the Atlantic Air building, the Chief of Security would be the first to investigate, especially if he was in the middle of celebrating the safety aspects of the company.

Later that evening Kieran McGuire made his assault on the Atlantic Air building. Getting into the premises was easy, he merely reported to the desk just before closing and made a few enquiries about flight times. He then simply took an elevator to the third floor, where he hid in the men's room until the staff had all left.

He didn't have long to wait. The Atlantic Air personnel were all anxious to finish on time so that they could get up to the Sheraton to join in the celebrations. Once the building was clear Kieran forced entry into one of the smaller offices where he set up his equipment and prepared his makeshift bomb. This entailed working out and preparing the optimum length of fuse that would allow him enough time to clear the area. There was no way he could have planned this in advance, because he hadn't known the layout of the building. However, he had noted where the generator room was on his way to the elevator, and had estimated how long it would take to climb the stairs and get back into the office. Kieran wanted to be at a vantage point as quickly as possible so that he could monitor the reaction of the outside world to the explosion. He had estimated that a five-minute fuse would give him sufficient time to get back into position, so he cut the lacing cord to the appropriate length, then made for the generator room to position the bomb. When Kieran entered the room, he headed straight for the fuel tank of the emergency generator, removed the tank cap and poured in a packet of sugar. Once the generator was activated, the sugar would then feed through the system and stop the fuel igniting, bringing the machine to a grinding halt. Having dealt with the emergency backup system, Kieran's next task was to sever the mains cable that supplied power to the building. He did this by simply strapping the bomb alongside the cable.

Meanwhile, at the Sheraton, Roy Stirling was giving a press conference to an assortment of TV and newspaper reporters.

'Mr Stirling, is it true that you are taking credit for work that should be rightfully attributed to your predecessor Alex Stenton?'

'Nope, you've got that wrong on two counts, buddy. One, Alex Stenton is not my predecessor. I'm merely standing in for him as he was unable to attend himself on this occasion. And two, we're not celebrating one man's success here, but the success of a whole enterprise. Since the emphasis is on safety and security we thought that it was only fitting that the office of chief of security should symbolically represent that particular area of involvement. All right, gentlemen, any more questions?' said Roy in thinly disguised smugness.

'Yea, I've got a question,' a voice called from the back of the crowd. 'If you're acting chief of security, shouldn't you be down at the Atlantic Air building investigating the explosion that took place ten minutes ago?'

There was a sudden roar of laughter from the crowd of reporters and onlookers who surrounded Roy Stirling.

'Listen, wise guy,' said Roy through his teeth. 'If you don't have anything constructive to ask, why don't you take a hike? Or perhaps you would like me personally to show you the way.'

'I ain't kiddin' mister. I just got a call from my office three minutes ago. Apparently the explosion knocked out the lighting system. If you don't believe me, look for yourself. You can see the Atlantic Air building from that window behind you.'

The whole crowd including Roy Stirling rushed over to the window. 'Hey! The guy's right enough. The building's in total darkness.'

'Yea, so it is,' shouted another.

Roy was speaking his thoughts out loud by this time as he pushed his way through the crowd. 'What the hell is this, anyhow? What kind of stunt are they trying to pull?'

'What's your next move Mr Stirling?' shouted one reporter.

'What the hell do you think it's gonna be?' he replied sarcastically. 'I'm gonna investigate this one myself. And if I find out that this is some kind of hoax...'

He didn't finish his implied threat, but left it hanging there menacingly as he stormed out of the building. Roy Stirling was really angry by this time. He didn't mind standing in for somebody else to help out, but being publically embarrassed was something else. He jumped into his car and roared off at high speed toward the Atlantic Air building. His knuckles were showing white as he angrily gripped the steering wheel. It took him just eight minutes to get there.

By the time he arrived the building was surrounded by onlookers, and a team of firemen were trying to determine exactly where the explosion had originated. Two of the firemen had just extinguished a minor fire that had broken out after the explosion.

'Let me through!' shouted Roy, as he tried to force his way to the front. When he finally broke through, he approached the fire officer who seemed to be in charge of the operation, 'Look, my name's Roy Stirling. I'm acting head of security for this building. Do you mind telling me what happened here?'

'We don't know yet,' replied the fire officer. 'We haven't had time to fully investigate.'

'Anyone been in the building yet?' asked Roy.

'These two men here, they put out a minor fire on the ground floor. We weren't allowing anybody in there until your people came along. You see, it's a complete blackout and we don't have layouts of the building. From what I can make out, it was a bomb that went off and who knows? There may even be another one in there just waiting to go.'

'OK. Leave it with me, Chief,' said Roy. 'I'm going in there to have a look around. It looks like they've knocked out the emergency generator system as well, so you people better stay clear until I come out again.'

Roy Stirling went into the building alone and immediately made for the generator room.

By this time Kieran had the major advantage of having his night sight, as he had been in the dark for much longer than Roy. He had positioned himself in a utility closet opposite the generator room, from where he could observe anyone who came to investigate.

Roy Stirling had thrown all caution to the wind at this point and his driving force was pure anger. He blundered his way through the darkness, stumbling over pieces of rubble created by the explosion.

He was just about to enter the generator room when Kieran made his move, reaching out and grabbing Roy tightly around the neck, at the same time ramming the steel tube into his back as hard as he could.

'Not one word,' he said vehemently. 'If you so much as breathe too loudly, you're a dead man.'

Roy froze instantly. His anger immediately drained away from him, as he broke into a cold sweat.

'Right, now,' said Kieran. 'I want you to take out your gun with your left hand and give it to me. Nice and easy now. There's a good lad,' said Kieran sarcastically as he took the gun from him. 'We're now going to quietly walk up these stairs until I tell you to do otherwise.'

Kieran took Roy Stirling up two flights of stairs and walked him down the corridor to the far side of the building where he pushed him into one of the offices. Once inside he ordered Stirling to sit down and then tied his hands to the back of the chair. By this time Roy had recognised the Irish accent and had already deduced who it might be. Kieran lit a candle and put it on the desk in front of Roy.

'There now,' said Kieran as he sat down on the desk. 'You and I are gonna have a wee talk and, if I like what you say, then you've nothing to worry about.'

Roy had composed himself by now and was starting to feel a bit more confident, although this confidence was based on rather dubious grounds. He had been thinking about how Kevin had responded to his bullying, remembering how he had managed to completely dominate him without great difficulty. This had left him with little respect for Irishmen in general. This was Roy Stirling's limited logic.

'Why the hell should I tell a bum like you anything?' said Roy with disdain, rather riskily testing the mettle of his opponent.

'Oh, would you be wantin' a good reason now for speakin' to me?' said Kieran, laying on the accent. 'Well let me see now,' he said as he removed Roy's necktie.

Roy was completely baffled by this, and wondered what was going to happen next.

'Right, if you're not going to be speakin' to me, you won't be usin' your mouth for a while, so I'll just be makin' sure you keep it shut,' added Kieran as he gagged him with the tie.

This only succeeded in confusing Roy still further, as he awaited Kieran's next move with trepidation.

Kieran leant over the desk and reached into his holdall from which he produced a can of kerosene and made a big display of opening it. He then walked over to Roy and poured the contents of the can all over him. Roy was in great discomfort as he felt the kerosene soak through his clothing and on to his flesh. The smell of fumes was almost choking him as he suddenly burst into a fit of coughing. His eyes fell on the candle and fear welled up inside him as its role took on a new significance. He was quick to realise its silent threat.

'Now, I'm going to be asking you once more Mr Stirling, and I'll be expecting a more cooperative response this time.' Kieran was deliberately exaggerating his accent. He wanted Roy to know who he was. He wanted him to expect violent revenge, so as to instil maximum fear.

Roy Stirling was shivering, due to shock and the sudden awareness of what could happen next. He was only too conscious of how vulnerable he was.

'Now we don't have a lot of time, Roy, so just in case we have any more aggravation, I'm gonna put all my cards on the table.' Kieran then produced the second pipe bomb and held it up to Roy's face. 'Do you know what this is?'

Roy shook his head vigorously.

'Well now, this ... this is what we call back home a pipe bomb. It's not unlike the one that blew up in your generator room, only this one's a wee bit smaller.'

Kieran stuffed the pipe down the front of Roy's trousers, leaving only the fuse exposed. He then took out a penknife and cut a slot in the candle about one inch away from the flame. In this slot he placed the end of the lacing cord protruding from Roy's trousers.

Roy looked down in horror at the explosive device. He began to stare at the candle in an almost hypnotic trance, terrified to take his eyes from it as if he could somehow suspend its burning by sheer willpower alone.

'There now, Mr Stirling. This is gonna be our little clock,' he said, pointing to the candle. 'So now I don't have to prompt you any more, for all you have to do is watch the candle and answer my questions. Now isn't that fair?'

Roy nodded his head vigorously in agreement, as Kieran removed the gag and put his pocket tape recorder on the table.

'Yes! Yes,' said Roy, his voice trembling with fear. He could feel the blood draining from his face and a cold sweat seeping through his pores. He was utterly convinced by this time that he was in the hands of a psychopath.

'Perhaps you would like to discuss the consequences of not stopping the clock in time?' said Kieran.

'OK, OK. You've had your fun, now get on with it, just. Just get on with it. Good God man, what are you waiting for?' said Roy almost pleadingly.

Kieran switched on his recorder and began his interrogation. He asked Roy who had been behind the plot to assassinate the Labour leadership, the reason behind it, and why it had been necessary to kill Kevin and his mother.

Having now reduced Roy to a state of absolute terror, Kieran found him to be very willing to give immediate responses to his every question. Roy was certainly terrified of the consequences of not cooperating as he sensed that this was a madman who was perfectly capable of allowing the bomb to explode. But there was another reason why he was being so cooperative, and that was that he didn't intend to let Kieran leave the building alive, even if it meant that both of them went up in smoke.

Outside the building Gregg Donoghue had arrived on the scene and was in the process of having the area cordoned off. Gregg knew that it had to be a trap and was cursing Alex Stenton for insisting that Roy shouldn't be told about the bait plan. Had Roy known, thought Gregg, he wouldn't have been so stupid as to rush in to investigate this thing on his own. Although, on second thoughts, the guy is such a hot head that he may well have done just that. According to the fire chief, Roy had entered the building 20 minutes ago, and there had been no sign of life since. The chief told Gregg that he had been concerned, but was reluctant to act until another Atlantic Air official appeared. After all, the fire was out and he had no authority to enter the building, especially after being told not to take any action by the company's chief of security.

Gregg's mind was working overtime, trying to figure out the best move. He figured it would be wise not to send anyone else in until the people from the power station had arrived and reconnected the lighting system.

'How long until the power people get here?' Gregg asked.

'I reckon they should have been here by now,' said the Fire Chief.

Just then a large truck pulled into the forecourt of the building. 'That looks like them now,' he added.

'Thank God!' replied Gregg. 'Perhaps we'll get some action around here. At least once we get the lights operating we'll be in a better position to establish just what's going on in there.'

Gregg was thinking to himself that Alex Stenton was going to be really mad when he found out about this fiasco. If he didn't get Roy out of this one alive, Stenton would be only too pleased to set him up as the next bait for the little Irish punk.

The electrical people unloaded their equipment and were about to enter the building. Gregg stepped forward, stopped one of them, and flashed his ID. 'How long will it take to get these lights restored?'

'Take it easy, bud, we've only just arrived. You gotta give us time to size up the damage. I'll let you know as soon as I can.'

Gregg was starting to get a bit jumpy. He knew it had been a foolish question to ask, but his impatience was getting the better of him. OK, he said to himself, that's it. I'm damned if I'm waiting any longer. I'm going in. Gregg called over to one of his men and informed him of his intention, and left instructions for them to enter the building as soon as the lighting was restored.

Whilst all this was going on, Kieran had decided that it was time to terminate the interrogation, as it wasn't safe for him to hang around much longer. He switched off the tape recorder and slipped it into his pocket. Then he removed the fuse from the candle which had by this time burned down to within an eighth of an inch of being ignited. He turned to Roy with the intention of replacing the gag over his mouth. Roy Stirling saw his opportunity and was quick to take advantage of it.

Forgetting his kerosene-soaked clothes, he quickly raised his knees up into his chest then kicked out with all his might at Kieran's mid-section, sending him tumbling over the other side of the desk. As Roy dropped his feet back onto the floor his leg caught the lit candle, knocking it on top of him. Instantly, there was a whoosh as Roy's clothes ignited, turning him into a human ball of fire. He stood up screaming and shrieking with pain as the flames enveloped him. The papers that had been lying on the desk were also alight and the chair that Roy had been sitting on just seconds ago was now a raging inferno.

Kieran had recovered from the blow and was trying to make his way to the door across the blazing carpet. It was only a matter of seconds now before the whole office would be engulfed in flames. It was certainly too late to save Roy Stirling and it was going to be touch and go whether he would get himself out. He worked his way round the burning desk then threw himself at the doorway, jumping over the flames that were threatening to cut off his only means of escape. Kieran launched himself with such force that his body passed through the doorway, and he rolled across the corridor floor, thumping against the opposite wall.

Just as he did, he heard a loud explosion behind him. It was the pipe bomb that Kieran had placed in Roy's waistband. 'Good God!' he shouted aloud. Poor bastard, he thought. I never meant this to happen. Then Kieran heard a noise coming from the other end of the corridor. It was Gregg Donoghue running up the stairs.

When he arrived at the top, Gregg could see flames coming from the doorway of the blazing office halfway along the corridor. He ran towards it and, as he approached, he saw, through the heat haze, a man struggling to his feet. He stopped just short of the burning room.

The two men stared at each other for a moment. In the flickering light of the blazing flames they could clearly see each other's faces. A loud cracking sound distracted both men and, as they turned towards the noise, the office door and half that section of the wall tumbled into the corridor between them, amidst great billows of smoke and ash. Gregg jumped back to avoid the burning debris. He rubbed his eyes as the smoke began to take effect. Kieran had gone and there was no way of getting past the debris to pursue him.

Kieran was already making his way down the stairs, taking them three at a time, when suddenly the lights flared up all around him.

Standing at the foot of the stairs, with his back to him, was the engineer who had just switched on the lights. Kieran seized advantage of the situation and leapt down the last ten steps, landing on top of the engineer, propelling him head first into the wall. The engineer collapsed in a heap on the floor, knocked unconscious by the impact. Kieran removed the engineer's green overalls and pulled them over his own clothes. He then picked up his safety helmet and made for the exit. He was in luck, for after the lights had been reconnected, the firemen and a number of Gregg Donoghue's men were rushing to enter the building. In the following confusion Kieran was able to escape. Once outside he discarded the overalls and blended in with the crowd.

As Gregg Donoghue rushed down the other stairway, he bumped into some of his own men. 'Where is he?' shouted Gregg.

'Who do you mean, sir?' replied one of his men in bewilderment.

Gregg looked at him disdainfully, then a second man said, 'Wait a minute, there was an engineer leaving the building as we came in...'

'That would be him!' shouted Gregg. 'Get after him.'

As Gregg and his men ran out of the building they were just in time to see an old grey-haired gentleman shouting toward a moving car, 'Hey! Hey! Come back here, come back with my car!'

Kieran drove off at high speed while Gregg and his men made for their cars. As soon as he got into his, Gregg started firing orders into his CB, setting up road blocks to intercept McGuire.

Kieran headed up Rock Creek and Potomac, which was a road running alongside the Potomac River. He was being pursued by a whole string of Black and Whites, with sirens wailing. As he approached the Theodore Roosevelt Memorial Bridge he aimed for the river, then opened the door and leapt from the car. Ten seconds later the car crashed into the side of the bridge with an enormous bang, then rolled over into the river.

It was dark and so Kieran concealed himself amongst the shrubs at the side of the road. From his hiding place he could see the patrol cars pulling up alongside the bridge, just in time to see the car disappear below the surface of the water. The darkness allowed Kieran to make his way safely to the main highway, where he hitched a lift north in a truck.

18

Jim Hollis called into Frank Mariano's office to give him an update on their investigations. 'Morning, Frank.'

'Oh come in, Jim, sit down. What have you got for me today?'

'Well, there were some fireworks in the city at the weekend which relate to our current inquiries. I thought I'd put you in the picture.'

'Yes. I heard we had an explosion. It was the Atlantic Air building wasn't it? Don't tell me we've got terrorists in Washington?'

'No, I don't think so.'

'Anybody hurt?'

'There was one fatality. It was Roy Stirling.'

'What? Not the Roy Stirling we are investigating?'

'I'm afraid so.'

'OK. What happened?'

'All we know at the moment is that someone set off a bomb in the Atlantic Air Building, cutting off all the power supplies. They even knocked out the backup generator. Roy Stirling took it upon himself to investigate personally, so we don't know exactly what happened. Anyway, another bomb exploded and another fire broke out. The firemen managed to contain the fire and eventually brought it under control. They found Roy Stirling's charred body amongst the debris, with a hole in his stomach the size of a grapefruit.'

'What on earth caused that?'

'Forensic reckon he must have taken the full impact of the bomb blast.'

'My God, this is getting more and more intriguing. OK. Do we know anything at all about who could be responsible for these explosions?'

'Well, one guy was seen leaving the building, although nobody seems to have got a close look at him. Apparently he stole a car and was chased by a number of Black and Whites. The chase ended at the Theodore Roosevelt Bridge when the car crashed into it and ended up in the drink. They pulled the vehicle out but there was nobody in it. Either the guy got clean away or he's still somewhere in the river. They're starting to drag the river this morning.'

'Who was in charge of the investigation?'

'A guy called Gregg Donoghue. He's FBI.'

'FBI? What on earth is their interest in all this? Shouldn't this be a local matter?'

'We don't know what their involvement is yet. Do you want me to make contact with his office?'

'No! Definitely not. We don't want them to know that we're even interested, not yet anyway. There's something not right about all this and I want to gather a lot more information before we let anyone else in on it. All right, see what you can find out about this Gregg, but do it quietly, not through official channels. By the way, any news from Ireland yet?'

'Yes, our man arrived back yesterday. I've just finished debriefing him.'

'What's the story?'

'Well, it seems that Alex Stenton was seen in the company of James Bankhead, a known activist and member of an Irish extremist organisation. We don't know what business he had with him, although our records do indicate that Tom Casey has been under suspicion, for quite a while now, of supplying arms to both sides. But we haven't been able to get anything specific on him.'

'What? Gunrunning? Is that what you think his trip was about?'

'Well, we don't really know what his trip was about. We're just collecting information.'

'I can't see Alex Stenton being openly involved in gunrunning. I figure there's got to be something else. Was there any action taking place while Stenton was over there? You know what I mean. Any sectarian killings take place at that particular time?'

'Well, there was one incident, but we haven't been able to make any connection yet.'

'Oh? What was that then?'

'A Mrs Bridie McGuire and her son Kieran were reported killed after a bomb exploded in their home. The local police are a bit puzzled by this one because the father, who was a well-known activist in the IRA, died quite a few years ago. The younger son Kevin was also a member, although the police strongly suspect that he has skipped the country, probably to the States, but they don't know for sure. The remaining family were definitely non-active, and the mother was known to have spoken quite openly and vehemently against the sectarian killings since her husband was killed. She had also strongly discouraged her elder son Kieran from taking any interest in the IRA. He held a fairly responsible job as an accountant in the local bank. So, you see, there doesn't seem to be a lot of reason for killing them.'

'Yes, I see what you mean. Well, look, see if you can find out if there's any record of the younger brother's entry into the States. What's the latest on Tom Casey?'

'Oh, not a lot there I'm afraid. Except that his consortium seems to have made heavy investments in the UK and it's all commercial work too. There doesn't seem to be any military involvement at all, which is most unusual for Tom Casey.'

'Oh, that doesn't surprise me. The Labour government put paid to all Tom Casey's military interests in the UK and it's cost him dearly. That's why I'm surprised that he's having any dealings with this government at all. It's all a bit suspicious to me.'

'That's all the more reason for keeping an eye on him. OK, Jim. Keep me informed will you?'

It took Kieran two days and a night to get to Buffalo. He had hitched a lift on a timber truck as far as Williamsport, a small timber town on the River Susquehanna in Pennsylvania. Williamsport was also a holiday resort with a rail link all the way to Buffalo, so Kieran had taken a train for the rest of the journey. It was 12.30 in the afternoon when his train arrived in Buffalo. He had told Linda to cross the border on her own if he didn't show up on the third day, and this was it. He was a bit worried by this time, as he didn't know how long she would wait for him.

Back in Washington, Gregg Donoghue received a phone call from one of his agents. 'I've just had a report from the Border Police in Buffalo. It seems that a girl answering the description of Linda Johnstone has been seen twice near the Border Bridge in Buffalo.'

'Was she on her own?' said Gregg excitedly.

'Apparently she was. They say that it looked as if she was waiting for somebody.'

'I'll bet she was,' said Gregg. 'Look, I don't want her apprehended, not yet anyway. So tell them that under no circumstances is she to be detained.'

Gregg's main concern at the moment was McGuire, and now that he knew where Linda was, he could use her as bait. It was now only a matter of time before he showed up. So all Gregg had to do was to get out there and keep an eye on her until Kieran turned up. Then he could bag both of them. Gregg sent word back to the border police to take note of her car and its licence number. If she decided to go across the border, they were instructed to let her go and inform the Canadian authorities to keep an eye on the car until he arrived. Gregg Donoghue could hardly believe his good fortune. This was certainly a breakthrough and it had come when he needed it most. He quickly made preparations to fly to Buffalo.

Linda Johnstone was standing by her car, parked close to the Border Bridge. She was anxiously looking at her watch and wondering if Kieran was going to show up. It was fast approaching decision time. Was she prepared to go it alone, or should she wait, but for how long? She looked at her watch again. It was now nearly one o'clock. He should have been here by now, she said to herself. Oh God, please let him be all right.

It was just after one when Kieran approached the bridge on foot, anxiously looking ahead to see if he could make out Linda amongst the gathering crowds of tourists who were queuing up to cross the bridge into Canada. He noticed one of the border police and decided to stay out of sight, so he hid behind a parked car. From there, he could see that the patrolman was looking intently in one particular direction. Kieran looked over to see the source of his preoccupation: it was Linda. She was pacing up and down by the side of the large blue station wagon.

Oh God, he thought to himself. Don't tell me they're on to her. I daren't approach while he's watching. Kieran started to weave his way through the parked cars in an effort to get closer to her car. At that very moment Linda decided to get into the vehicle and was walking towards it.

Kieran whispered loudly, 'Linda!' She stopped in her tracks. 'No! Don't look round, Linda. You're being watched by the patrolman.'

'Is that you, Kieran?'

'Yes. Carry on what you're doing. Get into the car and take out the keys, then go and open the rear door. Act as if you've forgotten something and leave the driver's door wide open when you go to the back.'

The open car door obstructed the patrolman's view and, when Linda opened the rear door, Kieran quickly appeared from behind the adjacent car and jumped into the rear of the station wagon.

'OK, Linda. This is it. No time to explain. It's now or never. Just close the door, get into the car and make for the bridge. We're crossing the border now.'

Linda threw the car rug over Kieran then quickly did as she had been instructed. She drove the car over to the queue for the bridge, where they waited for at least 15 anxious minutes. Meanwhile, the patrolman had rushed to his box and made a phone call to the Canadian authorities.

'She's on the move,' he said, 'but she's still on her own.'

'OK,' said the voice at the other end. 'You know what to do. Just let her go quietly through and we'll take it from there.'

Much to Linda's surprise and great relief, she was allowed to drive through unhindered. Once across the border she kept on driving. Kieran spoke to her from the rear of the car. 'Well done, Linda, you've got us through. Keep checking your mirror though, to see if we're being followed.'

'I think we're being followed already,' she said.

'OK, it's up to you now. You're gonna have to do something to lose them.'

'But how?' she said desperately.

'I don't think they're going to stop you now. If they were, they would have stopped you at the border. I think perhaps they're waiting to see where you're headed first. They probably expect you to lead them to me.'

'Oh! What am I going to do?' she said impatiently. 'How am I going to lose them?'

'Now don't panic. The hardest part is over. We're across the border. Just wait for your chance.'

'Look, I'm no speed driver. I get nervous when anyone drives over sixty. There's no way I'm going to outdistance these people.'

'Listen, I've got an idea. What you'll have to do is find a lot of traffic. Try and keep at least two or three cars in front of them. They won't want to get too close to you either, as they won't want you to know that they're following. Look for a busy tourist spot or a major bridge, anywhere where there is likely to be a build-up of traffic.'

'Then what?' asked Linda.

'Then I'll slip out of the car when you slow down, and you can drive on. What I want you to do then is take the car somewhere and dump it, after which you can make your way back to where you dropped me off.'

'And how do you propose I do all that?'

'Look for a diner, Linda. Make like you're stopping for something to eat, then slip out the back way and try and get back to me somehow.'

'You make it all sound so simple.'

'We're gonna have to make it work. It may be our last chance. Now that I know what this is all about, I realise that these people mean business, but I'll tell you all about that later.'

What Linda found most aggravating was the fact that much of the traffic was going in the other direction, heading for Niagara Falls. She thought to herself how easy it would have been if she had been going the other way. She could see a sign ahead of her that said 'Welland Canal', and decided to head in that direction. It turned out to be only minutes away, and the traffic in front of her had already started to slow as they approached the inevitable bottleneck at a busy canal crossing.

Linda, seeing a gap in the traffic just three cars ahead of her, seized her opportunity, pulled out sharply and made for the gap at speed, just managing to squeeze in before the gap closed as they neared the canal bridge. Linda's manoeuvre had taken place so suddenly and unexpectedly that she surprised the occupants of the pursuing car. They quickly pulled out to follow, thinking that she was up to something. This turned out to be a bad move on their part for, as the bottleneck formed, all the gaps in the traffic were closing up and they were unable to get back in line. The pursuers were forced back quite a way before they were able to rejoin the queue of traffic. It couldn't have worked out better for Linda and Kieran, for now there were at least 14 cars between them and the following vehicle. As they approached the bridge the traffic slowed to a crawl, and Kieran made his move.

'Remember,' he said to Linda. 'Remember, Welland Bridge.'

Kieran slipped out of the rear door of the car and down the embankment at the side of the bridge. This was watched in utter amazement by the driver of the car behind who followed Kieran's every move in open-mouthed bewilderment. Kieran concealed himself under the bridge and prepared for a long stay.

Linda carried on across Welland and followed the traffic towards a place called Beamsville. It seemed ages before she finally came across a diner. This one was situated at a major junction just east of Brantford. By this time the pursuing vehicle had caught up and it followed her into the car park of the diner. Linda waited for a few moments to see what her pursuers would do, but they didn't move from their vehicle so she got out of the car and entered the diner. She was absolutely starving by this time, for it had been hours since she last had something to eat. Linda went up to the counter and ordered two hamburger rolls and a cup of coffee. The second roll she put in her bag for Kieran.

As the diner was quite full Linda was forced to share a table. Her table companion turned out to be a friendly truck driver who struck up a conversation with her. During the conversation, he asked Linda where she was heading. She told him that her car had broken down and she wanted to head back towards Niagara Falls. The trucker said that she was in luck, because he was headed for Rochester and Niagara was on his route.

'But just a minute,' said Linda contemplatively. 'I didn't see any trucks out there when I came in.'

'Don't be so surprised,' said the trucker. 'You were travelling west, so you naturally came in that door, but eastbound traffic use the door on the opposite side of the building. Didn't you notice that this station was built in the middle of a junction?'

'No, I'm afraid I was just so glad to find a place to stop.'

By this time they had finished eating and the trucker said, 'OK. Are you ready to go?'

'Yes I am,' said Linda.

'Right then, follow me.'

As Linda stepped outside the other door she suddenly realised why the trucker had referred to it as a station, for there was a gas station in the middle of a large forecourt. They climbed into the truck and were on their way.

Back at Welland Bridge, Linda met up with Kieran once again. Kieran by this time was cold, wet and shivering. He had been waiting out in the open for nearly two hours, during which time there had been a heavy fall of rain. He had had no way of knowing how long it would be before Linda returned.

When they met they hugged each other very tightly. So much

had happened in those three days that it had seemed an eternity for both of them. It had also been three days of uncertainty, but long enough to make them realise just how much they meant to each other. As they hugged, Linda remembered the hamburger that she had bought for Kieran.

'Hey! You must be starving,' she said. 'Just wait and see what I've got you.' She produced the roll from her handbag, and Kieran grabbed it and stuffed it greedily into his mouth.

'What next?' she said. 'Where on earth are we going to hide? It seems like even the Canadian authorities are after us now.'

'Don't worry, Linda. We'll find somewhere. But for the time being, we're going back to Niagara.'

'Niagara?' she said in disbelief.

'Yes. That's the last place they'll expect us to go. We can soon lose ourselves among the tourists and honeymooners. Talking of which, it wouldn't be a bad idea if we were to sign in ourselves as a honeymoon couple.'

'Don't you go getting any ideas, Kieran McGuire. What I said before still holds.'

'You sure are one stubborn lady,' he said. 'Anyhow, I for one will have to get my head down for the night because I'm absolutely shattered. It'll also give us time to think about our next move, and I can tell you what happened in Washington.'

'I really don't think I can take much more of this, Kieran. I'm tired of running, and my family will be worried sick. I must get in touch with them somehow. I simply must,' said Linda.

Kieran pulled her towards him to comfort her. 'Let's get a room first and then we can discuss this in comfort. No point in the two of us catching cold now, is there?'

They were surprised at how long it took to find a room. Apparently it was peak season for honeymoon couples. They were everywhere. Eventually Linda and Kieran were able to find a room at a Holiday Inn by the falls. It was a typical, up-market honeymoon suite, with all the mod cons, spacious, attractively furnished, draped with velvet and a king-sized waterbed in the middle of the room.

Kieran buzzed for room service and ordered up a large pot of coffee. Tired though they both were they still had a lot of talking to do. Kieran gave Linda a graphic description of what had taken place in Washington. He also let her hear the tape recording that Roy Stirling had made. She was astonished at the length to which these people were prepared to go in the name of business interests and at the number of lives they were willing to take.

Where will it end? she thought to herself. Linda was also worried about her family. She now realised that they too were at risk, and how much more dangerous it would be for them if she were to return. Despite all these fears Linda was determined to make some kind of contact with her family before they left Niagara.

Kieran interrupted her train of thought. 'Look, Linda. We have some real serious decisions to make tonight. We have to consider a complete change of strategy.'

'What do you mean?'

'Well, for one thing, it looks like it was a bad move coming to Canada. I guess I underestimated their influence. We're gonna have to go further afield.'

'Like where?' said Linda apprehensively.

'Listen, when I decided on Canada, I thought we would be safe from the American authorities. I figured that, even if they did manage to continue pursuit over the border, Canada was a big enough country to get lost in. But I'm not so sure any more. I think I'd feel a lot safer back home in Ireland.'

'Ireland!' exclaimed Linda, who was just about at the end of her tether. 'And how do you propose we're going to make that mighty leap?' she said sarcastically.

'Look, simmer down. We're both in this together. If you've got a better idea, then I'm only too willing to listen.'

Linda said nothing. She just stared blankly at the wall.

'I don't know how we're gonna get there yet, but we're gonna have to find a way,' said Kieran.

'But didn't you say that they had killed your mother in Ireland?'

'Yes, I know, but I've got friends over there, enough to make the difference. As a matter of fact, I've got friends back home who would be only too happy to start a war with them.'

'Oh no, Kieran! Hasn't there been enough killing already?' asked Linda despairingly.

'I'm sorry, Linda. I didn't mean that. I was only letting off steam. But I still think we would have a better chance on home ground. You may even get a chance to see your mother and father while we're over there,' he said in an effort to cheer her up.

'As much as I'd love to see them, I don't know if I could put their lives in danger by visiting them.'

'Well first things first. We're gonna have to find a way for you to get in touch with your family in Washington. That's our first priority. OK?'

After some debate, Kieran convinced Linda that writing a long letter to her family would be far more beneficial than phoning. She would have enough time to say all the things she wanted to, instead of making a quick phone call and worrying all the time about the call being traced.

As Linda settled down to write her letter, Kieran took out some maps to investigate an idea that he had been toying with. He had remembered that his Uncle Peter had served four years in the Merchant Navy, and that two of those years were spent on a cargo ship that carried grain from Canada to England and Scotland on a regular basis. He remembered his uncle telling him that the round trip took approximately six weeks. It was all coming back to him now. Old Pete used to tell him about his trips up the St Lawrence to Montreal, where they would pick up the grain. He seemed to remember that there was another port of call in the St Lawrence that had a French name. Now what was it? Baie something or other. Then it suddenly occurred to him. Baie Comeau. That was it, at the mouth of the St Lawrence. Now all he had to remember was the name of the ship, or even the company. Then he could look up the shipping journals and see if that trade route still operated. Kieran couldn't remember whether Pete had ever mentioned the name of the company, but he was sure that the ship's name had come up a few times.

What was it? *Avon*, that's it, or something *Avon*. He decided to let it rest for a while, hoping that the name would return to him later. Meanwhile, it was time to try the idea out on Linda, to see how she responded.

'Linda, I think I've got a way of getting us back to the UK.'

'You have?'

'Well, I've got a game plan to work on, but we'll have to check out a few things first. There's a chance that we might be able to get a ship back.'

Kieran then went on to give Linda a rough outline of what he had in mind. Later that evening they both settled down to a long overdue sleep, with Linda enjoying the waterbed while Kieran had to settle for the couch.

The next morning they made plans to travel to Montreal by train. As they left the hotel, Linda persuaded Kieran to let her have a look at the Great Horseshoe of Niagara Falls before they moved on. Kieran took her over to the large crowded car park directly opposite the Falls. It was a spectacular sight to behold: a continuous wall of water, 200 feet high causing an almost deafening crescendo. The water spray from the Falls was so dense that it created a heavy mist over the whole area.

As they both stood there staring at the Giant Falls they heard a loud whirling, whistling noise in the distance. It gradually grew louder and louder until, quite suddenly, a large helicopter came thundering into view. It seemed to appear from nowhere out of the mist. It hung in the air, hovering over them, creating great gusts of wind and spreading the spray from the Falls all over the vast crowd of spectators, soaking them as they desperately fought and pushed each other in their efforts to get out of the way.

Once the crowd had dispersed enough to create sufficient space for the helicopter, it landed abruptly, dropping to the ground. The door flew open and two men appeared in the doorway, as four uniformed policemen ran towards the machine. One of the men in the doorway produced ID and showed it to the first policeman. Moments later the four policemen pushed back the inquisitive crowd, creating a way through for the two mysterious visitors.

As the lead man in the doorway stepped down on to the tarmac Linda suddenly stepped back, giving a loud lingering gasp as she quickly put her hand to her mouth in a vain attempt to stifle her cry.

Kieran, stirred by Linda's movement, said, 'Wait a minute. I know that guy! He's the one who came after me in the Atlantic Air Building. He certainly doesn't hang about.'

'I'm not surprised, Kieran. That's Gregg Donoghue.'

'What!'

'Yes! We'd better get out of here quickly, and quietly.'

Gregg had a photograph in his hand and was showing it to two of the uniformed policemen, who were shaking their heads in response to his questions.

Kieran and Linda tried squeezing their way back through into the crowd. Eventually, they broke through. Kieran hailed a cab; they jumped in and he asked the driver to take them to Wilson. He had originally planned to go to the railway station, but it was obviously too late to pursue that course of action. Wilson was on the coast of the lake near Niagara River. He was hoping that they could pick up a boat there that would take them to Kingston on the other side of Lake Ontario. The travel brochure had advertised a boat trip up the St Lawrence which ran from Kingston. As it was turning out, this could be a far better alternative to the one he had originally planned.

It was certainly a safer and more discreet way of travelling to Montreal. It took only 45 minutes to get to Wilson, but it was two hours before they managed to find someone with a boat who was willing to take them to Kingston. The trip across the lake was over a 120-mile stretch and took them eight hours.

It was now 11.30 in the evening, which meant that they would have to make another overnight stay before they could catch the morning steamboat trip that would take them all the way to Montreal. As Linda and Kieran settled yet again into a hotel room, Linda commented on how sad it was that they were making all these fantastic journeys across Canada, visiting all the places she would have loved to have seen under different circumstances. But being chased as if she was a fugitive from the law was turning her life into a nightmare.

'I can remember not too long ago, when I didn't have a care in the world!'

'What did you say?' exclaimed Kieran. 'Say it again.'

'Say what again?'

'Wait a minute. Yes that's it. You said, "I didn't have a care in the world." '*Cairnavon*! You've triggered off the name of the ship that I've been trying to remember for the last twenty-four hours. *Cairnavon*! Linda, you're a genius,' he said as he grabbed her cheeks between his hands and kissed her gently on the mouth.

Next morning Linda and Kieran were up bright and early to catch the paddle steamer. Kieran picked up a shipping journal on his way to the boat. He intended to study this at length during the trip. On arrival at the pier they were both pleasantly surprised to see before them what turned out to be a replica of a three-deck paddle steamer, complete with twin stacks. It was a beautiful sight to behold, rigged out in period style.

Their journey down the St Lawrence turned out to be a fascinating one which they both enjoyed tremendously. For the first time in a long while they felt safe and secure, and were able to relax and enjoy themselves. Of course, it was meant to be a fun trip, as it was designed for tourists to see the best parts of the river while enjoying the luxury and comforts provided for them on board this quaint old-style paddle wheeler. Linda and Kieran took full advantage of the facilities provided: good food, wine and pleasant surroundings. They sunbathed on the upper deck, taking in the breathtaking views as the boat paddled its leisurely way down the river. They even explored the boat's magnificent casino where Linda won $150 at the roulette wheel, a game she had never played before.

A fancy-dress ball had been organised in the late afternoon and all passengers were expected to participate. Linda and Kieran were only too pleased to join in and, using a bit of ingenuity and improvisation, they were able to concoct a pirate's outfit for Kieran while Linda dressed as a slave girl.

It seemed a lifetime ago since they had been able to relax and enjoy themselves, during which time they had both lost people whom they were very close to. It was not surprising, therefore, that they ended up in a state of euphoria. Linda even got a little drunk on the generous quantity of wine which was freely available to all. Despite this, Kieran kept a cool head, although trying hard not to spoil Linda's enjoyment. He tried to slip away for a while so that he could study his shipping journal, but Linda wouldn't hear of it. She insisted that he stay and have one more drink with her. So Kieran relented and joined her in a last drink. As it turned out, that was one too many for Linda, for she soon felt dizzy and became unsteady on her feet when she tried to move from their table. Kieran helped her down to the cabin and lifted her on to her bunk.

'Oh Kieran, I'm so embarrassed. What must you think of me? I'm ... I ...'

Linda dropped off into a sound sleep. Kieran left her to sleep it off. He thought to himself as he looked at her, poor Linda. I bet that's the first time she's been drunk in her life. Boy, is she in for another new experience when she wakes up.

He scanned through his journal looking for a ship called the *Cairnavon*. He was unable to find it, but he did spot the *Cairndhue*. He thumbed through the pages looking up the particulars of this ship, and discovered that it belonged to a company called the Cairn Line. There were four ships belonging to the company and two of them were on the same trade route and carried grain from Canada to the UK. Kieran consulted the section on the ship's time tables and discovered that the *Cairndhue* was at present in Quebec, due to arrive in Montreal that very night. This was the best break he had had since the whole episode started. He looked towards Linda and was about to share his excitement with her, but thought better of it. Instead, he went back to his journal to see if he could establish how long the *Cairndhue* was to be in Montreal.

Kieran found out that it would take three days to discharge the ship's cargo, and another three to reload her with grain. So he was going to have at least six days to find a way of getting himself and

Linda on board. Travelling legitimately as passengers was out of the question, as this would attract the attention of the authorities, so somehow he and Linda would have to become stowaways, a prospect that Kieran was beginning to find quite exciting. But to do this, he would have to enlist the aid of a crew member, one who was prepared not only to smuggle them on board, but also to conceal them for the duration of the trip. Considering the trip was to take 12 to 14 days this was going to be no easy task. He lay back in his bunk while he thought about the next possible move. The drink started to take its effect on Kieran for, within minutes, he too was fast asleep.

The paddle steamer arrived in Montreal harbour early in the morning. Linda and Kieran were both recovering from the night before, although Linda was still feeling some consequences of her indulgent drinking. Kieran was quite surprised at how well she was dealing with this new experience of a hangover.

Kieran had no intention of wasting time in Montreal as there was so much to do and so little time. Their first move after leaving the paddle steamer was to find accommodation somewhere in the city. As soon as they were organised in a hotel, Kieran left Linda and headed back to the docks to see if the *Cairndhue* had arrived on schedule. Fortunately, Montreal was an open dock, so there were no police gates to contend with. His journal had told him which dock the ship was due to arrive at so it didn't take long to locate, especially since it turned out to be the only ship tied up to that particular quayside. Kieran was surprised at her size. She was a much larger ship than he had anticipated. The *Cairndhue* was 12,000 tons, and was probably a Sam Boat, a class of cargo ship hastily built by prefabrication methods and had only been expected to last for the duration of the war. Kieran moved up close to her massive black hull and noted the company's colours on the funnel. This was red and sported a large white triangle with a black band around the funnel's edge. The superstructure was white and showed up in stark relief against the black hull. As he walked towards the stern, he could clearly see the heavily embossed name '*CAIRNDHUE*', in large, bold letters. He decided not to hang around the ship too long in case he became conspicuous. Besides, he had seen enough for the time being. As he walked away he thought to himself, so that's the sort of big beastie that old Uncle Pete used to sail on. Not quite what I had imagined.

Kieran headed for the first bar on the waterfront, with 'Joe Beefs' emblazoned in red neon lights above the door. Kieran remembered his uncle telling him about this bar. Apparently it was part of the routine that took place when they went ashore in Montreal. They always made a point of having a couple of beers in Joe Beefs while they made their minds up about what they wanted to do when they went into the city. But, according to Pete, there had been many a night when they never got past Joe Beefs. Pete had also said that the barmen always knew most of the crews that shipped into that particular quayside, for very few of them got as far as the city without dropping into Joe Beefs first. And, like Uncle Pete, some of them never got beyond that point. They were often quite happy to sit there all night and get drunk before staggering back to the ship. Kieran planned to make use of this knowledge in his attempt to make contact with one of the crew.

When Kieran first entered the bar he was amazed at the sheer size of the place. It was an enormous open-plan area with dozens of little tables surrounded by traditional Wheelback Windsor chairs, bar furnishings which he remembered seeing in bars back home in Ireland. There was a large bar extending from wall to wall of this massive room. However, despite its size, there were very few people in attendance behind the bar. Kieran took up position on a stool at the bar, and ordered a cold beer.

He decided to try his luck right away and called to the mountain of a barman, 'Hey Jim!'

'Joe's the name,' bellowed the giant.

'Oh, I'm sorry,' said Kieran. 'Not Joe Beef, the owner?'

'Yes, that's right. The very same.'

'I wonder if you can help me, I'm looking for a deckhand from the *Cairndhue*. Do you know if any of the crew has been in here?'

Joe pointed to one of the tables by the window and said, 'I think these two over there are from the *Cairn* boat.'

Kieran hadn't expected to be quite so lucky so immediately, so he was a bit taken aback. However, having made the inquiry, he felt obliged to follow it through. He approached the table and asked the two seamen if he could have a word.

One of them pulled out a chair beside him and gestured to it, saying, 'Yeh! Sure, Paddy. Sit down and give us your craic.' The man had obviously cottoned on to Kieran's accent.

Kieran sat down beside them and said, 'I hear you're off the grain boat that arrived this afternoon.'

'Yeh. That's right, Paddy, the *Cairndhue*. I'm Sandy and this is Jim.'

'My name's Kieran.'

'Right then,' said Sandy. 'What do you want to talk to us about? Do you know one of our crew?'

'Well, not exactly. You see, my uncle used to sail on the *Cairnavon*.'

'Hey! I used to sail on the *Avon*,' said Jim. 'What was your uncle's name?'

'McGuire. Peter McGuire.'

'Nope! Never knew anybody by that name. I guess it must have been before my time.'

'Can I get you guys a drink?' asked Kieran.

'Sure thing, that's one thing we'll never refuse, eh Sandy?' said Jim as he winked at him and laughed.

Kieran went to the bar and ordered up a round of drinks. He was feeling very pleased with himself, for he had made contact with two of the crew at his first attempt and things seemed to be going well. He had reckoned that it might take a couple of days to get this far.

Kieran spent the next two hours drinking with Jim and Sandy, telling them the tales his uncle had told him, although Jim and Sandy also had a few of their own to tell. They all got quite merry as they drank, for they had knocked back a few beers by this time.

Kieran sensed that Jim and Sandy were obviously settled in for the rest of the night so he made some excuse to get away, but arranged to meet them again the next night. He didn't want to push his luck too far. The fact that he had been able to initiate contact was good enough for the first night. Besides, he was too drunk to start any serious negotiating.

It took another two drinking sessions before Kieran felt confident enough to broach the subject of getting on board. By this time he had grown quite fond of Sandy, who had turned out to be a carefree lad from Edinburgh. But Jim was a different proposition. His manner was more brash than carefree, and Kieran sensed that there was a darker side to him. He had also noticed Jim blatantly light up a joint on at least two occasions during their drinking sessions, which might have explained his brashness. It certainly explained why he got pretty high on relatively few drinks. Jim's smoking habit had given Kieran an idea. He knew that he would have to give them some explanation for wanting to leave the country as a stowaway, and telling them the truth was out of the question, so he had to concoct a credible story that would explain his situation.

On the third night Kieran waited until Jim and Sandy were approaching the merry stage before he brought up the subject, although he had already prepared the ground by indicating his intention of going back to the UK in the near future.

'Hey, guys. When are you heading back to the UK?'

'Day after tomorrow,' replied Sandy.

'What are the chances of me going back with you? Do you think the skipper would let me work my passage?'

Sandy didn't even take time to think about it. 'No chance, man. Not on a regular ship like the *Cairn*. Now if it was a Panamanian that would be different. These guys can hire and fire as and when they please. They can even leave you stranded in a foreign port. But British ships insist that you sign articles before you join and that usually means a two-year contract, especially if you're going deep sea.'

'Oh, I didn't know that,' said Kieran. 'Gee, that's a shame. I was kinda looking forward to going home with you guys.'

Kieran was wondering how they might respond to a more direct approach. He had decided to tell them that he and a friend were caught smuggling $5000 worth of heroin into Canada and were at present out on bail. They had planned to jump bail and leave the country but their passports had been taken from them so their only chance was to stowaway onboard ship. Kieran suspected that such a story just might appeal to their sense of adventure. He put out a few more feelers to test their reaction before actually putting it directly to them.

When he finally got round to it, he was quite surprised by their response. For the first minute, there was complete silence. Kieran was sure he had done the wrong thing. They both seemed to have sobered up in a hurry.

Sandy was first to break the silence. 'Are you for real? Is this on the level?'

'Look, guys, I know I'm asking a lot but if you people don't help us then we're gonna be spending some time behind bars. We're not exactly big-time drug dealers. This was a one-off situation ... believe me, we've learned our lesson.'

'I'm going to need some time to think about this,' said Sandy. 'I don't mind helping out a fellow countryman but what you're asking is real risky stuff.'

'What's in it for us?' said Jim. 'That's assuming that we can take you!'

'Aw, don't be such a mercenary bastard,' joined in Sandy. 'Can't you see the guy's in real trouble? And all you can think about is what you can get out of it.'

'Wait a minute, Sandy! We're putting our own necks on the line here. There's no harm in getting some return for it, is there?'

'OK, OK,' interrupted Kieran. 'I don't want you people fighting over this now. I'm perfectly willing to pay. But let's discuss this tomorrow. Meanwhile, we can all sleep on it.'

Kieran went back to the hotel that night feeling really pleased with himself, for now he had given them two good reasons for helping him. Sandy had sounded quite genuine in his concern for Kieran's plight. He was also willing to help for nothing. But Jim seemed to be better motivated by the chance of some financial reward.

The whole situation was starting to look encouraging. Kieran decided not to tell Linda at this stage how he was progressing. He thought that he'd better wait and see how the lads responded the next day.

Linda had been reading the local newspaper in Kieran's absence and had noticed a report claiming that the Canadian authorities were looking for a dangerous fugitive who had smuggled himself across the Canada–USA border at Buffalo. It went on to claim that he was wanted by the American FBI on suspicion of murder and terrorist activities in Washington. Inside the paper there was a picture of Kieran when he was 19. Linda showed the article to him as soon as he got in.

'Where on earth did they get hold of that awful picture?' asked Kieran.

'Never mind the picture. Have you read the article? They're on to us even here in Montreal, and now they have a picture of you.'

'Don't worry, Linda. It's unlikely that anybody will recognise me from that picture.'

'But where did they get it?' she asked.

'From Ireland, I expect,' replied Kieran.

'I hope this doesn't mean that your name's plastered all over the papers in the UK as well.'

'Now come on, we don't know that yet. This is no time to start panicking.'

In the light of this new development, together with Linda's obviously growing concern over the situation, Kieran decided to tell her about his progress in negotiating a passage back to the UK. He had hoped that she would find the news encouraging. Linda was delighted, for she was starting to feel that the authorities were closing in and that their only hope was to leave the country. Her main concern now was that it should be as quickly as possible.

The next day, when Kieran met up with Sandy and Jim, he was told that they were prepared to do what they could to help. Sandy told Kieran that he and Jim had managed to secure some accommodation for them. Kieran hadn't mentioned the fact that his partner was a woman for fear that it might create further complications. Sandy figured that the best place to conceal Kieran and his companion would be in what he called 'the infirmary', a medically equipped double cabin which always remained vacant in case of emergencies. No one but the steward ever went near the place. He was responsible for cleaning it out once a month, and had done that already, so he wouldn't be going in there again until after docking in Newcastle.

'What if there's a genuine emergency?' enquired Kieran.

'We'll just have to play that one by ear, but don't worry about it. Jim and I will be keeping an eye on things. We'll see that your needs are provided for. We haven't had time to work out what's going to happen at the UK end, but we'll work something out on the trip over.' Sandy was feeling quite pleased with his preparations and was glad that he was going to be able to help Kieran as he had come to like him over the past four or five days. 'Do you think you and your friend will be able to manage with that?'

'Manage!' said Kieran in amazement. 'I don't know how we're gonna be able to thank you enough. You couldn't have been more helpful.' Kieran was overwhelmed by Sandy's enthusiasm.

Then Jim intervened. 'Wait a minute, Sandy. You haven't told him what the fee is yet, have you?'

Sandy didn't answer. He just looked at Jim in disgust.

'It'll be $1000,' said Jim.

'What!' exclaimed Sandy. 'Are you nuts or just plain greedy?'

Kieran sensed that an argument was about to start, so he quickly intervened, trying to nip it in the bud. 'Look, it's OK, honestly. That's all right by me,' said Kieran. 'I figure that's a fair price under the circumstances. Especially when you think about the risks you guys are taking.'

'See! I told you so,' said Jim to Sandy. 'I knew it was no big deal asking for a thousand bucks.'

Sandy didn't speak, but continued to look at Jim disdainfully.

Jim was visibly embarrassed by the silence and tried to cover it up by again addressing Kieran. 'You realise you'll have to pay in cash.'

'Right,' said Kieran, anxious to get this agreement finalised before it blew up out of all proportion. 'That's OK, Jim. I anticipated that and brought cash with me.' Kieran pulled out his wallet and counted out $500 into Jim's hand. Jim was beaming by this time as if he could hardly believe his luck. 'I'll give you the other $500 when we're safely at sea,' said Kieran. He turned to Sandy. 'Right, Sandy. If that's OK, what are the arrangements for getting us on board and when would you like us to be there?'

Sandy told him that it would be best if they could both get on board that night as they expected to sail the next day on the late afternoon tide. 'If you and your friend get down here for midnight, we'll slip you on board and settle you in the infirmary, then we can get you both battened down before we sail. I hope you haven't got too much luggage?'

'Nope, we're travelling very light.'

'Right, midnight it is then,' said Sandy.

That night, Kieran and Linda boarded the *Cairndhue* under cover of darkness. Sandy met them at the gangway and smuggled them on board. He was quite surprised to find out that Kieran's friend was a woman, and had mixed feelings regarding the possible consequences, 'A word of warning, Kieran. Keep her well out of sight. There's no telling how the boys will react if they find out there's a woman on board and, for God's sake, keep Jim away from her. He tends to think he's God's gift when it comes to women.'

'OK, Sandy. I get the picture. Let's get to the cabin.' Sandy saw that they were safely installed in the infirmary and locked them in until the ship was under way.

At four o'clock the next day, the *Cairndhue* weighed anchor and headed out to sea. Linda and Kieran were on their way to Newcastle.

19

Back in London, Bill Rice was conferring with Ian Scott, his second in command.

'We don't seem to be getting anywhere fast on this Edinburgh Parade killing. It's time we stepped up our range of investigation. What says you, Ian?'

'Yes, I think you're right. Most of our enquiries are pointing to the US, so it's time we sent someone over there.'

'What do you have so far?'

'There seem to be two lines of investigation stemming from local police enquiries. The Glasgow police have identified a man who appears to be a strong suspect in this case.'

'Oh, and what's the evidence so far?'

'Well so far, we have discovered that he runs a small security firm in Glasgow. You know the sort of thing. They compile lists of names of people who have questionable backgrounds, not unlike our Suspect Index, except that this is a commercial system like InfoLink. Access to their files is sold to industry. They also screen personnel for local firms.'

'OK,' said Bill. 'What's the connection?'

'It seems that this man Simpson was spotted near the Camera Obscura on at least three occasions. His final visit was reported to have been on the day of the explosion.'

'Explosion?' questioned Bill.

'Yes. On the day before the shooting there was an explosion in the Camera Obscura tower, putting it temporarily out of action. There's no doubt that this was part of the preparation for the killing that followed. Didn't I put that in my report, sir?'

'Yes, I remember now. Sorry about that. I'm afraid I've been out of town for the last week on another case. The minister recalled me to give this investigation priority. Please, carry on will you?'

'Where was I? Oh yes. I was about to say the fact that the man was in the area at the time is not remarkable in itself. What is interesting, though, is that when you line this information up with all the other bits and pieces, a definite pattern seems to take shape.'

'How do you mean? What sort of profile do you have on this guy anyway?'

'He was an officer in the security services of the army during the war. Part of his function was to filter out Nazis trying to get into this country after the war was over, but he seemed to be more interested in identifying communists and left-wingers in general. He was eventually drummed out of the forces because of his right-wing tendencies.'

'Do you mean he was discharged?'

'No, but he was asked to resign his commission.'

'I see,' said Bill. 'But surely you don't think that this was reason enough for a political assassination. And why would he wait so long?'

'No, we don't think that that was the motive in itself, although it's a possibility we can't rule out.'

'What about his firm?' asked Bill. 'Is there anything there worth following up?'

'Yes, I was coming to that. That's our second line of investigation. The real owner of E&F Securities turns out to be an American multinational, CLC Industries.'

'Ah yes, I remember now. We discussed it earlier.'

'Yes. CLC would appear to have a definite interest in the outcome of the British elections. Inquiries into this company have revealed that they were in the middle of negotiating a hundred million dollar contract with the Conservative government and were sure to lose this contract under a Labour administration. This may all be circumstantial at the moment but there does appear to be an excellent motive on the part of CLC, and now we have an even more tangible link in the shape of this man Dave Simpson. Well, sir, that's where we are at the moment.'

'Have you pulled this man Simpson in for questioning yet?'

'No, not yet.'

'Why haven't you?'

'Well, because we wanted to see who was behind him and what the CLC connection was. Besides, I didn't think we were likely to get much information from him at this point.'

'Right, we'll have to send someone over to the States to follow this up. Leave it with me for a while and I'll see if I can pave the way by making contact with my opposite number over there. OK, Ian, I'll call you back later.'

Bill Rice made a call to Frank Mariano – a call that he was most reluctant to make, for he remembered cutting Frank short when he inquired about the case two days after the event.

'Oh! It's you, Bill,' said Frank rather overeagerly. 'I wondered when you'd get round to calling me back. Well now, what's happening over there? You got everything tied up in that assassination attempt?'

Bill Rice knew that Frank was having a go at him but he was trying to take it in his stride. He figured that he'd have to eat some humble pie, but hoped that Frank wouldn't revel in it.

'No, we haven't tied it up yet,' said Bill with thinly disguised anger in his voice. 'As a matter of fact, that's what I'm phoning you about. We're particularly interested in a company called CLC, and I wondered if there was anything you could tell us about them?'

'Umm! CLC. Isn't that one of our multinationals? What exactly is it you want to know?'

'Well, to start with, perhaps you could give me a profile of their business interests together with a list of subsidiaries?'

'I see,' said Frank. 'Well, you'll have to let me check my files, but I'll get back to you as soon as I can, OK?'

'Yes, sure, Frank. Thanks for your help.'

When Bill Rice hung up he was furious. That bastard knows something and he's not letting on. I know it. I can feel it in my bones. This'll be him getting revenge for my not involving him from the very beginning. Looks like I'll have to go over there myself. There's no way he's going to give me information on the phone. This one's gonna have to be eyeball to eyeball.

Frank Mariano called Jim Hollis to his office. 'Jim, it looks like the British have finally got round to investigating CLC and they want our cooperation.'

'Will we be cooperating, sir?'

'Of course we will, but not before I make them sweat a little first. I'll teach them to leave me out in the cold when I offer my help free and gratis. Meanwhile, see if you can prepare a report for them. I expect they'll be sending somebody over here soon. This is not the kind of investigation you can conduct over the phone. Don't include everything we know in that report, whatever you do. Just give them enough to whet their appetites, just a rough outline of our investigations. I'll fill in some of the details verbally. I want to know just how much information they have on this case before we pool our resources.'

Bill Rice was regretting being flippant with Frank Mariano, for it now looked as if he was going to need his full cooperation. He had hoped that he would have been able to send Ian over for this one but knew that Ian would be no match for Frank, especially if he was in a non-cooperative mood. Bill called Ian back into his office.

'Ah! Ian. Look, I had hoped to give you a trip to the States but it looks like I'll have to go over there myself. However, I'd like you to take care of things for me while I'm away. Keep me informed of anything that crops up relating to this case and I'll let you know if I get anything worthwhile from the Yanks, though somehow I have my doubts this time. Oh, could you arrange a flight to Washington for me, the first available one tomorrow. I don't want to do it through my secretary. Let's keep this little trip to ourselves.'

'Sure. How long do you intend staying?'

'I don't know yet. It depends how much help we get from our American cousins.'

Ian Scott was relieved that he didn't have to go to the States, for his wife was expecting their first baby any day now, and she'd never have forgiven him if he was out of the country when it happened. Besides, he wanted to find out more about this Mr Simpson. He was sure that there were other areas to explore.

The next day Bill Rice was on his way to America. Bill was a 6 foot 4 giant of a man, who weighed 18 stone. Normally he was a good-natured, easygoing kind of a guy, but this was not surprising considering his rather large proportions: people tended to be polite to him purely because of his size, so consequently he never experienced much friction in his social life. As a matter of fact Bill had great difficulty in understanding why anyone would want to cause friction with another human being. This led to his taking an interest in the criminal mind and eventually to his joining the service.

Bill found the flight to Washington a pleasant one. Weather conditions were good, the plane was on schedule and he simply loved flying. He was like a big kid when it came to flying. He always had to have a window seat so that he could see what was going on and he enjoyed the thrill of taking off and landing. He would have loved to have been a pilot, but he had less than 20:20 vision.

About half an hour before the plane was due to land in Washington, Bill tried to prepare himself for his meeting with Frank Mariano. He had met Frank before on two other occasions and had found him to be quite a likeable person. He also realised that Frank would be a bit miffed that he hadn't been involved in the early inquiries, but figured that he had had good reason to exclude Frank, especially from enquiries concerning a political assassination. Frank should have been able to understand that.

Bill took out his report on the Edinburgh Parade killing and revised its contents. It wasn't much of a report, but then they didn't have much information on the case. He decided to prepare a list of questions about CLC: Who are the key men in the company? How active is its security system? He was finishing this list when the signal came on for him to fasten his seat belt as the plane was making its final approach to land.

They arrived in Washington ahead of schedule. After clearing customs Bill took a cab to the Watergate Building, where he booked into a two-roomed suite. He had chosen the Watergate because it was the nearest hotel to the CIA headquarters. As soon as he got into his room he phoned Frank Mariano.

'Hello, Frank.'

'Oh hi, Bill. Hey, look, I was just about to phone you.'

'No need,' said Bill. 'I've just booked into the Watergate.'

'The Watergate? Why you son of a gun. Why didn't you tell me you were coming over? I could have arranged to pick you up and you could have stayed at my place.'

'It was a last-minute arrangement and I didn't want to put you to all that trouble. I was hoping to see you some time this evening.'

'Of course, no problem. Look why don't I take you out someplace and show you a bit of Washington? Gee, I do wish you'd warned me you were coming across. We could have prepared something special for you.'

'Oh, a night on the town would be just great. I'll look forward to that. Where can I meet you?'

'Tell you what, I'll pick you up from the Watergate around eight-thirty,' said Frank. 'I'll see you then.'

After a shower and a change of clothing Bill was ready for something to eat so he headed for the dining room. It turned out that he was too late for a proper meal but the head waiter directed him to the hotel restaurant, where he picked up a quick snack in the shape of two large hamburger rolls, a side salad and a large glass of milk. Bill had no aversion to American fast foods for, being a bachelor, he appreciated their convenience. After the meal he decided to take a walk around Washington and familiarise himself with his new surroundings. This also allowed him time to adjust to the different environment.

Bill spent the next two hours wandering around, taking in the sights. He did some shopping and picked up a few souvenirs. By the time he arrived back at the hotel he was dead beat and thoroughly exhausted. It wasn't only the walking that had got to him but the heat as well. When Bill got to his hotel suite he unloaded his packages and made straight for his bed. His head barely touched the pillow before he was out like a light.

Two and a half hours later the phone at the side of his bed rang, waking him with a start. 'Hello. Mr Rice?'

'Yes, speaking.'

'There's a Mr Mariano at reception, waiting to see you. Shall I send him up to your room?'

'Er, em, no. No. Tell him I'll meet him in the hotel bar in about fifteen minutes.'

Bill looked at his watch. That time already? He immediately jumped out of bed and into the shower. It was the quickest and most effective way of wakening himself up.

It took him exactly 20 minutes to shower, dress and get down to the bar.

Frank didn't have any difficulty identifying Bill, for he towered way above everybody else in the room.

'Oh, there you are, Bill. It's real good to see you again.'

'I'm sorry about this. I didn't mean to keep you waiting. You must think me very rude indeed.'

'Not at all,' said Frank reassuringly.

'But really,' insisted Bill. 'I must explain. You see, I spent two hours wandering all over the city this afternoon, and when I got back to the hotel, I just collapsed onto my bed. The next thing I knew, was the phone ringing, and being told that you were waiting for me in the hotel lobby.'

'OK, I accept your apology and your explanation. Now will you tell me what you would like to drink?'

'Oh, well, I'll have a whisky, a large one.'

'One large Scotch coming up,' said Frank as he signalled to the bar attendant. 'Well, what's brought you to Washington in such a hurry?'

'There's some pressure afoot to get this case resolved. Someone seems to think we're dragging our feet.'

'Is that the case you were asking about on the phone? The one you think CLC is involved with?'

'Yes. I got the impression that you might have some information that could be useful to us.'

'Well, I'll tell you what got me interested in this case initially.' Frank then went on to tell him about the discussion that took place on board Tom Casey's yacht. Bill Rice was all ears. 'So you see when we got notified about the Edinburgh Parade killing, I remembered this little tête-a-tête and put two and two together. That's why I phoned you at the outset.'

'Yes,' said Bill rather disconsolately. 'And that's when I snubbed you on the phone. I'm afraid I thought you were just trying to stick your nose in where it wasn't wanted. I don't know how many kinds of fool you must think I am, but I can only apologise once again. How about we call a truce and make a fresh start.'

Frank could see that Bill was genuinely contrite and endeavouring to restore the status quo. He was only too happy to agree. 'Sure. Let's put all this nonsense behind us and see what we can do to get to the bottom of this case of yours. Hey! Wait a minute. What am I saying? It looks like I'm involved anyway, now that we're investigating an American company.'

Now that the air was cleared between them they were able to make some progress. After some verbal exchanges of information, Frank handed Bill the report that Jim Hollis had prepared for him.

'This is a rough outline of our investigation into CLC. You browse over it and tomorrow we'll get our heads together and take it from there. But that's enough about work. I'm here to show you the Washington night life. By the way, have you eaten yet?'

'No,' said Bill. 'But I've certainly got an appetite.'

'Good,' said Frank. 'I've got a great restaurant in mind.'

The next morning Bill spent two hours browsing over the report that Frank had given him the previous night. He then made a call to Ian Scott in the UK. After that he headed for Frank's office.

'How are you feeling this morning, Frank?'

'Not too bad. Hey! That was some night we had. It's been a long time since I was last on a drinking session like that. I see you've recovered quite well.'

'Oh, I'm fine. I read over your report this morning and found it quite interesting. I see that Atlantic Air is one of CLC's subsidiaries and that you're currently investigating their head of security, Alex Stenton. Well, this morning I phoned my office and asked them to check our files to see if we had anything on him. It seems that he was one of our people from way back, about eight years ago. He was dishonourably discharged from the SAS.'

'Yes, we're aware of that. We keep a record of that kind of information. Have you seen his profile yet?'

'No, not yet. My office is preparing one for me. They're going to send it over.'

'OK, but you can have a look at what we have on him meantime. I think you'll find it interesting reading. He seems to be quite an unsavoury character.' Frank reached into his desk and pulled out a folder which he handed to Bill.

'How come you let him into the country in the first place, especially with a dishonourable discharge?'

'Oh, we didn't know about his DD until later, when we investigated him during our inquiries into this case. You see, we don't check every detail of every application to enter the country. If we did, we would be so bogged down with paperwork that the system would come to a grinding halt. I guess he just slipped through the net.'

'Anyway, why is he such a prominent feature of this enquiry?' asked Bill.

'We don't know that he is yet. We began by making routine enquiries into Tom Casey's chief lieutenants and we came up with all this interesting information – and when it comes to interesting, this guy's a star. We know that he spent three days in Ireland recently and we're trying to find out why. Anyway, that's enough from me. What about you giving us some information, Bill?'

'Yes, you're right. It's time I showed you my report. I've got it here,' said Bill, opening his briefcase. He handed the document over to Frank and waited until he had read it.

Now that they had read each other's reports, things started to slot into place. For one thing, Frank hadn't known about CLC's

Glasgow-based subsidiary, E&F Securities. They both realised that this company would be an excellent outlet for covert operations, due to both the nature of its business and its proximity to the target area.

So far they had established that Tom Casey was a prime suspect for four reasons. Firstly, his company stood to make substantial financial losses which were evident from recent contractual negotiations with the previous Conservative government. Secondly, Tom Casey's strong verbal attacks on the Labour administration and its proposed policies which Frank witnessed. Thirdly, CLC had covert connections in Scotland in the shape of E&F Securities, whose manager was a prime suspect of the British government. Fourthly, there was Alex Stenton, one of Tom Casey's lieutenants, who had an unsavoury background and links in the UK.

20

The *Cairndhue* had been at sea for three days and Kieran and Linda were getting settled into a routine. Sandy had arranged to bring them food twice a day and they had free access to all the other amenities that they required. There was even a shower in their cabin so, all things considered, they were pretty comfortable. Their biggest problem now was combating the sheer boredom of being locked up in the cabin 24 hours a day. It was too risky for them to venture out on deck in case they were spotted by any of the crew. However, after the third day, Sandy agreed to take them up on deck during the night and offered to keep watch for them while they stretched their legs. Sandy took them to the stern where they would be concealed from most other parts of the ship and where there would be less traffic of crewmen. There was also enough deck space for them to walk around freely.

It had been some time since they had left the sheltered waters of the St Lawrence River and entered the Atlantic Ocean. There was quite a heavy swell and Linda was feeling a bit squeamish. It was the first time on the open sea for both of them and they were swamped with mixed feelings about the whole experience. As they sat out on the open deck breathing the night air, Linda's eye was caught by the rhythm of the swell, and she gradually became more and more aware of the motion of the ship as it gently rose and fell with the waves. Soon she could feel the nausea and internal turbulence that is only associated with sea sickness. This hadn't occurred earlier because she had been too preoccupied with the experience of being a stowaway on board a cargo ship, and with enjoying the splendid views of magnificent landscapes as the ship sailed down the St Lawrence.

But now they were on the open sea. Now there were no distractions of beautiful scenery. All she could see was the vast expanse of grey uninterrupted ocean and the continuous movement of the waves that seemed to lift the ship even higher on every crest, until all her senses became alerted and she was acutely aware of any and every pungent smell that surrounded her. She tried desperately to fight it and avert her eyes from the turbulent waters of the sea. But soon they were fixed on a new object that swayed rhythmically with the motion of the waves. Wherever she looked she could see movement, always the same steady to and fro getting increasingly greater as time went on. There simply was no escape, so she closed her eyes and tried to occupy her mind with other distractions.

But this also failed, as she only became more and more aware of the internal turbulence of her stomach. She could feel its contents churning inside her, which triggered off in her mind thoughts of all the things that she had eaten before, their smell and what they looked like. Her mind was swamped with memories of past greasy dishes. To escape this mental torture, she opened her eyes wide and tried to take deep breaths of sea air, and again she became aware of the waves and the ship's movement. Linda could feel the contents of her stomach rising inside her. Her head span and she was feeling quite dizzy. She quickly rose to her feet, holding firmly to the safety rail.

Kieran was calling to her, asking her, 'What's wrong Linda? What's wrong?'

But to Linda his voice was distant and hardly audible, as her mind and all her senses were too preoccupied with the struggle to control her body functions which were about to break loose at any second. Once on her feet, Linda rushed over to the ship's rail, oblivious of any danger, totally engrossed with her immediate predicament. As she reached the rail her stomach seemed to explode as it desperately tried to empty its contents in one mighty rush. Linda yielded to the inevitable, and opened her mouth just in time to make way for the rising accumulation of vomit as she emptied the entire contents of her stomach. When it was over she stood there gripping the rail, drenched and covered with the spray of the sea. She was completely spent, weakened and distraught by her nauseating ordeal.

By this time Kieran had realised what was happening but felt totally helpless and frustrated with his inability to rescue her from her distress. He moved over to the rail and put his arm around her. Linda just stood there, numbed by the whole awful experience.

'Come, Linda. It's time to go below deck. I'm sure you're going to feel much better now.'

Kieran took her down to the cabin and helped her into her bunk. She was so exhausted by her ordeal that she fell asleep right away. He put a blanket over her then settled down on his own bunk. He too was tired, and fell asleep soon after.

Next morning Kieran was awakened by hammering on the cabin door. He quickly got up and answered the door. It was Jim.

'Well, aren't you going to invite me in?'

'Em er, well...' Kieran was trying to think of a way to prevent him from entering but, before he could, Jim had already pushed his way into the cabin.

'Well, how are our passengers settling in then?' Jim could see that Kieran was confused and tried to put him at ease. 'Oh! You'll be wondering why I'm here instead of Sandy? It seems that one of the ABs wanted to swap watch with Sandy for a couple of days as he wasn't feeling too good, so Sandy won't be able to make his usual visits. So, it was up to me to stand in. How are you doing anyway? Where's your friend?' said Jim looking around the cabin. Before Kieran could answer though, Jim was walking across to Linda's bunk. 'What, still in his kip is he?'

'Yes, he's feeling a bit under the weather,' said Kieran forcing himself in front of him. 'I think we'd best leave him alone until he's feeling better.'

'What's wrong with him? Seasick! It's amazing how some guys just can't take it.'

'Aw, he'll be all right,' said Kieran. 'He'll be as right as rain tomorrow. Some of us just take a little longer to adjust.'

'Anyway,' said Jim. 'I only stopped by to let you know the change in the usual arrangements. I'll be bringing your food for the next few days until Sandy is back on his usual watch.'

After Jim left the room, Kieran wakened Linda. 'How are you feeling today?'

'Oh,' she said, 'I'm feeling a bit groggy.'

'I'm not surprised,' said Kieran. 'You had a rough time last night.'

'Yeh, I know. I was seasick. Boy was I seasick. It's such an innocuous name for such a dreadful, disgusting and loathsome illness.'

'Listen, Linda. We've just had Jim in here.'

'Jim? Who's Jim?' said Linda impatiently.

'Jim is Sandy's friend. He's the guy who insisted on the thousand bucks for our passage.'

'Oh, that Jim,' said Linda as she remembered. 'So what's the problem?'

'I'm not sure, but Sandy was very reluctant to let him know that there was a woman on board.'

'Why should that make a difference?'

'I don't know. Maybe it's an old nautical taboo that it's unlucky to have a woman on board, or perhaps it's something more basic like he can't be trusted with women. Whatever it is, we'd best be careful. So far, he's still unaware. You were fast asleep with the blanket over your face when he was here, so he didn't have a chance to find out. I'd like to keep it that way if we can. We've got enough problems without taking more on board. Anyway, are you feeling any better?'

'I feel a lot better. But I don't think I ever want to go through another night like that. I thought I was going to die.'

'You know, my Uncle Peter told me that he was only ever seasick once, and that was on his first trip to sea. He said the secret is just to keep yourself occupied, be active and not to think about your surroundings. Just to get on with whatever you have to do.'

'Is that how you're dealing with it?'

'Yes, and it seems to be working for me.'

When Jim next returned, it was with their midday meal. Kieran had already arranged with Linda that she should be in the shower when he arrived, so as to keep her out of sight. Linda, for her part, was getting a bit peeved with what she saw as unnecessary subterfuge.

When Jim entered the cabin with their tray of food, he was quite chirpy, and was joking about the rough weather and its consequences on anybody who didn't yet have their sea legs. He had also brought along a packet of dry cornflakes.

'Hi there,' said Jim. 'Where's our sick passenger now then? Is he feeling any better?'

'I'm afraid he's having a shower at the moment. You know, trying to freshen up. It makes him feel better when he's doing something.'

'Yea, that's the idea. Keep your mind off it. Look, I brought along these cornflakes just in case.'

'Just in case of what?' Kieran asked.

'In case he can't eat anything. I know that on my first trip at sea, I practically lived on cornflakes for the first three or four days. It's about the only thing I could keep down.'

'That was very considerate of you,' said Kieran. 'But I don't think it'll be necessary. I think he's got his appetite back now. He said he was feeling quite hungry today.'

'OK. Suit yourself. I'll see you later. *Bon appetit,*' he said with a half smirk on his face as he left the cabin.

When Linda came out of the shower she was evidently a bit annoyed. 'Must we keep up this charade? How on earth do you expect me to hide every time he appears, especially when he's going to be coming twice a day? There's no way we can keep this up for another eight days, no way.'

'I don't expect him to be in attendance for the rest of the trip,' said Kieran. 'Sandy knows the situation. He'll probably take over again in the next couple of days.'

'No!' said Linda. 'No, we'll just have to confront him with the truth. Better that we tell him ourselves than that he finds out by accident. Besides, he's being paid well for his services. What right has he got to be choosy?'

'Maybe you've got a point. It might be better to tell him before he gets suspicious.'

IAN FERRI

What they didn't know was that Jim was already on to them. He had first become suspicious when Kieran barred his way when he tried to approach the bunk that morning, and he wasn't buying the shower story either. When Jim left the cabin he decided to hang around for a spell outside the door. It was just long enough to hear Linda's feminine tones as she was sounding off to Kieran. So that's it, thought Jim. Our other guest is a woman. Now that's interesting. I wonder why Sandy never mentioned it. Perhaps he planned on keeping her all to himself. We'll just have to see about that.

That night, the weather conditions got even rougher as the wind reached gale force and beyond. It had risen to force nine by eleven o'clock that evening, causing the ship to pitch and roll very heavily as the helmsman steered her into the wind. Linda and Kieran were finding it very difficult to stay upright for any length of time and their cabin was strewn with clothing, broken crockery and upturned chairs rolling across the floor. They were both unprepared for such rough seas. Neither of them had experienced the like before and they hadn't bothered to batten down any of the more vulnerable pieces of cabin equipment.

One of the advantages of really rough weather is that there's no time to be sea sick. Linda's mind was occupied with other things, like trying to control her own movements with one hand, while trying to stop things falling on top of her with the other. Hence the first rule of the sea, which says that you keep one hand for yourself and the other for the ship.

Kieran and Linda eventually clambered into their bunks, but only after they had abandoned all hope of sitting in a chair for longer than 30 seconds. Kieran, who had a fore and aft bunk, tried desperately to jam himself securely into it, but to no avail, for he fell out every time the ship rolled to port. This was much to Linda's amusement, and she laughed heartily every time it happened. Linda, whose bunk was thwart ships (pointing port and starboard) didn't have this particular problem, as the ship didn't pitch as much as it rolled, so she was able to secure her position quite successfully.

By midnight, the gale had subsided a little and the ship was becoming more stable but Kieran, who had dragged his bedding and mattress onto the floor, was taking no chances. He was staying put. He eventually accomplished a level of stability by laying his mattress on the floor and squeezing it in between the lockers and his bunk support. Ultimately they fell asleep, but more from exhaustion than anything else.

During this time, Jim had been lying back on his bunk smoking a joint with a glass of whisky in his hand. He seemed quite oblivious to the weather conditions. His mind was more occupied with the memory of the girl's voice and the brief but significant glimpse he had of her when he looked through the slats of the ventilator on the cabin door and saw her come out of the shower.

By morning the storm was over and conditions had returned to the norm, which amounted to a gentle roll and a barely perceptible pitch. When Kieran awoke he had a stiff back and was aching all over from the bumping and knocking about of the previous night. He thought to himself, if this is life on the ocean waves, you can keep it! He sat up, looked round the cabin and could hardly believe his eyes. It looked as if a bomb had hit it. There was debris everywhere. This is gonna take a month to clean up, he thought to himself.

Linda stirred a few minutes later. 'So that's where you decided to sleep,' she said smilingly. 'I wondered when you were going to make up your mind. One minute you were in your bed, the next you had decided to get up again!'

'Very funny,' said Kieran. 'Well, you just feast your eyes on that lot. Maybe that'll take the smile off your face.'

Linda looked round to see what he was talking about, then suddenly shot up into a sitting position. 'Good Lord!' she exclaimed. 'What a mess. We're never going to get this cleaned up before Jim comes back.'

'That's as maybe, but we'd better get up and get dressed right away. There'll be no long lie-ins this morning.'

Linda and Kieran were barely dressed when they heard a loud banging on the cabin door. It was Sandy. 'Quick you guys, you'd better get out of here in a hurry. The skipper has just told the steward to get up here and check the place out for storm damage once he's finished clearing up the dining room. Hope you haven't started tidying up yourselves yet?'

'No, we haven't,' said Linda. 'There wasn't time. Where can we go?'

'Oh, no need to worry about that, you can both come down to my cabin for a couple of hours, at least until the steward's finished up here. Try and get all your stuff together and see if you can clear out without leaving any sign of your being here. I'll give you a hand with all that bed linen. We'll have to take it down with us to my cabin.'

'What about the rest of the crew?' said Kieran. 'Won't they see us?'

'No, they're all too busy tidying up their own cabins. I guess there were a few of us got caught short last night. That was some gale. I've been through a lot worse, mind you, but that one seemed to creep up on us suddenly and it hit us with a bang.'

When they eventually got into Sandy's cabin, Kieran asked where Jim was. 'Aw, he'll be up on the bridge right now. It's his turn on the wheel.'

'What on earth does all that mean?' said Linda.

'I think Sandy means that it's Jim's turn at the helm. I thought there had been some switching around of watches?' said Kieran. 'Isn't that why Jim brought us our food?'

'Oh yes. But that's all been sorted out now. The guy I stood in for is back on watch.'

'I see,' said Kieran. 'By the way, how are we doing for time? Do you think the weather has held us up much?'

'No, I shouldn't think so. There's a following wind brewing out there that's gonna push us all the way home if it keeps up.'

'Not more rough weather?' interrupted Linda.

'Oh, just a little,' said Sandy with a smile. 'What's wrong, Linda? Don't you like life on the high seas?'

'Not much,' replied Linda sheepishly.

'Never mind, the first two years are the worst,' said Sandy teasingly.

'You two make yourselves comfortable and I'll see if I can organise some coffee for us.'

The three of them chatted about life at sea in general, and Sandy tried to assure Linda that it wasn't all rough weather and hard times.

'There's been many a time that I've crossed the Atlantic when the sea was like glass,' he said. 'The crew used to lie out on deck and sunbathe. There's nothing like breathing in sea air to clean out the old lungs. But you landlubbers wouldn't know much about that. You'll be too used to the smog of the city. I guess I'd better go and see if that steward's cleaned out your cabin yet. Hey! This isn't such bad service after all, now is it? I bet you weren't expecting a cabin steward on this trip, eh?'

Sandy was back within ten minutes to let them know that it was all clear for them to return to the infirmary. Although initially concerned about the unexpected interruption to their routine, Linda and Kieran had found it a welcome break to the monotony of daily life in the cabin. Linda was very relieved to see the cabin back in order. It had been a nightmare of a mess when they left. Sandy had given them a pack of playing cards to take back with them, so they both settled down to a game of Gin Rummy.

Later that evening, Jim knocked on their door. As Kieran wasn't expecting a caller, he didn't open it until Jim spoke through the door ventilator and said, 'It's Jim here. Sandy wants you to come down to the cabin. He's got something worked out, to get you and your friend ashore when we get to Newcastle. He'd like to discuss it with you.'

Kieran turned to Linda and said, 'You wait here. I'll find out what this is all about.' He opened the door and said to Jim, 'I thought Sandy was supposed to be on watch?'

'Yeh, this is normally his watch,' said Jim. 'But he swapped over so that we could have a get-together.'

Kieran followed Jim down to Sandy's cabin. When he went in, he was surprised to see that Sandy wasn't there and turned to Jim questioningly. Jim explained that he was probably up in the mess organising the coffee.

'Wait here. I'll go and check,' said Jim.

As he was leaving the cabin, he said to Kieran, 'By the way, I'll lock this door behind me, just in case any of the crew should put their head in. You know, to borrow a book or something. I won't be long.'

In actual fact, Sandy was still on watch and Jim was heading straight back to the infirmary. He had got hold of the steward's pass key, so he was able to let himself in when he arrived.

When he entered the cabin, Linda was already in her bunk. Although she was awake, she hadn't stirred because she fully expected it to be Kieran. By the time she realised that it wasn't, it was too late. Jim had already put his hand over her mouth and the other behind her head.

He said, 'One word from you, and I'll break your neck.'

Linda immediately tensed up and tried to struggle free. Jim responded by giving her head a sharp twist, just enough to inflict a measured amount of pain, and to show Linda that he meant what he said. She froze, as a surge of excruciating pain passed down her neck.

Jim spoke to her. 'If you scream there's a good chance that you'll turn out the whole crew, but then I'll just have to explain to them how I found a stowaway on board. Then you and your friend will both be handed over to the authorities. Do you really want that to happen?' Linda shook her head. 'Now there's a good girl,' said Jim. 'I like a woman who knows when to keep her mouth shut.' Jim slowly removed his hand from Linda's mouth.

'Kieran will kill you if you as much as lay a hand on me!' snapped Linda.

'Oh, do you think so?' said Jim defiantly. 'Don't you think that would be kinda foolish under the circumstances? Anyway, he's otherwise engaged at the moment. He won't be bothering us for a while.'

'Haven't you been paid enough?' shouted Linda, trying desperately to play for time.

'Only in money darling, only in money. But we both know that there are other things that money can't always buy, now don't we?'

Kieran had been waiting for ten minutes or more in Sandy's cabin and was wondering what the hold-up was. He was also starting to get agitated and suspicious. It had already occurred to him that it just might be a set-up, but he had dismissed that thought as being irrational. He kept telling himself that it wasn't that big a ship, that there was nowhere on board that you couldn't get to in less than ten minutes. Was it really necessary to lock the cabin door? Kieran was having great difficulty convincing himself that nothing was wrong. He began to feel extremely uncomfortable about being locked in a cabin while Linda was left on her own up in the infirmary. The more he thought about the situation the more suspicious he became, until he could take no more. He looked around the cabin for another way out but there was none other than the porthole and he didn't think he would manage to climb through it. By this time he was feeling like an animal in a locked cage, and was determined to break free somehow.

Back in the infirmary, all Linda's efforts to keep Jim talking were quickly becoming exhausted. She changed tack, and had now allowed him to believe that she was prepared to cooperate with him and yield to the inevitable. Jim had started to remove his clothes, and Linda waited until he was in the process of removing his jeans. Then, when he was at his most vulnerable, she acted.

She quickly grabbed hold of the rail at the side of her bunk with both hands, then pulled herself forward with all her might and butted Jim in the face with her head. He let out a yell as he went reeling backwards towards the opposite bulkhead, banging his head on the heavy steel plate. Blood streamed from his nose, which looked as if it was broken. Jim was stunned for a few seconds as he fell to the floor. He shook his head, blood running down his face which now wore a tortured expression of pain but quickly turned to a grimace as thoughts of revenge filled his mind. By the time he got to his feet there was murder in his eyes and he lunged towards Linda with outstretched, grasping hands. Just before he reached her a large fist hit him a tremendous blow to the side of the jaw which spun him a full 45 degrees before he collapsed unconscious on the floor.

Linda looked up to see Kieran breathing heavily and towering over Jim's stunned body.

'Oh Kieran!' she cried. 'Thank God you arrived in time. I honestly thought that I was done for. He was going to rape me and I butted him in the face...' The rest of Linda's words were lost in the deluge of tears which followed.

'You're safe now Linda,' said Kieran as he wiped away the tears from her face with his hand. 'It's all over. There's no way he's gonna harm you any more. Not while I'm here.'

'What happened?' asked Linda. 'Did you see Sandy?'

'No Linda. It was all a set-up to get me out of the way so that he...' said Kieran, pointing to Jim, 'could come up here and ... well you know the rest.'

'What about Sandy?'

'Sandy's still on watch. I'm gonna have to get in touch with him as soon as he finishes. I really don't know how we're gonna sort this one out, Linda. I truly don't.'

Fortunately for all concerned, there was a noisy sea outside splashing heavy waves against the side of the ship, so nobody had heard the rumpus caused by the exchange of blows. Kieran used Jim's belt along with his own to tie Jim's hands and feet. He then gagged him with a handkerchief. They waited until it was time for Sandy to come off watch and by that time, Jim had recovered.

'Right smart ass!' said Kieran. 'I'm going down to get Sandy to see if we can sort something out here, but if you make one wrong move while I'm away, you're a dead man! Got it?'

Jim, who was considerably subdued by this time, nodded in acknowledgement.

Kieran found Sandy in his cabin and told him what Jim had done and how he himself had only just managed to escape through the porthole in time to stop Jim attacking Linda. Sandy was outraged at what Kieran was telling him. He made threats of throwing the bastard over the side, as he put it. Kieran knew he had to calm Sandy down before he could let him anywhere near the infirmary. Then Kieran and Sandy spent a few minutes trying to figure out what to do next.

After a while, Sandy jumped up and said, 'Hey, wait a minute. I don't see why anything should change. There's no way that little bastard's gonna squeal.'

'How's that?' said Kieran. 'I've threatened him, but I can't guarantee that'll hold him for long, especially after the mess he's in.'

'No. I've got something else in mind,' said Sandy. 'Something much more threatening to him. Let's go get him.'

They headed for the infirmary. When they arrived Sandy could see evidence of the distress that Linda had been through and he apologised for Jim's behaviour. He untied Jim and forced him up to a standing position.

Sandy said, 'Leave this to me. If he knows what's good for him, he won't be bothering you again, otherwise the skipper's gonna be hearing about that hoard of hash he's got stashed away under his bunk. He's probably been using it himself. I'll bet that's how he had the courage to come up here in the first place, the little rat.' Sandy then grabbed Jim by the back of the collar and dragged him out of the cabin.

There were no other major events during the rest of the voyage. Jim did not come near the infirmary again and the *Cairndhue* arrived in Newcastle on schedule. Sandy was able to keep Linda and Kieran out of sight when the custom's officers boarded the ship and carried out their search for contraband. As soon as the custom's officials were all below decks, Sandy was able to smuggle them both off the ship. Once ashore, they would have to fend for themselves. Newcastle was an open dock, so they were able to walk out without being challenged.

21

From Newcastle, Linda and Kieran took a bus to Stranraer. Kieran had been anxious to leave the area as quickly as possible, in case Jim reported them to the authorities after all. From Stranraer they caught the ferry to Larne the same day, although Linda wasn't too enamoured of the prospect of going on yet another sea voyage. She reckoned that she had seen enough of ships to last a lifetime.

Kieran spent the two-hour crossing telling Linda all about Ireland and describing what life was like in the country. Linda had lived in towns or cities all her life and couldn't imagine what it was like to live anywhere else. Kieran, however, had painted such a vivid picture that by the time he had finished she could hardly wait to get to the farm. She was also looking forward to meeting his Uncle Peter, who she had heard so much about.

As soon as they arrived in Larne, Kieran made for a telephone box and called Peter. He wanted to let him know of their arrival as soon as possible and to establish whether it was safe for them to go to the farm. Peter was delighted to hear that he was alive and well, and reassured him that it would be safe to do so.

After the call they stopped at a local hotel for a meal while Kieran made enquiries about hiring a car. An hour later they were on their way. It was a three-hour drive, two hours on the motorway and another hour on single-track roads through miles of lush Irish countryside. By the time they arrived they were both very tired and travel-wearied. Big Peter was there to meet them when they got to the farm gate. He gave them both a warm, hearty welcome and made a special fuss over Linda.

'And where did you find this fine beauty of a girl?' inquired Peter. 'Is this your first trip to Ireland, ma lass?'

'I'm afraid so,' said Linda.

'You mean to say that you travelled all the way to America, before you'd even visited Ireland? My goodness, you should be ashamed of yourself,' teased Peter. 'Come on inside. I've got a hot meal ready and waiting. I expect you must be hungry after all that travelling.'

Linda, who had been a bit overawed by the sheer size of the man, found the warmth and friendliness that he exuded a welcome surprise.

During the meal Kieran became so excited while trying to relate the events that had overtaken them that he was having great difficulty articulating his thoughts quickly enough and found himself stumbling over his words. Peter was amazed at what they had been through, and was utterly astonished at their ability to evade the authorities of two countries and make good their escape to Ireland.

'That's some ordeal you two have been through. Thank God you're both safe and well,' said Peter. 'When I didn't hear from you for so long,' he said directing his words to Kieran, 'I felt sure that something had happened to you. But now I know why you didn't contact me. You've obviously never had the time.'

Linda, for her part, was just too tired to keep pace with it all and found herself dozing at the table.

'My goodness, girl, what am I thinking? You poor wee lassie! You must be thoroughly exhausted!' exclaimed Peter. 'Look, you can hardly keep your eyes open. Kieran, will you show her through to her room and see that she's comfortable while I clear up in here?'

'Sure,' said Kieran as he helped Linda from the table. 'I hadn't realised, I'm sorry Linda.'

'Oh no, I'm the one who should apologise. Your uncle must think me ever so rude, but I'm just so very tired.'

'Don't be silly, lass. After all you've been through I'm surprised you're not already in hospital from sheer exhaustion.'

Once Linda was safely tucked in bed Peter broke out a bottle of Bushmills, considered by some to be among the finest of Irish whiskeys. He and Kieran then settled down in front of a large peat fire while Kieran continued his story. He also let Peter hear the tape that he had made while he questioned Roy Stirling. Peter could hardly believe his ears as Kieran told him of their adventure. He was particularly impressed by Kieran's improvisations in making pipe bombs, of all things. 'Where on earth did you get an idea like that?' asked Peter.

'Ouch, it was just something we used to experiment with as kids, when we were at school.'

'Why, lad,' said Peter, 'your own father would have been real proud of you, bless his soul. So he would. We could sure have used the likes of you in the old days, when your dad and I were fightin' the good fight.' Peter produced a large Sherlock Holmes-style calabash pipe and proceeded to fill it with a huge handful of black, pungent tobacco. 'Well then, what are your plans for the future? Or haven't you made any yet?'

'I'm not quite sure what my next move's gonna be,' said Kieran. 'Up until now, we've just been looking for a safe haven where we can both rest and relax for a while, without having to look over our shoulders all the time.'

'Ouch, you'll both be safe here ma lad. Nothing's going to happen to you, not if I can help it. Have you thought about contacting the British authorities yet? I bet they'd be only too pleased to get information on anybody trying to knock off their election candidates, especially if there was a government agency behind it, and it sure sounds that way to me.'

'I don't know who I can trust any more,' said Kieran. 'Perhaps these killings were initiated from this end. We just don't know. It could well have been the opposition who organised it, or maybe I'm getting paranoid about all this.'

'Never mind, Kieran, drink up lad. It's time we were turnin' in anyway and we can go into this tomorrow. You must be dead beat yourself and I've kept you up too long already. Come on now, it's time you got some sleep. By the way, that's a real brammer of a girl you've got there. I hope you appreciate her?'

'Isn't she something?' said Kieran. 'But that's a whole new story, and you're right, I'm far too tired to start another episode tonight. See you in the morning.'

* * *

Gregg Donoghue, having lost all trace of Kieran and Linda, had no option other than to convey this unpalatable news to Alex Stenton. Gregg was informed by the Washington office that Alex was in London with Tom Casey. That's all I need, thought Gregg, for Tom Casey to find out that we are looking for somebody who he thinks is already dead.

Gregg put his call through to London and reported the current situation to Alex Stenton. He was surprised by Alex's response, or rather lack of it, for Alex didn't make any fuss.

Alex knew that would be futile, especially over the phone. Anyway, he had already tried threats as a means of motivating Gregg to be more productive, but that too had proved futile. He just said coldly, 'I'll get back to you later,' then hung up.

Alex was fast coming to the conclusion that Gregg Donoghue was a luxury the company could no longer afford. His inability to complete his assignments, along with his repeated failures, were costing the company dearly. It was time Gregg Donoghue was dealt with, but for the moment Alex had far more pressing business to attend to. It was now up to him to locate Linda and Kieran.

He sat back from his desk to think for a while. There was no way that he could pick up a trail that had already gone cold in Canada, from an office in London. But he couldn't just leave it hanging there; he had to do something, and fast. Then it suddenly struck him: where else would an Irishman go, who was on the run in a foreign country? Where would he eventually head for? Then it suddenly occurred to him: home of course. Where else? He's got to start heading in that direction sooner or later. Perhaps it's time I prepared a wee reception committee for him, for when he does decide to return!

Alex picked up his phone and got in touch with his Irish connection. He instructed them to establish whether Kieran McGuire had any relations in Ireland that he might try to contact, and to monitor the area in case he turned up. If he did, they were to eliminate him on sight.

It took the paramilitaries just one week to track down Peter

McGuire and to set up constant surveillance of the farm. They were already there when Linda and Kieran arrived. During their enquiries they had found out that Peter McGuire had been an activist and was therefore almost sure to be armed. So they decided that it would be too risky to repeat the kind of attack made on Kieran's house. Besides, there was far too much open ground to cover, so the decision was made to wait until all the occupants left the building.

Peter McGuire did not go to bed, although he did grab a couple of hours sleep in his chair. From then on he tried very hard to stay awake throughout the rest of the night. Despite his assurances to Kieran, Peter was well aware of the possible dangers that lay ahead and was especially mindful of the people who had so brutally killed Kieran's mother. Peter had tried to trace these assassins during Kieran's absence but had been unsuccessful. He knew that whoever had the power to activate these killers in the first place could certainly do so again. It was only a matter of time before they discovered that Kieran was back in Ireland, and it wouldn't take them long to locate the farm.

Peter got out of his chair and went to the kitchen. Having established that all around him was quiet, he lifted the carpet and a few floorboards, exposing a large polythene package which he lifted out and unwrapped. Inside was a sub-machine gun, a Soviet Avtomat Kalashnikova 7.62 millimetre assault weapon, thought to be the most efficient and reliable in the world. In Vietnam even the American Marines prized the AK-47. They would abandon their M16s whenever they found a Kalashnikov amongst the bodies of the Viet Cong. The M16 was supposed to be a far superior and much lighter weapon but it was forever jamming, unlike the hardy, all-weather AK which could be soaked in mud for days yet still be an effective and reliable machine.

Peter picked up the weapon and ran his fingers over the length of it, caressing its cold, smooth finish. He hefted it experimentally and sighted along its barrel. It had been a long time since he had used the weapon, but it still felt good in his hands. Peter unwrapped an ammunition clip and rammed it home into its base. He looked at his watch. It was six o'clock in the morning and the sun was well above the horizon. Peter replaced the floorboards and then concealed the loaded rifle in a cupboard beside the window. It was time to get another hour's sleep before he prepared breakfast for his two guests. Peter's tiredness had eventually caught up with him and the drink had also taken its toll. This time, when he settled into his comfortable armchair, he fell into a deep sleep that lasted three hours.

Kieran woke him. 'Hey! Come on sleepy head, wake up. Don't tell me you've been sleeping in that chair all night?'

'What? What is it?' said Peter, startled by the rude awakening as Kieran shook his shoulder. 'Oh, it's you, Kieran,' he said, momentarily confused. 'What time is it?'

'It's nine o'clock already,' replied Kieran. 'Hey. I thought you were the early riser around here,' he teased.

'I tell you what, Kieran. You get the breakfast started, while I get washed up, there's a good lad now. I'll be with you in a jiff. Oh, is Linda up yet?'

'No, not yet,' said Kieran. 'I thought I'd let her sleep on for a while, since she was so tired last night.'

'Oh good, a good idea,' said Peter. 'Thank God for that. I wouldn't be wanting her to think that I was in the habit of sleeping in a chair, now would I?'

By 9.30, Linda was up in time to join them for breakfast, feeling totally refreshed after a good night's sleep. All three settled down to a hearty breakfast, starting with a bowl of porridge, followed by a large fry-up of bacon, eggs, black pudding and tomatoes.

During the meal Peter suggested that they should put their heads together and plan their next move. He was trying gently to keep them aware of the urgency of their situation, because he didn't want them to lapse into a false sense of security. Linda jumped in at that point and said that she had hoped to visit her parents in Edinburgh.

'Do you really think that's wise?' said Peter. 'These people who are looking for you will expect you to do just that very thing, now won't they?'

'I don't see how they could,' she replied. 'It's unlikely that they even know that I've left Canada. Don't you think it'll be all right, Kieran?'

'I'm not so sure. I think what Peter is trying to tell us is that if our pursuers stop to anticipate what our ultimate destination might be, then Scotland or Ireland would be a logical conclusion for them to come to. But we don't want to be too pessimistic,' said Kieran, trying to reassure her. 'If there's a chance for you to safely see your parents, then we'll certainly be taking advantage of it. But don't forget that Jim on the *Cairndhue* took a hell of a beating, and I reckon he may be itching for revenge. All it would take would be an anonymous phone call to the authorities and they would know that we were over here. I don't mean to scare you I'm just trying to be careful. Let's wait and see if there's a way we can check it out first.'

'Listen, Kieran,' said Peter. 'You know that I have no love for the British authorities but my advice to you is to get in touch with them. It's about time this thing was out in the open. They're certainly not going to be too happy about the American authorities interfering with British internal affairs now, are they? Particularly when it comes to killing senior politicians.'

'We don't know that the American authorities are involved,' replied Kieran.

'But did you not say that the FBI was after you?'

'Yes I did, but I know who he is, and he may well be a renegade working for this guy Tom Casey.'

'Well then,' said Peter, 'all the more reason for contacting the authorities. Let them find out who's at the bottom of this, and let them start putting pressure on the people who are pursuing you and Linda. It may even take the heat off you for a while. I suggest you start by sending copies of your tapes, together with an explanatory note to MI5. Or is it MI6? I can never remember which is which. I think one of them looks after internal security while the other deals with external affairs.'

'Do you really think that would be wise?' said Kieran. 'We may end up with the British on our tails as well.'

'I think that's a risk you're gonna have to take. The people who are after you have already come as far as Ireland to kill. They also seem to have plenty of resources to draw upon. That's why I think the American government may be involved.'

'I've still got an open mind on that one,' insisted Kieran.

'Anyway,' continued Peter. 'You two definitely don't have unlimited resources, and you can't go on running all over the globe now, even if you had. No, I reckon it's time to make a copy of the tapes here and now, so that we can send them on to the powers that be.'

Kieran pondered for a while as he thought over what Peter had said, then turned to Linda, saying, 'Well, what do you think, Linda? You've got as much at stake as I have. I think it's time you contributed something to this discussion.'

Linda took a minute or two before answering, then said, 'I agree with your Uncle Peter. We can't go on this way for ever. It's time we started hitting back.'

'That's the spirit, girl,' said Peter. 'That's the spirit.'

'OK,' said Kieran. 'We'll give it a try. Let's do it. If you copy the tapes, I'll get started on a letter and we'll send them off today. No time like the present, eh?'

'And I suppose that leaves me with the dishes,' said Linda jokingly.

By 1.30 that afternoon Kieran had prepared a package to send off to the British authorities and was getting ready to drive into the nearby village to post it. Linda and Peter went with him to the car. As Kieran opened the car door, Peter saw a reflection on the windscreen. It was a man on the hill opposite, in the process of aiming a rifle. Peter immediately pushed Kieran into the car and shouted to Linda to get down, at the same time grabbing her arm and pulling her to the ground. Just as they hit the ground, two bullets whizzed by them and struck the rear door of the car.

Peter shouted to Kieran, 'Get going, move!'

Kieran started the car and pulled away just as another barrage of shots struck the car and completely shattered the windscreen. Kieran looked over to see Linda and Peter making a run for the house. He immediately pulled hard left on the steering wheel and swerved the car round to cover them, by bringing it between them and the sniper. As he did, the side of the car was strafed with bullets and both near-side tyres were penetrated, bringing the vehicle to a sudden stop. Kieran lunged for the far-side door in an attempt to make his exit from the car and, just as he was turning the handle, a bullet pierced his upper right arm, causing instant and excruciating pain. Fortunately for Kieran the forward momentum of his body, together with the velocity of the bullet, propelled him with such force that as he released the door he rolled out of the car. He experienced still further pain as his wounded arm made heavy contact with the ground.

As his body came to rest about 10 feet from the car, he heard a sudden burst of gunfire coming from the direction of the farmhouse. It was Peter returning fire. Thanks to Kieran's covering manoeuvre with the car, he and Linda had safely made it to the house, allowing Peter to make use of the Kalashnikov which he had so carefully prepared the night before. Peter gave three bursts of fire, then the shooting abruptly ceased from the top of the hill.

Kieran looked up towards the house, to see Linda opening the door and beckoning him to move towards her. He crawled clear to the sheltered side of the house, and was able to make his way to the door unimpeded by gunfire. Once inside, he joined Peter in the kitchen.

'Can you see them?' he asked Peter.

'No, not any more. They've taken cover. They're probably planning their next move.'

Just then Linda noticed the blood pouring down Kieran's arm 'Kieran! You've been shot. Look at your arm, you're all covered in blood!' She rushed to attend to it.

'It's OK, Linda, the bullet went right through. There are no bones broken.'

'Never mind it's OK,' came back Linda angrily. 'We'll have to get something on that right away, to stop the bleeding.'

Peter looked round to assess the damage to Kieran's arm. 'You in pain, son?' he asked caringly.

'Nothing I can't handle,' replied Kieran.

'Aw, you'll be all right,' said Peter. 'But you'd better do what she says. Linda, take Kieran into the other room. You'll find a first aid kit in a cupboard by the fireplace. See if you can put a dressing on his wound.'

'Will you be all right on your own, Peter?' asked Kieran.

'What do you mean on my own? I've got my trusty AK here to keep me company. Don't you worry, I'll be fine.'

'What if they try to circle around behind us?' asked Kieran.

'It'd be too risky for them, son. That hill out there is the only cover they've got, the rest is open ground. But just in case, you'd better watch the other side of the building while you're through there. Look, there's a rifle and a box of shells below the floor boards in front of the fireplace. Go get it and leave all the doors open so we can talk. Go on now, get that wound covered, will you? These guys are not going to be making any more moves for a while, not now that they know that I can outgun them.'

Linda took Kieran into the other room and, while he retrieved the rifle, she found the first aid kit. While she was dressing his wound, Kieran said, 'Looks like we're in the thick of it again, Linda.'

'Never mind,' she said. 'This time we've got a friend, a good friend and one we can trust.'

'Yes, you're right there. Thank God for Uncle Peter. He sure saved our bacon this day.'

After some silent waiting Kieran shouted through to Peter, 'What do you think their next move's gonna be, Pete?'

'I'm not sure,' was the reply. 'I think they may wait until dark, then try and sneak up on us. Trouble is, I don't know how many of them are up there. I've only seen two so far. Our big problem is that they might send for help... By the way, Kieran, what condition was the car in, when you left it?'

'Useless. There's no way we're gonna be using that machine again,' replied Kieran. 'They did too good a job of immobilising it.'

'Well,' said Peter, 'whatever their plans are, we'd better start thinking about getting you two out of here soon.'

'We're not leaving here without you,' was Kieran's reply.

'You'll do what you're bloody told,' said Peter angrily. There were a few moments of embarrassing silence until finally Peter said, 'Listen Kieran, there's a van in the outbuilding... I think we should make a run for it as soon as it's dark.'

'Can't we just phone the police?' Linda said desperately.

'No, I'm afraid not. The first thing our visitors did was cut the phone lines. They probably did it last night.'

Just then, another burst of fire opened up, shattering the upper window just above Peter's head. He dived for cover then, as soon as it stopped, he retaliated with a couple of bursts from the AK.

'What on earth was that all about?' shouted Kieran.

'I think they're trying to remind us that they're still around,' Peter said, then all was quiet again.

Peter thought he heard a noise and shouted through to Linda and Kieran to shush and listen. He could just hear the faint murmur of a car engine starting up in the distance, and gradually it grew fainter until there was silence again.

'That's it,' said Peter. 'That's just what I've been waiting for. Right, Linda, you get all your things together along with Kieran's. Put everything into one suitcase. We don't want any excess luggage on this trip. Do it now, Linda, on you go.'

'Right,' said Linda. 'I'm on my way.'

'Good girl.'

'What do you have in mind, Pete?'

'I've been thinking that these guys figure we're stranded out here because they've knocked out our only means of transport. They obviously don't know about the van. They must have used their own vehicle to send for help.'

'How do you know that?'

'I think I heard a car starting up a minute ago, and the noise seemed to fade into the distance. This is in our favour at the moment, because if anyone is left up there they are probably without transport and won't be able to pursue us. I don't know how long it will take them to rally support, but to hell with waiting. I think we should take our chance now, and make a run for it.'

'Sounds good to me,' agreed Kieran.

'Good. Now look, here's the key for the van. When I give the word, you make for the outbuilding with Linda and all that gear, and get that bloody van moving. Leave the rear door open once you get under way, and I'll join you as soon as I can.'

Peter crawled over to the window and scanned the brow of the hill. At the highest point of the hill, he caught sight of a sparkle of sunlight glinting on glass. It was the gunman, using binoculars and panning the building for signs of movement. Then suddenly he disappeared below the edge of the hill. Peter figured that it could be as much as ten minutes before they made another check on the house, and decided that now would be a good time to start moving. Ten minutes was all they needed to get under way.

He shouted to Kieran. 'This is it boy! Let's go!'

Kieran took hold of the suitcase that Linda was carrying and they both made a run for the outbuilding. When they got there, Kieran threw the large barn door open, then dashed inside and jumped into the van. Linda scrambled to the back of the van, opened the rear doors and climbed inside.

'Are you ready?' shouted Kieran.

'Yes. I'm ready.'

'OK, let's do it,' said Kieran, as he rammed the gear stick into first and released the brake. He gave the engine full throttle, released the clutch and they were off. The van shot out of the barn at high speed and sped towards the back window of the main farmstead, where Peter was waiting for them. He leapt from the window and jumped into the back of the van. They were on their way.

As they cleared the building the assailant, who had heard the roar of the engine, was standing on top of the hill poised with his rifle, waiting for the vehicle to come into view. As it did, he let go a volley of gunfire. Peter was ready with the Kalashnikov and immediately returned fire. The assailant dived for cover and hit the ground. The van sped towards the closed farm gates and crashed through at high speed, followed by further shots from the hill top. By this time, they had a good head start and were fast moving out of range. In the van, there were hoots and shouts of nervous excitement as they finally drove clear of the farm.

On top of the hill, the gunman stood up and extended the aerial on a Tx Radio. 'Mike! Mike! Come in!'

Finally, after a few seconds of crackling, a voice came through the static, 'Right, Charlie, got you loud and clear. Go ahead.'

'They went for it. We've smoked them out, and they're heading towards you in a green Volkswagen van.'

'We'll be ready for them, but you stay where you are, in case they try and double back when we stop them.'

'Will do, over and out.'

Linda and Kieran were indulging in the relief of the moment, laughing and squeezing each other's hands in their joy. Peter, on the other hand, was not quite so demonstrative. He felt that it had all been a bit too easy and was refusing to relax until he was certain that they were in the clear.

'Peter! Hey, Peter,' shouted Kieran. 'Come on, cheer up. We made it didn't we? Get up here beside us.'

'Yes, come on,' joined in Linda. 'Come up front and join us.'

Peter shrugged his mountainous shoulders and responded to their pleading by clambering up to the front of the van. As they rounded the next bend a small hump-back bridge spanning the river appeared before them. Perched on top of the bridge was a dark blue Ford Escort.

'Get off the road!' shouted Peter. 'Get off this bloody road!'

Kieran reacted instantly and veered off the road into a grassy meadow. He headed towards a wooded area lying about half a mile in front of them.

'That's far enough, Kieran. Stop right here. Stop, I said!' he yelled.

The van lurched to a halt. Peter threw open the back doors, jumped to the ground and put a new ammunition clip into the Kalashnikov.

'That's it,' he said with venom in his voice. 'No more running. It's time I showed these bastards just who they're up against.' He turned to Kieran and Linda and said in a commanding voice that dared them to argue with him, 'You two stay right here, and don't move an inch from this spot.'

Peter started running back towards the bridge. 'Come on, you cowardly bastards, let's be havin' you!' he said under his breath.

The Escort had already started moving and was speeding towards him. Peter stood his ground with the AK at hip level and waited for just the right moment. The car was aiming straight at him and loomed larger and larger as it gathered speed, narrowing the gulf between them.

'That's it, me laddies, come and get it.'

He opened fire and blasted the car with bullets. He stood firm, determined to empty the whole clip into the vehicle. There was no way he could miss, by now the car was too close. Bullets poured into the interior, smashing and destroying anything and everything in their way. The car did not deviate from its path, but followed a straight line to its inevitable destination.

The Escort hit Peter at high speed, killing him outright and throwing his body clean into the air, before continuing on its deadly journey, until it collided with a resounding crash into a large tree and rolled over onto its side. The petrol tank exploded and the car burst into flames. It finally came to rest on its back, while the flames continued to burn furiously, consuming the interior, together with its occupants.

Linda screamed. 'No! No! No! Why did he do it? Why did he have to kill himself?' She then lapsed into hysterical tears.

Kieran grabbed her arms and pulled her body into his, squeezing her tightly within his arms. She was sobbing uncontrollably. Kieran too was crying. They stood there in each other's arms, weeping until they could weep no more.

Then Kieran clasped her face between his hands and tilting her head, looked straight into her eyes and said with great emotion, 'He gave his life, so that we could live! As it says in the good book, "Greater love hath no man, than he who lays down his life for another." Are we going to waste what he gave us?'

Linda didn't utter a word, but her eyes spoke volumes.

'Come on then. Let's go,' said Kieran.

They climbed into the van and drove off, without another word passing between them for the next hour. Kieran saw the strain on Linda's face and was concerned about her physical and mental condition. He suggested that she should climb into the back of the van and lie down for a while, as there was at least another hour's driving ahead of them. 'There's no point in both of us sitting up here,' said Kieran. Linda did not speak as she climbed into the back and stretched out on the floor of the van.

By the time they got to Larne it was nightfall and there was still two hours to wait for the ferry. Kieran took Linda into one of the local bars and ordered a double brandy for her and a pint of Guinness for himself.

'I don't drink brandy,' she said abruptly.

'Drink it,' said Kieran. 'It'll do you good. Believe me, you need it.'

'What are we doing in here anyway?' said Linda. 'How could you? How could you, after what we've just witnessed?' She made to leave the bar.

Kieran grabbed hold of her wrist and jerked her back. 'Look here!' he said sharply. 'I'm just as hurt as you are. After all, it was my kin who died.'

Linda didn't speak, but tears welled in her eyes.

Kieran softened his tone and explained to her that the drink would loosen her up, that it would relax her and help to dissipate some of her tension. 'After what you've been through, a doctor would be administering morphine injections by now. This is the next best thing I can think of. Come on now, please drink it.'

Linda finally relented and drank the brandy. During the next two hours, while they waited for the ferry, there was little conversation between them. Kieran wanted to discuss what they should do when they got to Scotland, but Linda wasn't interested. She was still in a state of shock. She just sat there, completely numbed by the whole experience. Eventually, it was time to board the ferry and they were once more on the move.

22

Jim Hollis walked into Frank Mariano's office and said, 'Hello Frank. Look, I've been doing some digging around at the immigration headquarters and I've discovered that their people in New York received a call from the forty-ninth precinct saying that they were holding a Kevin McGuire, who was trying to claim political asylum.'

'When did this happen, Jim?'

'About three months ago, Frank.'

'I see. What was the outcome?'

'Well, they sent one of their people along to investigate but by the time he got there, this Kevin McGuire had gone. He was told that the FBI were handling the case and that they'd taken McGuire into custody. And guess what? Gregg Donoghue was the arresting officer. There was also a bogus CIA agent.'

'CIA?' questioned Frank.

'Yes. Roy Stirling was with him and he was carrying a CIA identification card. Obviously a phoney.'

'Of course, but he's dead now, isn't he?' Frank inquired.

'Oh yes. He's the one who got killed during the bombing of the Atlantic Air building.'

'Yes, I thought so,' said Frank. 'I think it's time we had a word with this guy, Donoghue. Let's see if we can bring him in for questioning. Who's our linkman with the FBI, Jim? We'd better go through channels with this one.'

'Sam Torrance is our liaison with the FBI.'

'OK Jim. Let me have a word with him first. See what I can come up with. I'll get back to you shortly.

Frank's conversation with Sam Torrance was barely informative. All he was able to establish was that Donoghue was somewhere in

Canada working on a case and that he was not permitted to inquire about the nature of the case he was currently investigating. What Frank did find out, though, was that Gregg Donoghue was no ordinary FBI agent. He was a section head and was responsible for numerous FBI investigations. Frank called in Jim Hollis and told him the news.

'It looks as though we're not going to get much cooperation with this one, Jim. Apparently the guy's on some case in Canada at the moment so we can't get hold of him until he returns. Sam will notify us when that happens, then you and I can go over and have a word. Meantime, though, we can make some further inquiries in Ireland. Now that we've established a link between Donoghue, McGuire and Roy Stirling, there's obviously some connection with Alex Stenton's trip to Ireland, especially when it took place at the same time as the McGuire family were murdered. I just don't believe in these kind of coincidences.'

'All right,' said Jim. 'I'll get that organised. By the way, how are things going with Bill Rice, Frank? Has he been able to contribute anything worthwhile?'

'Yes he has. His people are currently investigating a security firm in Scotland that turns out to be a subsidiary of CLC Industries and the guy running it is one of the suspects in the Edinburgh Parade killing.'

'Hey! How about that? This thing is really starting to piece together, isn't it?'

'It sure is, but we still need hard evidence, a lot more than we've got. Proving a link is certainly not going to be enough in this case, but we're getting there. I'd be a lot happier if I knew what the FBI connection was. That's what's bugging me at the moment. This guy Gregg Donoghue is a senior operative and I'd like to know what he's been up to.'

Ian Scott made an emergency call to Bill Rice in Washington.

'Oh hi, Ian,' said Bill. 'How's the new baby coming along?'

'Fine, she's fine. I don't think I've got used to the idea of being a father yet. It's such an awesome responsibility, bringing a child into the world. Fiona seems to take it all in her stride though. She's simply over the moon.'

'Don't worry. You'll get used to it. Well, what do you have for me then?'

'Oh yes. Well, I'm phoning to tell you that something extremely important has come up, but it's not something that can be discussed on the phone.'

'Tell me what you can.'

'Well, I have two cassette tapes here that have been sent to the office along with a brief explanatory note.'

'Oh! Can you tell me who sent them?'

'They were sent to us by a Kieran McGuire. Does the name mean anything to you?'

'No, I can't say that it does.'

'Well listen, Bill. The contents of these tapes are vital to our inquiries into the Edinburgh Parade killing and they're far too sensitive to be sent by post, so what do you want me to do?'

'The only thing that you can do, Ian, is to bring them over. That's if you can manage to tear yourself loose from that new baby of yours for a little while.'

'Oh, I think I'll manage that. I think Fiona will be only too pleased to get me out from under her feet. And what with her mother and her sister being on the scene all the time, I need a break from female company.'

'Sounds like you're having a hard time. OK, how soon can I expect you over here?'

'Let me see now. This is Tuesday. I'll need a couple of days to clear things at this end first. Let's say Thursday afternoon.'

'OK. Let me know what flight you're on and I'll pick you up at the airport. Oh by the way, give my love to Fiona will you?'

'Sure thing, Bill, see you soon.'

Two days later Ian was on his way to Washington. It was a routine and quite uneventful flight. He spent most of his travelling time going over the transcripts of the tapes and the reports that he had brought with him. Ian, who had been looking forward to the sunny Washington weather that he had heard so much about, was quite surprised to find torrential rain when they eventually arrived at Dulles airport. As soon as he cleared customs he headed for the arrivals lounge and was pleased to see that Bill was already there waiting for him.

'What's the idea of bringing this nasty weather with you?' asked Bill. 'I thought I'd left all this behind in England.'

'So did I,' replied Ian. 'I was looking forward to all that sunshine you were telling me about.'

When they got into the car Bill told Ian that he had booked him into the Watergate in a room adjacent to his own.

'Not the Watergate?' said Ian questioningly. 'This has got to be the irony to end all ironies.'

'Are you referring to the Nixon affair?'

'Well, the Watergate was certainly the centre of political intrigue during that era and didn't the Nixon tapes play a significant role in bringing down that administration?'

'So, what're you getting at? Come on, the suspense is killing me. What's this irony you're talking about?' said Bill showing his impatience.

'All right, then, look at it this way. The Watergate investigations were inquiries into the misuse of the state security system for internal political ends.'

'Yeees,' said Bill, tapping his fingers on the steering wheel.

'Well then, here we are using the very same premises to investigate the possible misuse of the state security system, only this time for external political ends.'

'What!' said Bill indignantly. 'Just what exactly are you trying to tell me? Are you saying that the CIA may have had something to do with the Edinburgh Parade killing?'

'No, not the CIA, but I am suggesting that the FBI may well be involved.'

'Good God!' exclaimed Bill, now starting to get very agitated. 'Talk about covert activities,' he muttered to himself.

'I'd rather not say any more until you've heard the tapes for yourself,' said Ian, sensing that he had gone too far and that he'd been too flippant with his remarks.

By the time they got to the hotel, Bill Rice was practically at fever pitch with anticipation. When they arrived outside Ian's room, Bill suggested, 'Look, Ian, just you give the tapes to me. I'll get them set up and you can join me once you've got organised. I'm just along the hall in 3B.'

'Yes, sure,' said Ian as he rummaged through his briefcase for the tapes. Ian had never seen Bill quite so worked up before and was regretting his somewhat premature discussions in the car. Ian handed Bill the tapes, then went to his own room.

He was pleasantly surprised by the smart ultra-modern decor. It had almost every modern convenience you could possibly want, from a jacuzzi to satellite TV. Ian decided not to spend much time unpacking. He wanted to be there when Bill played the second tape, the one containing Roy Stirling's statement. He thought that his presence might have a dampening effect on Bill's response.

When Ian got to Bill's room he found that he was already halfway through the first tape. Bill signalled him not to speak so he pulled up a chair and sat down. They both listened in silence until the tape ended.

'What do we know about the people mentioned on this tape?' asked Bill.

'At the moment very little, but we're still making inquiries. I think you'll find the other tape even more revealing.'

Ian moved over to the machine and changed the tapes, then returned to his seat.

'Like a drink, Ian?'

'Love one. What have you got?'

'Oh, I've still got some of my duty-free Canadian Club.'

'That'll be fine. It's a good whisky.'

Ian had heard this tape before. As a matter of fact he had heard it several times in his own office, so he spent most of the time observing Bill's face as it went through a whole spectrum of facial expressions in response to Roy Stirling's revelations.

When the tape was finished, Bill sat back in his chair and thought for a moment.

'Well, before we can act on any of this information, I would like to know something about the authenticity of these tapes.'

'We're checking all we can.'

'Has this information been documented yet?'

'Oh yes, completely. I have copies in my briefcase. I also made copies of the tapes but they're in the London office. These are the actual tapes that were sent to us.'

'Didn't you say something about an explanatory note when you were on the phone?' asked Bill.

'Yes I did. That's in my briefcase as well. I'll get these papers now.'

While Ian was out of the room Bill examined the cassettes and discovered that they were of British origin, a point that he confronted Ian with on his return.

'Oh yes, sir, they are. But that doesn't mean to say that the originals were. It's more than likely that these are copies that were sent to us. No, I don't think we're going to get much from the actual cassettes, but the package they came in had a Stranraer postmark on it. That in itself might prove useful inasmuch as it was posted recently, indicating that the person who sent the package was in Scotland at that time.'

'Stranraer,' said Bill. 'Why Stranraer? You know that name means something to me but I can't think what it is.'

'I think I might know. It's a ferry port, handling traffic between Scotland and Ireland.'

'Yes of course. That's it. Thanks, Ian.'

'Yes and ... here's the explanatory note, sir.'

'Oh! Good and thanks again.'

Bill read through the note several times before he spoke. 'Look, we'll have to locate this guy pretty quick. He seems to be the key to this whole case and, according to this,' he said, pointing to the note, 'he seems to be a witness to the making of at least one of those tapes.'

'I've got men out looking for him right now, sir. He's already given us his name, and from that and the information on the first tape about his brother Kevin, we were able to trace where he comes from. Kevin is already on our files and from there we got an address and were able to locate Kieran's former employers. They gave us his full description.'

'You have been busy, haven't you?'

'Well sir, you did leave me in charge and I thought it best to get things moving as quickly as possible. Have the CIA thrown any light on this?'

'As a matter of fact they have, but it was all speculative until you brought these tapes over. Frank Mariano told me from the start that he suspected that Tom Casey was capable of such an operation, and he was only referring to the Parade killing. If we're to believe what's on these tapes, his suspicions are more than confirmed. We now know what the follow-up plan is: having failed to take out the party leadership in his efforts to manipulate British policy, he's now trying to destabilise the economy. You've got to hand it to the guy, he's certainly got some balls.'

'At least we know that the CIA is not involved.'

'Yes, but we haven't ruled out the FBI yet. For all we know, they could be using this man as a front.'

'How are you going to play it? Are you going to give Frank access to all this information?'

'I don't know if I should. I don't want to put him in a position where he may have a conflict of interest.'

'Why don't we give him part of the information and then wait and see which way he jumps?'

'That's a very tempting proposition you have there, young man, but it's too risky. For one thing, I've only just managed to build up a good rapport with Frank after a bad start, and we're going to need all the help he can give us. For another, the CIA are in a far better position to investigate the FBI than we are so, if we want that kind of cooperation from them we'd better put all our cards on the table. I don't think we've got much choice, son. What I'll do is call a meeting between the four of us.'

'Four, sir?'

'Oh, sorry, I was forgetting you haven't met Frank's aide yet. He seems to be a real capable guy and I think you'll like him. His name's Jim Hollis. Well, I hope you slept on the plane, as you're not going to get much sleep tonight. I want us both to go over every bit of this information until I know it off by heart.'

'That's all right by me.'

Bill Rice and Ian Scott were up until the early hours of the morning going over all the material that Ian had brought with him. They also discussed various lines of further investigation. It was three in the morning before Bill decided that it was time for bed.

At the meeting the next day Frank Mariano was utterly astounded by the information that Bill was relating to him. When he and Jim Hollis listened to the tapes they could hardly believe their ears.

Suddenly the office was a hive of industry. Frank had three phones on his desk and at least one of them was occupied at any one point in time. Now that they had the big picture, now that they knew what Tom Casey and his confederates were ultimately planning, everything began to fall into place. All these weeks and months of patient investigation were now being rewarded. This was what Frank had been waiting for. This was all that he needed to start the wheels in motion. Many hours were spent and endless cups of coffee were drunk as they collated all the information that lay before them and planned the best course of action.

As the British were already doing all they could to find Kieran McGuire, who they suspected was in Scotland, there was no need for the Americans to take any action in that area. Frank decided to channel all his initial inquiries into establishing the whereabouts of all Tom Casey's syndicate members so that he could keep them under close surveillance. His next move was to be a joint venture with the British, to investigate just how deeply the British economy had been penetrated by the syndicate's activities. It was collectively agreed not to arrest Alex Stenton, at least not for the moment, although they probably had enough evidence to do so. Stenton was considered to be too close to Tom Casey and they didn't want to show their hand prematurely.

Frank Mariano arranged a meet with his FBI opposite number, with a view to finding out exactly what Gregg Donoghue was up to. He had already made up his mind that if he didn't get any cooperation this time, he would put out an all-points bulletin on Donoghue, and have him arrested on sight. Frank figured that for his immediate short-term goal, Gregg Donoghue would be the prime target. He suspected that Gregg was probably a renegade operative, employed by the syndicate. He was determined to have him picked up for interrogation, one way or another.

This time, Frank had an interview with a senior FBI administrator who proved to be yet another obstacle. His response to Frank's revelations was curiously guarded and he refused point blank to give Frank access to Gregg Donoghue's file or to give him any information relating to the project that Gregg was currently working on. Frank was informed that this was an internal affair and that it would be handled by the department. However, he was promised that there would be an immediate inquiry and that he would be notified of the findings as soon as they were known.

Frank was angry. He had expected much more. OK, he understood that they should be allowed to conduct their own inquiries into internal affairs but this was more than just an in-house problem. The political implications of this case could be extremely far-reaching and, in these circumstances, he had expected a little more interdepartmental cooperation. For the time being Frank's hands were tied. No way were they going to let him interrogate Gregg Donoghue. But Frank was not prepared to leave it at that. He needed to know what the FBI policy was on this matter and he felt that they were being deliberately obstructive. He decided to give them one week to come up with the answers he needed, and if they didn't, he was going to act independently and order his men to find Donoghue and bring him in for interrogation.

23

By the time they arrived in Stranraer, Kieran had already decided that he was going to take Linda to see her family, regardless of the risks involved, for by this time he was deeply concerned by her mental state. She was obviously still in shock and had so far resisted all attempts to bring herself out of it. Kieran figured that a family reunion was just the therapy she needed. He was very aware that Gregg Donoghue and Co. might well be waiting for them in Edinburgh, but it was a chance they would have to take.

As they sat waiting for the ship to tie up, Kieran told Linda his intentions. 'Linda, I think it's time you got in touch with your family.' Kieran waited for a reaction before continuing.

For a brief second her eyes sparkled as she savoured the thought, but then they quickly dulled again. She turned towards Kieran and stared at him. 'Are you mad?' she said incredulously. 'Do you honestly expect me to lead these killers to my family? Are they also to become victims of these murderers?'

Kieran reached out tentatively to touch her arm but she pulled it away sharply. 'Linda, Linda, listen to me,' he said pleadingly. 'We don't have to ...'

'No!' she shrieked. 'If I go anywhere near them they'll all die. Everywhere I go somebody dies.'

'That's enough!' said Kieran sternly. 'Now stop it, get a hold of yourself!' he shouted.

She turned her face away from him, to avoid his rebuke. Kieran grabbed her by the shoulders and swung her around towards him. He could see the tears well up in her eyes but to Kieran this was a good sign for it meant that she was coming out of shock.

'Listen Linda ...' She struggled briefly, but Kieran was insistent.

'Listen to me.' He spoke quietly, in softer tones. 'I know we've both been through a terrible ordeal, but this is not the time to give up. We're going to see this thing through, believe me. Stop blaming yourself. That's going to get us nowhere. Look, I've thought it through. I've been speaking to one of the passengers and he told me that there's a bus scheduled to leave for Edinburgh soon after we dock, and we're going to be on it.'

Linda burst into tears. She threw her arms around Kieran and said pleadingly, 'Oh Kieran. Do you really think there's a chance? Do you think I can safely see my family without endangering them?'

'Don't worry. We'll see that you do. From now on we're calling the shots.'

'Yes, you're right, we must try. Oh please God. Please let it happen,' she said tearfully.

'But first, you'll have to tell me exactly where your family live. Or, better still, is there a neutral place where we can arrange to meet them?'

All at once Linda was bubbling with life again. Kieran had been right: the prospect of meeting her family had instilled new life into her. He realised that he had broken through her depression and that now she was well on the road to recovery.

Within the hour they were on the bus to Edinburgh. During the journey, they discussed ideas for meeting up with Linda's family. Linda suggested that they should get in touch with an old girlfriend who used to work with her in the electronics factory. Through her they could arrange to meet her mother and father at a predetermined location. They both agreed that it would be too dangerous to go directly to the house. Linda mentioned that her mother, who was a keen gardener, had a fascination for exotic plants and had often taken her as a child to the Botanical Gardens. This seemed to them to be an appropriate meeting place where Linda and her family could be reunited.

As soon as they arrived in Edinburgh, Linda phoned her friend Sandra, told her that she wanted to surprise her mother, and arranged for Sandra to go to the house and tell her mother that an old friend from overseas would like to meet her at the Botanical Gardens.

Everything went like clockwork. Linda was waiting alone near a lily pond at the prearranged time. She had positioned herself discreetly by an oak tree overlooking the pond. She watched tearfully as her mother approached the bench at the edge of the water. It had been four years since she had last seen her mother. Linda could see a distinct difference in the way her mother walked. In that short period of time her health had deteriorated considerably. She was stooping a little and her once brisk walk was now reduced to a much shorter, steadier pace. Linda saw that her mother was wearing her favourite camel overcoat that she kept for special occasions. She watched silently as her mother made a slow inquisitive scan of the area before she sat down on the bench.

Linda was anxious to rush over and hold her, to tell her how much she loved her and how much she had missed being with her, but she restrained herself for a few moments longer as she tried to mentally adjust to the situation. She was trying to deal with the flood of memories that were threatening to overwhelm her, memories that had been triggered off by the appearance of her mother in her favourite environment.

Linda's mother opened the large brown Italian leather handbag that Linda recognised as the one she had sent her two years ago for her birthday. From the bag, her mother produced a pair of spectacles and put them on. She again delved deeply into the handbag and this time produced a little black book with gold edging on the pages, which she began to read. Linda could restrain herself no longer and slowly walked over towards her mother who was now engrossed in the book.

As she approached her mother, she finally managed to speak and chokingly said, 'Hello, Mum. Remember me?'

Her mother slowly looked up, her eyes peering over the top of her glasses expectantly, for she had instantly recognised the voice of her daughter. She looked at Linda and blinked as if she could hardly believe her eyes, then quickly removed her spectacles and said questioningly, 'Linda? Linda, my baby!' she cried as she threw her arms open invitingly.

Linda rushed over and embraced her mother and they both wept with joy as they squeezed each other tightly.

'What's that you're reading Mum?' said Linda, trying to distract her mother, while she fought to control her inner feelings of joy.

'Oh. Oh this! This is my pocket Bible. It gives me great comfort in times of need and I've been reading it a lot lately, I can tell you. But Linda, where on earth have you been? We've all been worried sick ever since your uncle phoned and said you had suddenly left home without explanation. And your Auntie Mary's been frantic with worry too. Oh come here,' she said. 'Give me another hug. Oh it's so good to see you. My prayers have certainly been answered.'

Linda spent the next hour and a half explaining to her mother some of the nightmare that she and Kieran had been through, but she was very careful to filter out the worst of her recent experiences, such as the killings she had witnessed in Ireland. She wanted to spare her mother any unnecessary suffering.

Her mother listened in stunned silence to Linda's incredible tale. She searched her mind in vain for some reassuring words that would put her daughter's mind at rest. 'Have you been in touch with the British authorities yet?' she asked.

'Yes. When we arrived in Stranraer we sent off what information we had, but there's no way of knowing how they'll respond. You see, we just don't know who we can trust any more. Kieran is planning to phone them from Edinburgh in a couple of days, to see what their reaction is to our information.'

'Why wait two days?' asked her mother impatiently. 'Why don't you phone right away?'

'We're hoping to give them some time to check our story.'

Linda could see the strain on her mother's face as her frustration became more and more apparent. She thought it prudent not to pursue this line of conversation and tried to change the subject. 'Listen, Mum. You haven't told me what's been happening here since I last heard from you. How's Dad been keeping?'

There was a pause before her mother answered. She needed time to adjust her thoughts. Then she told Linda of all the good things that had happened since she had last made contact with them. How her father had eventually got a job as a postman after being on the waiting list for two years, and how delighted he was with the work. She said that she had not seen him so happy for a very long time. She went on to say that they had been away for a holiday to Dubrovnic in Yugoslavia. She was now in full flow with her news and Linda was delighted to see the enthusiasm with which she was telling her story.

'Oh yes, and while I remember, we made friends with a local family in Dubrovnic. They took us to a place called Medjugorje. Have you heard what's been happening there?'

'No, I don't think so,' said Linda. 'Should I have?'

'I had hoped that the whole world would have heard about Medjugorje by now,' her mother said mysteriously. 'But never mind, that's a whole new story. Your father's certainly a changed man since he's been there, I can tell you. As a matter of fact, we've just arranged another trip to Dubrovnic next week. Our friends invited us back for another fortnight, so I hope you're going to see your father before we go. He'd be very angry if he found out you'd been to Edinburgh and hadn't been to see him.'

While Linda and her mother strolled through the gardens, Kieran was trying to find some accommodation. They had already decided that it wouldn't be wise to stay with any of Linda's family and the fewer people who knew of her presence in Edinburgh, the better. It had been arranged that Kieran would pick Linda up from the gardens as soon as he found a place for them to stay.

Kieran fairly quickly managed to find room and board in a small hotel in Gilmore Place on the south side of Edinburgh, and was now anxious to get back to Linda to find out if there had been any inquiries made about them at the family home. As the gardens were on the north side, Kieran had to travel across the city to get there. By the time Linda and her mother had explored the entire north section of the gardens and returned to the bench by the pond, Kieran had arrived and was sitting there waiting for them. Linda introduced her mother to Kieran.

'So this is the young man who has done so much to save my daughter's life.'

'Hello, Mrs Johnstone. I've heard a lot about you and I'm very pleased to meet you at long last,' said Kieran politely.

They all sat down and talked for a while longer. Kieran asked Mrs Johnstone if there had been anyone making inquiries about her daughter. She was able to reassure him that as far as she knew, no one had been asking questions about either of them. Kieran was relieved to hear this for at least it suggested that, so far, they were still ahead of the game. He had already programmed himself to take every new day as a bonus, and each bonus gave them just enough time to stay one jump ahead. Perhaps they would have time to sit it out until they could contact the British authorities again. There was still a chance that the authorities would help them. They would just have to wait and see. Kieran and Linda agreed to meet Mrs Johnstone at the same place two days later, by which time they hoped to have heard from the authorities.

Meanwhile, in London, Alex Stenton received a call from his Irish connection, informing him of the disastrous confrontation that had taken place near Peter McGuire's farm and warning him that Kieran McGuire was still on the loose.

'That's twice you bastards have let me down!' roared Alex. 'Have I got to do every bloody thing myself?'

He slammed down the phone and sat there for a moment silently simmering, his mind frantically searching for a solution to his dilemma. He thought to himself, this guy McGuire is either the luckiest bastard in the world or the smartest. Or maybe I'm just surrounded by a bunch of incompetents. Talking of which … Alex grabbed the phone and dialled a long-distance number, 'Hello, Gregg?'

'Yea, speaking.'

'Listen, Gregg, Kieran McGuire was spotted in Ireland thirty-six hours ago.'

'In Ireland!' cried Gregg. 'How on earth did he get over there?'

'Never mind that now. We've got to find him before he makes contact with the British authorities. He was in a skirmish with some of our people over there but the stupid bastards let him escape and there's no telling where he'll head next.'

'I think I know where he might go,' said Gregg. 'We may be able to trace him through the girl.'

'How do you mean?' asked Alex.

'Well, I happen to know that she comes from Edinburgh. I figure that she couldn't resist being that close to her family and not drop in to see them. It's a good bet that's where they're headed next. They may even be there now.'

'OK, Gregg. Let me put it to you straight. This is your last chance to clean up this mess once and for all. You botch this one, son, and I will personally make sure that you'll have good reason to regret it. You understand me now?' said Alex menacingly. Gregg didn't respond to the threat. 'Do you understand me?' repeated Alex in a louder and more threatening tone.

'OK, OK. I got the message,' said Gregg.

'All right then. I want you to take the next available flight to Edinburgh and solve this problem once and for all. I don't care how you do it, but do it. Let me know the minute it's over. I'll be in London for another week and that's exactly how long you have to get back to me with a positive result.'

Gregg hung up abruptly, leaving Alex squirming with exasperation. Alex leant back in his chair. He was still apprehensive and began considering the possible consequences of yet another failure, for he had little faith in Gregg Donoghue's ability to come up with the goods. What was needed was some kind of backup situation, one that would automatically follow through should Donoghue prove incompetent yet again.

Then it suddenly struck him. 'Of course, the very man!' he exclaimed out loud. Why the hell didn't I think of it before?

Alex made another call, this time to Dave Simpson in Glasgow. 'Hello, Dave. Alex Stenton here!'

'Oh! Hi Alex. It's good to hear from you again. What can I do for you?'

'I've got another job for you. Do you remember Kevin McGuire?'

'How the hell can I forget? It was me who wet-nursed him through the last job. Don't tell me you're sending him over again?'

'No. Mr McGuire is no longer with the organisation.'

'I think I understand. What do you have in mind?'

'Kevin McGuire has a brother, Kieran, whom we are most anxious to trace. It's imperative that we find him as soon as possible. I'd like you to locate him for me.'

'I see,' said Dave. 'What do we know about him so far?'

'Well, first of all I have reason to believe that he may be in Edinburgh. He's travelling with a girl called Linda Johnstone who has family somewhere just outside the city.'

'Is that Johnstone with an "e"?' asked Dave.

'Hang on. I'll check my notes,' said Alex. After a short pause he was back on the line. 'Yes Dave. It's spelt with an "e".'

'Good,' said Dave. 'That cuts my work down considerably. Can you tell me anything at all about the girl?'

'All I can tell you at the moment is that she's approximately twenty-four years old and that she moved to the States about four years ago.'

'That's all we've got?' asked Dave.

'I'm afraid so.'

'OK, Alex. Leave it with me. I'll see what I can do.'

'Now listen. All I want you to do is find them and keep them both under surveillance until I arrive. Phone me at this number as soon as you've located them.'

'Don't worry. If they're in the Edinburgh district, I'll find them. I'll be in touch. Bye.'

Dave Simpson got to work as soon as he hung up the phone. His first task was to sift out from the Edinburgh telephone directory the number of Johnstones who lived in the outlying districts of Edinburgh. This would hopefully shorten the list considerably. Dave was in luck, for he managed to reduce his list to 57 names. He then gave his secretary the task of checking on the names with a view to establishing which of them had a daughter in their twenties called Linda. This was a much easier task than one might think, for there are many ways of cross-referencing that would yield this kind of information. Within two hours his secretary had it pinpointed, Mr W Johnstone, 14 Grove Street, Dalkeith. Dave's next task was to assign a couple of agents to monitor the family, and wait until Kieran and Linda made contact.

The instant that Gregg Donoghue put down the phone, following his conversation with Alex Stenton, it rang.

He picked it up again and a voice on the other end said, 'Gregg, I've just received a signal from Washington. They're trying awfully hard to locate you. You're being recalled to Head Office.'

'Didn't you tell them that I'm working on a case?'

'They already know that, but this is a priority recall. We can't ignore it.'

'Don't quote me the rule book, son!' said Gregg patronisingly. 'Tell them I'm out in the field at the moment, and you're unable to make contact. I've got one more week's work to do, then I'm finished.'

'A week? I don't know if I can hold Head Office off that long. It's more than my job's worth!'

'Look, son, consider this an exercise on initiative. You stall them for a week and I just might reconsider my assessment report on you, all right?' Gregg didn't wait for an answer. He hung up.

That night Gregg Donoghue was on a flight to Prestwick airport in Scotland. Dave Simpson might have had a head start on him, but Gregg knew something that Mr Simpson had yet to find out, for he knew exactly where Linda's family lived. Being a long-established agent, Gregg was naturally inquisitive about any new person he met. He had long since established where Linda came from during their many conversations together, when he and Kathy had been out in foursomes with Linda and her current boyfriend. Gregg had a memory like a neat filing system, with the added benefit of instant recall. He remembered that Linda had told him that her father was a coalminer from Dalkeith, a small town about 10 miles outside Edinburgh.

24

Kieran had taken Linda back to the hotel, where he wanted to talk to her about their present situation, but she was too preoccupied with thoughts of her family to take on such a serious conversation. She was indulging in the delights of her happiness. Kieran, however, was determined that she should not be lured into a false sense of security by the familiarity of her surroundings.

'Listen to me, Linda. I don't mean to frighten you but I just don't know where we can run to next if we don't get help from the British.'

'Kieran,' said Linda firmly, 'I'm well aware of the seriousness of our situation. I don't need any reminders from you.' She could have bitten her tongue when she realised how sharply she had spoken, especially after all they had been through together. She saw the hurt look on Kieran's face and regretted her words. 'I'm sorry, Kieran. I didn't mean to be so rude. I don't know what I was thinking of.'

Linda had suddenly started to appreciate that he too was under a great deal of strain and must be near to his own limits of endurance. Kieran didn't respond to Linda's apology and she was anxious to restore the status quo.

'I know!' she said cheerfully. 'Why don't we go out and have a night on the town. Let me show you the sights of Edinburgh. It's really a wonderful city and I used to know it so well.'

Kieran looked at her and smiled. It was good and uplifting to see her happy face beaming at him so encouragingly. He wondered at her ability to rally such resources in the face of such adversity. He wanted very much to respond to Linda's encouragement to lighten their mood, but her talk of Edinburgh had triggered off other thoughts in his head. He had begun to ponder over the irony of their new location. It had not escaped his notice that they were now in the very city where the seeds of their present predicament had been sown, in the city where his own brother had cold-bloodedly killed a politician. But Kieran, realising that he was thinking himself into a morbid state, decided that it was time to abandon these unpalatable thoughts. Linda was right. Why shouldn't they go out on the town? There was simply no point staying indoors worrying about tomorrow.

'Right,' said Kieran. 'You're on. Let's go see what Edinburgh's got to offer a couple of pleasure-starved tourists.'

Linda thought it would be a good idea to show Kieran some of the major tourist attractions, so that afternoon she took Kieran on a Grand Tour of Edinburgh. They started off at Holyrood Palace where they were given a conducted tour of the royal premises. After that they took a slow walk up the Royal Mile, with Linda pointing out the many places of historical interest. Edinburgh Castle lies at the top of the Royal Mile and was their next destination. It was a beautiful sunny day, which allowed them to see Edinburgh at its very best. Kieran was impressed by the magnificent views to be seen from the castle. From there it was only a short walk to Princes Street where Linda was eager to go shopping in the stores that she remembered from her years in the city before she left for America.

By early evening Kieran was growing weary of shopping and was anxious to explore some of the more social venues of the city. 'Hey, wait a minute,' he said. 'I don't know if I can handle all this culture and shopping in one go. Don't you think it's time we went for a meal, and then perhaps we could go for a couple of drinks? What says you?'

'I wondered when you would get around to asking me that,' said Linda. 'I must admit you've held out pretty well though. OK, let's go for a meal first, then I'll introduce you to Rose Street which runs parallel to Princes Street.' Linda explained to Kieran that it used to be famous for its many drinking dens and that the locals would often try a pub crawl from one end to the other, almost a mile away.

'Hey! That sounds like a good idea,' said Kieran.

'You really want to have a go?' asked Linda.

'Yea! Why not? We haven't had a good drink since we came down the St Lawrence. I think we owe it to ourselves. How about it?'

She was only too pleased to see Kieran spark into enthusiasm again. Under normal circumstances, Linda would never have dreamt of undertaking such an exercise but these were not normal circumstances. There was a lot of pain behind them which they both wanted to forget, so Linda decided that it was time she let her hair down.

'All right!' she said enthusiastically. 'Let's do it, but you watch what you're drinking. There are more pubs in Rose Street than you can hold drinks, so I suggest that you stick to half pints. I don't want to end up carrying you back to the hotel.'

'That's the spirit,' said Kieran. 'That's my girl. Now let's get some grub in us before we start, put a lining in our stomachs to prepare the way.'

Three and a half hours and eight bars later, Linda and Kieran had reached very near saturation point. As Linda had predicted, Kieran was hardly able to stand.

'I told you to stick to half pints,' she said, then burst into a fit of the giggles at the antics of Kieran as he tried in vain to walk unsupported across the pavement. 'Come here, you,' said Linda, as she grabbed hold of his arm just in time to save him from falling flat on his face.

'How come you're so damn sober anyway?' slurred Kieran.

'That's because I switched to soft drinks three pubs ago but I expect you won't remember that far back, considering the state you're in. I don't suppose you'll remember much of this in the morning either.'

'Aw, don't be daft, woman. I'll be fine in the morning, don't you worry yoursel' about that.'

Linda decided that further communication would be futile and concentrated all her remaining energy on getting Kieran into a taxi. Eventually she got Kieran back to the hotel. With the aid of a by now aggravated taxi driver, who Kieran had been teasing throughout the journey, Linda got him up to their room. She didn't even attempt to get him into bed, for he was just too heavy to manhandle, so Kieran was left to spend the rest of that night on a chair.

The next morning Linda was up bright and early and Kieran was still fast asleep in the chair when she made for the shower.

'Hey! Come on sleepyhead. It's nearly time for breakfast,' she said trying to waken him. 'Come on, snap out of it. How much did you have to drink last night anyway? I lost count after we'd been in the first six bars.'

'Oh, hi Linda, gee, have I slept here all night?'

'I'm afraid so. There was no way I could put you to bed, not in the state you were in.'

'Well, er ... you just go ahead. I'll join you downstairs later.'

By the time Kieran had showered and eaten some breakfast he was in better shape to deal with his lingering hangover.

But Linda was less sympathetic and was now ready to face the more immediate problems that confronted them. 'I don't think we should wait another day, Kieran. We don't know how much time we have before somebody catches up with us. We should try and get in touch with the authorities today.'

'Yes. I think you could be right there,' said Kieran. 'The quicker we know where we stand, the sooner we can make our own plans.'

Kieran had been unable to make direct contact with MI5, although he knew that this would be the department to deal with it, so he had sent his tape addressed to MI5 via New Scotland Yard, hoping that it would eventually make its way to the appropriate authorities. At this stage he had no option but to phone Scotland Yard direct to see how they had responded.

Kieran kept his conversation brief and to the point. 'Hello. My name is Kieran McGuire. I sent a tape to your offices a few days ago and I would like to speak to the people who received it.'

'I see,' said a voice at the other end. 'Just a minute and I'll make some inquiries for you.'

Two, then three long minutes went by and Kieran was just about to hang up when a voice came back on the line.

'Hello caller. Did you say you were speaking on behalf of Mr McGuire?'

'No I didn't,' said Kieran impatiently. 'I am Kieran McGuire and I want to speak with someone in authority.'

'Just one moment sir. We've located the department that received your communication. We're just trying to get hold of the section head who's dealing with it. Can you hold for just a little bit longer? His line seems to be engaged at the moment.'

Kieran was getting more and more impatient. He knew that there was a good chance that they were trying to trace his call and he was growing anxious. A full two minutes later another voice came on the line. This time, it spoke with a level of authority.

'Mr McGuire?'

'Yes. Speaking,' said Kieran.

'Yes, we received your communication. Would it be possible for you to come to our offices and discuss this matter further? Or perhaps we could send someone to speak to you. Where did you say you were staying?'

'I didn't,' said Kieran sharply, getting a bit angry with the time-wasting. 'I wanted to know what your response was.'

'Oh. Well, we're extremely interested in the information you have given us Mr McGuire but I'm sure you realise that we can't act on it until we have had a chance to meet you and discuss it. Why don't you tell us where you are and then we can arrange for someone to meet you. It's not the sort of thing we want to discuss on the phone, now is it?'

Kieran was convinced that they were playing for time and trying to trace his call. 'Look, I'll get back to you,' he said. 'I'll call you later.' Then he hung up.

On reflection, he thought to himself, what a fool I've been. Just what did I expect them to do anyway? Did I really think that they would guarantee us protection on the strength of an uncorroborated tape and a phone call?

Kieran told Linda that Scotland Yard was not prepared to discuss it on the phone and that he suspected that they had been trying to trace his call. 'It looks as if we've got two options open to us. Either we put our faith in the authorities and meet them on their terms, or we go it alone. It's up to you, Linda. What do you think? Bear in mind, though, that we're running out of hiding places.'

'I think we should let them sweat a little, at least until we've had a chance to examine the alternatives.'

It was becoming apparent now that Kieran was weakening in his resolve and Linda was trying harder to keep his hopes alive. 'Listen, Kieran. Why don't we wait until we've seen my father, perhaps he can help us?'

'Don't worry about me, I'm far from giving up. It's you that I'm worried about, you and your family. I don't think we should stay in Edinburgh too long, it's far too risky. Perhaps we should go up north for a while. It's less populated up there and it might be easier to hide in the open country.'

'No, I don't think we should move just yet. Wait until I've had a word with my father.' Kieran nodded in agreement.

The next morning Linda set off to meet her mother at the Botanical Gardens while Kieran went to the Waverley Station to find out about rail times in case they decided to travel north. Kieran had decided that they must now be extra careful, and had arranged for a taxi to pick him up at the hotel. He figured that travelling by cab would be less conspicuous than using public transport. When he got to the station he asked the driver to wait for him.

As he left the cab he noticed a dark blue Ford Escort pulling up just 15 feet behind them. Kieran wasn't sure why he should be taking an interest in this particular car but there was something about it that unnerved him. He tried to dismiss the thought from his mind and told himself that he was just being paranoid. All this cloak and dagger stuff was finally getting to him. He walked through the station looking for a ticket desk with the thought still lingering in his mind. It just wouldn't go away. He wondered if he had seen the car somewhere before then, quite suddenly, it struck him with a jolt. He broke out in a cold sweat as he remembered that he had seen it on two other occasions. It had been parked opposite the hotel the night before, and this morning there had been someone sitting in it when he left for the station.

Kieran saw the ticket desk ahead of him. He approached it slowly, at the same time trying to make out the reflection in the desk window. He didn't dare look round, for he was sure that he was being followed. As he got closer to the desk, he could see more clearly the reflection of a man standing some distance behind, looking in his direction. He asked the desk clerk for a timetable for trains running north. As Kieran moved away from the desk he kept one eye on the glass to see if the tall figure behind him would follow. His suspicions were confirmed, so he quickened his pace, thinking frantically of a way to lose this persistent pursuer.

Kieran noticed a large crowd forming queues by the platform to the left of him. He headed in that direction, hoping to lose the stranger amidst the throng. When he got to the platform he pushed his way through the gathering. As he did, he looked back, and saw that the stranger had now abandoned discretion and was tracking his every move as he boldly forced his way through the crowd towards him. Kieran was looking for an exit. He wanted to leave the station and make for the street where he would have a better chance of escape. Ahead of him lay a series of closed doors. He ran towards them and tried to open the first one he came to but it was locked. He hastily moved on to the next, which he found open and quickly entered. Kieran found himself in a large empty waiting room with no other exits. He was trapped.

Gregg Donoghue came running through the door behind Kieran and quickly sussed the situation. It only took seconds for him to realise that there was no other way out, that he now had Kieran cornered.

Kieran was standing at the far side of the spacious waiting room with his back to the wall. He looked hard at the tall menacing figure that stood between him and freedom. Gregg Donoghue was a large, powerful man whose build dwarfed Kieran's much leaner proportions. He had a gun in his hand which he made no attempt to use, but it hung by his side threateningly.

'OK you bastard! Your running days are over,' said Gregg, seething with anger and breathing heavily from the exertion of the chase. 'I've spent a lot of nights just thinking about what I was gonna do to you when this day finally arrived. Oh yes, there was never any doubt in my mind that it would arrive.'

Gregg Donoghue was savouring every moment of his triumph. Kieran could do nothing, for Gregg had full command of the situation and was standing with his back to the door, gun in hand.

'I'm gonna make you pay for every day and night I've spent tracking you down. Because of you my own life's at stake, and I don't take kindly to that. You're causing me too much grief, son, there's a whole lotta people who are very unhappy just knowing that you're still breathing. So it's either you or me, but one thing's for sure, only one of us is gonna leave here alive.'

While Gregg was talking, Kieran didn't take his eyes off the gun for a second. As Gregg moved towards him Kieran said, 'You fire that thing and you'll have every cop in the city down here before you can make another move. You're not in the States now. You just won't get away with it.'

'I don't need a gun to deal with the likes of you,' sneered Gregg. 'This is just to stop you running away. You're pretty good at that, aren't you? Come on, why don't you stand your ground for once and fight like a man?'

Kieran could see that Gregg was just oozing with confidence and decided to play on his ego. 'OK, big man. You want a straight go, then put down your weapon and let's even up the odds. Just maybe we'll find out who the real man is here.'

Kieran's last remark hit home and triggered Gregg into action, for he was now incensed by Kieran's sheer audacity.

'I don't need this, you bum,' said Gregg as he put the weapon back in its holster. 'I'm gonna tear you apart with my bare hands. You've got a whole lotta aggro to pay for, son, and I'm gonna enjoy every minute of this.'

Gregg then lunged at him. As he did, Kieran jumped, raising his left knee high into his chest, causing him to leap into the air while simultaneously thrusting his right leg forward and sinking the ball of his foot deep into Gregg's chest. Gregg's onward motion came to a sudden halt as he dropped on one knee, gasping for breath. It was probably the best executed Flying Migeri Kieran had ever performed.

As he was about to follow this up, the door suddenly burst open and a uniformed railway official shouted, 'Hey! What the hell is going on in here?'

Kieran seized his opportunity and kicked Gregg in the face, sending him reeling back on the ground with blood pouring from his mouth. He then ran for the open doorway. The bewildered official, seeing Kieran bearing down on him, quickly moved out of the way as Kieran bolted past him and through the door. Donoghue, enraged, scrambled to his feet and raced through the door after Kieran who, by this time, had made his way to the station steps leading up to Princes Street. He looked back to see that his assailant was only 20 feet behind him. This spurred Kieran on to move even faster, as he pushed his way through the incoming throng of people entering the station.

Gregg, driven by sheer rage, was bulldozing his way through the crowds and catching up. By the time he got to the top of the steps Gregg was only about 10 feet behind. Kieran, whose progress had been hindered by the build-up of pedestrians and commuters at the top of the stairs, decided to make a dash across the heavily congested Princes Street, dodging and weaving his way through the traffic. Gregg, his mind locked on his prey, didn't see the motor bike speeding along Princes Street as it overtook the double decker bus, for his whole being was fully occupied with the pursuit. He had but one single thought in his head: to stop Kieran. As Gregg reached the middle of the road, the bike hit him square on, with such force that it threw him several feet in the air and into the path of the oncoming bus. As he came down again he smashed into the windscreen of the double decker, which threw him back onto the road and continued its forward motion. The front wheels had rolled over Gregg's body before the driver was able to bring the bus to a halt.

Kieran didn't stop running until he was halfway along Princes Street. He had heard the smash of broken glass and the screeching of brakes. He guessed what had happened and thanked God that he had escaped with his life yet again.

Somewhere in the back of his mind, he considered the possibility that he was indeed living a charmed existence, for he had surely been on the brink of death so many times. Kieran thought about Linda. He knew that if they had managed to trace him, it was almost certain that they were also on to her.

25

Linda waved goodbye to her mother as she left the Botanical Gardens, then crossed the road towards the bus stop on the opposite side. As she neared the pavement, a large maroon Volvo pulled up alongside her with its rear door wide open. Hands reached out and grabbed hold of Linda, dragging her into the car. The whole exercise happened so swiftly that she barely had time to scream. The car moved off at high speed whilst Linda struggled furiously with her kidnapper.

Linda's mother, who had witnessed the whole incident, screamed and shouted after the car as it sped by. She ran out onto the road and noted the car's registration number. There was nothing more she could do. She just stood there and watched helplessly as the car moved towards the junction at the end of the road.

When Kieran arrived at the hotel he immediately started to pack his things. It was obvious that his pursuers now knew where they were and it was only a matter of time before others would follow. When he had finished packing his own clothes he started on Linda's. Where on earth is she? She should have been back by now. The more he thought about it the more concerned he became. Then it occurred to him. My God! Perhaps she was followed too. Oh God, please let her be safe, he said to himself. As these thoughts flashed through his mind, the phone started ringing loudly. When he picked up the receiver he thought to himself, at last, that must be her now.

But it was Linda's mother. 'Hello, hello! Is that Kieran?'

'Yes. Yes, this is Kieran, what's wrong?' he said, sensing the urgency in her voice.

'It's Linda!' she said. 'They've taken Linda.'

'Who? Who's taken Linda?' he asked. 'Now take your time and tell me exactly what happened, Mrs Johnstone.'

'I don't know who's taken her,' she said angrily. 'She was dragged into a car a little while ago. It just seemed to appear from nowhere. It wasn't until I saw Linda struggling that I realised what was going on. Oh my baby,' she said tearfully. 'Why are they doing this and who are these people?'

'Listen, Mrs Johnstone. Linda's going to be all right, believe me. You see, it's really me that they're after. They're only using her as a means of getting to me. When did all this take place?'

'Oh I don't know. Perhaps about ten minutes ago. It's taken me that long to find a phone box.'

'Right,' said Kieran. 'What I want you to do is to phone the police immediately. Did you get the car's registration number?'

'Oh yes, yes I did.'

'Good, then phone the police and tell them exactly what happened but, whatever you do, don't mention my name for it will only complicate matters further. I'll get back to you sometime tomorrow. OK, now don't worry. The police will find them. All they need is the registration and they'll be picked up in no time at all.'

Mrs Johnstone didn't share Kieran's optimism but wasn't staying around to argue. She was too anxious to get on to the police.

Kieran continued packing the rest of Linda's clothes. There was no time to waste. He had to get out of there as soon as possible. Within half an hour he had checked out of the hotel and was in a taxi heading for the other side of town. The taxi driver took him to a small bed and breakfast establishment in the Leith district.

At the police station where Mrs Johnstone's call was received, Inspector Angus McLean was in charge of the incident room. He recognised the description of the car and its registration. His first reaction was to put out a call for the nearest unmarked car to locate and follow the Volvo to its ultimate destination. Only minutes before, it had been reported that the same car had been spotted running a red light and speeding towards the Glasgow Road. In an effort to co-ordinate activities, the Inspector notified the Glasgow police of the situation. They too ran a check on the vehicle and discovered that the car was already subject to their inquiries. Undercover agents investigating the Edinburgh Parade killing had been monitoring the premises of E&F Securities. They had sighted the car leaving the area the night before. CID was also notified of the new development and orders were issued to cordon off the area as soon as the car appeared. By five o'clock that evening the police began to close the net. By 5.45 pm, the media had got wind of the story and were moving in with camera crews to report the event live.

Kieran McGuire, who had been watching the TV in anticipation of news coverage of the situation, was tuned in to the six o'clock news.

'We are going live to Glasgow central district,' said the newscaster, 'for a report on an alleged kidnapping. A young woman, who is yet to be identified, was reported kidnapped in Edinburgh early this afternoon and is being held by two men in the premises of E&F Securities. Police have surrounded the area and have ordered the occupants to leave the building. So far, there has been no response.'

Kieran watched the screen anxiously as the camera scanned the two storey building looking for some kind of movement inside. He started to say a silent prayer that Linda would come to no harm. Now that both the police and the media were involved, Kieran's position had taken on a new dimension. There was no way of telling what the consequences of this new development would be. The more people who were involved the more uncertain the situation became. Kieran's thoughts were disturbed by a sudden movement of figures on the screen. Four people were leaving the building ... three men with Linda walking in front of them.

'Thank God,' thought Kieran. 'They're surrendering to the police.' Kieran heaved a huge sigh of relief. His major concern for Linda's safety was now resolved. He reached over and turned off the TV. He wanted to think and the noise of the commentary was distracting him.

What next? he thought. Will the police hold Linda or will they release her right away? If they do hold her, how will she respond to questioning? So many questions were flashing through his mind. Kieran was feeling frustrated mainly because he was unable to move until Linda was set free. He was in a hurry to make contact with her but didn't know how, until he remembered Linda's mother. He had already arranged to phone her the next day. In the light of what had since taken place, Kieran decided to bring the call forward and phone her that night. As there wasn't a phone he could use on the premises, he had to make his way to a call box where he dialled the number and found it to be engaged. He figured that she might well be speaking to the police at that moment so he decided to wait for a while.

When he finally got through, Linda's mother informed him that her husband had already spoken to the police and had been told that Linda would be asked to stay over, at least until the three men had been fully questioned.

'Do you think that she'll be released tomorrow?' asked Kieran.

'Oh, I should think so. My husband plans to go through to Glasgow himself to pick her up in the morning. I've told him about the predicament that you and Linda are in, and he wanted to meet with you as soon as possible. Listen, I'll put you on to him now and you two can make your own arrangements.'

The following day was a Sunday, and Linda's father intended taking Linda to Mass on the way back from Glasgow, so he arranged for Kieran to meet them at St Mary's Cathedral in Edinburgh for the twelve o'clock service. Mr Johnstone had also suggested that he would try and get access to one of the Cathedral's private rooms so that they could all get together to discuss their situation.

Meanwhile, back at the Glasgow police station, the three men who had been arrested turned out to be Dave Simpson and two of his agents. It was obvious to them that the girl had no idea who they were and had no knowledge of their intentions. So as far as they were concerned, she was in no position to make credible charges against them. Dave Simpson claimed that it had simply been a case of mistaken identity. He said that his men were investigating a reported missing person who could be suffering from amnesia. The girl appeared to answer the description, so she was taken to Glasgow for later identification by her parents. His men wanted to apologise for any inconvenience that they may have caused her.

Although the police didn't believe a word of their story, they found that the case against the three men was disappearing through their fingers like quicksilver. Linda for her part was also causing the police concern as she was showing great reluctance to bring charges against them, and was considering accepting their apology. Linda pleaded ignorance about the whole affair. She said that she had no idea why the men should want to kidnap her, and that perhaps it had been a case of mistaken identity.

Linda was well aware of their intentions but knew that she daren't reveal them to the police, so to keep the police from being involved further, she stuck to her story and hoped that she would soon be released on the grounds that no charges were being made. The next morning Linda was picked up by her father and taken back to Edinburgh.

Meanwhile, a telex for Bill Rice had arrived at Frank Mariano's Washington office. 'Hey, Bill! Frank here, would you like to come up to my office. There's something coming in over the wire for you from London.' By the time Bill got to Frank's office, the telex had already started:

HAVE BEEN COORDINATING ALL INCOMING INFORMATION RELATING TO THE EDINBURGH PARADE KILLING STOP HERE IS AN UPDATE OF THE LATEST INFORMATION TO ARRIVE STOP ANOTHER OF THE MCGUIRE FAMILY HAS BEEN MURDERED IN IRELAND STOP IRISH POLICE HAVE RECENTLY ARRESTED A MEMBER OF THE PARAMILITARY GROUP WHO WAS INVOLVED IN THE MCGUIRE KILLING

STOP HE IS WILLING TO TURN QUEENS EVIDENCE AND HAS ALREADY IMPLICATED ALEX STENTON DURING HIS STATEMENT TO THE POLICE STOP SCOTTISH POLICE HAVE REPORTED THE ACCIDENTAL DEATH OF AN AMERICAN FBI AGENT IN EDINBURGH WHO WAS IDENTIFIED AS GREGG DONOGHUE STOP GLASGOW POLICE HAVE INFORMED US THAT DAVE SIMPSON OF E&F SECURITIES WAS RECENTLY INVOLVED IN A SUSPECTED KIDNAPPING OF A YOUNG WOMAN IN EDINBURGH STOP KIERAN MCGUIRE HAS TRIED TO MAKE CONTACT WITH US BY MEANS OF SCOTLAND YARD STOP THERE WAS AN UNSUCCESSFUL ATTEMPT TO TRACE HIS CALL OTHER THAN TO ESTABLISH THAT IT CAME FROM SOMEWHERE IN THE LOTHIANS SCOTLAND STOP ADVISE IMMEDIATE RETURN TO LONDON STOP MESSAGE ENDS STOP SIGNED ARCHIE LANGDON STOP

Bill Rice called Ian Scott into the office. 'Look what's just arrived, Ian,' he said handing him the telex.

Ian read the message and was surprised at the amount of activity that had taken place in such a short time. 'It looks like it's all happening back home, Bill. I guess it's time I got back to where the action seems to be.'

'You and me both,' said Bill. 'Listen, I want you to book us on the first available flight to London. I want to leave here tomorrow afternoon if we can. I'm sure Frank here could pull a few strings if you have any problems. What do you make of the report on Gregg Donoghue's death, Frank? It looks as if all the key characters in this case are turning up this way, doesn't it?'

'What the hell was he doing in Scotland anyway?' exploded Frank, giving full vent to his feelings. 'That's what I'd like to know! He was supposed to be in Canada, at least that's what his people told me.'

'What are you going to do now?' asked Bill.

'I'll tell you what I'm gonna do! I'm gonna raise hell with the Bureau, that's what. If they'd cooperated with me in the first place then maybe this guy Donoghue would be alive today. God knows if we'll ever get to the bottom of his involvement now. By the way, Bill, about this guy the Irish police are holding.'

'Yes, what about him?'

'Well, I presume you'll be going over to question him yourself?'

'Yes I will. Why do you ask?'

'I was wondering if you would take my man Hollis with you so that he can keep us in the picture. I would have gone myself but I'm afraid I've got my work cut out for me, chasing up the Bureau etcetera.'

'I don't see any problems with that, as long as he's ready to leave with us tomorrow. He'll be welcome on board.'

'Oh, he'll be ready,' said Frank. 'Well, it's sure been good having you over here, Bill. I hope you didn't find it too boring.'

'On the contrary, I've enjoyed my stay and I found your people to be most helpful.'

All three then shook hands and said their goodbyes.

Bill and Ian returned to the office that Frank had provided for them. 'I'd like to make one last phone call before we leave Ian.'

'Where to?'

'To London.' They entered the office and Bill picked up the phone and dialled London direct. 'Hello, Archie?'

'Oh, hi Bill. I take it you got my telex then?'

'Yes, that's what I'm calling about. Listen, I can't understand how the most wanted man on our list could actually make contact with Scotland Yard and our people were unable to reach him. Just what are you people playing at over there? Isn't it obvious that he wants to cooperate?'

'Yes, but I think that McGuire probably wanted some assurances from us before he was prepared to talk further.'

'So,' said Bill impatiently, 'why didn't you give him some?'

'The situation was unclear. I didn't feel that I was in a position to give him any assurances. I thought it best to try and stall him so we could put a trace on his call but I guess he realised what we were up to.'

'So you botched it,' said Bill angrily.

'I'm afraid so, sir.'

'Now he's never gonna trust us. I hope you realise that you may well have blown the only chance we're going to get?'

'There may just be another way of locating him. I understand that there's a girl travelling with McGuire. We found that out today from the Irish police. They say that the man they're interrogating claims that he saw a young woman on the run with him.'

'That's interesting,' said Bill. 'Do we know anything about this girl?'

'I'm afraid not. We don't even have a good description of her. But if they're in Scotland, there's a chance that that's where the girl comes from. Let's face it, a man on the run is always looking for friendly territory so it could be that the girl has connections somewhere in Scotland.'

'OK. You've given us something to think about on the way over. I expect to be in London sometime tomorrow. Meantime, I'd like to interview this man they're holding, myself.'

'No problem. I'll get on to that right away. Well, have a safe journey, sir. I'll see you sometime tomorrow.'

That evening, Bill, Ian and Jim Hollis got together to consolidate what information they had to date. Bill had been giving some heavy thinking to the latest information concerning McGuire's travelling companion. It had taken prominence in his mind ever since he phoned London, and some fresh ideas were germinating in his head that he was anxious to try out on his colleagues.

Bill opened up the discussion. 'My people in London tell me that McGuire has a young woman travelling with him. I don't know just how significant this information is but I was thinking that there could be a connection between this woman and the girl who was kidnapped.'

'Are you saying that they could be one and the same?' asked Ian.

'Well, I know that I may be clutching at straws but I'm just trying to make sense of what information we have. Put it this way, it's obvious that we're not the only ones who are looking for McGuire. He's certainly a key witness in this case and one who seems to know a lot about the people who are pursuing him, certainly enough to have his entire family wiped out presumably in an effort to silence them. So there's no doubt that these people mean business and they must be desperate to get hold of him. Let's assume for the moment that it is the same girl and that the people who are trying to find McGuire have located the girl he's supposed to be travelling with. It would make sense that they would want to kidnap her and hold her hostage to draw McGuire out into the open. If this is the case, then there's a good chance that McGuire's in Edinburgh at this very moment. That's where Archie said she was picked up, wasn't it, Ian?'

'Yes, you're right, and didn't he say that McGuire's call came from somewhere in the Lothian district? It certainly makes sense to me,' said Ian enthusiastically.

'What we want to know,' said Bill, 'is whether the Glasgow police are still holding the girl. Even if they're not, they're bound to have a good description and they should also have an address where she was staying. If only we can match the description with the one in Ireland. That's really all we need to make the connection.'

At this point, Jim Hollis, who had so far listened silently to Bill's scenario, interjected. 'Aren't we forgetting something here? If what you say is true, then surely the people who are looking for Kieran will also be aware of the girl's location?'

'That's true, but I'm hoping that they'll still be in custody. If not, we've got problems.'

'I can't think why McGuire hasn't surrendered to the authorities before now,' said Ian. 'He would surely have had a better chance of survival if he had. What's the US interest in him so far, Jim?'

'Well, we think that he had something to do with the killing of Roy Stirling. We also think that he was responsible for starting the fire in the Atlantic Air building in Washington. Perhaps he's afraid that the British authorities would extradite him to the States for trial. That would explain his reluctance to take refuge with them.'

'Right. I think we've speculated enough for one night,' said Bill. 'Maybe we should all sleep on it. Besides, there's nothing more we can do until we get over there so let's get some shut-eye and I'll see you both in the morning.'

26

That Sunday, Kieran met Linda and her father outside the Cathedral. After brief introductions they all went in to Mass. It was the first time in a number of weeks that Kieran had been to Mass. So much had happened in that short time he had almost forgotten the peace and tranquility of a church service.

Kieran prayed to God for guidance in their attempt to find refuge from their pursuers. He also prayed for his family, a family that he no longer had, for now he was the sole survivor. The thought had never occurred to him until this moment, but it compelled him to relive his loss. For once, Kieran was able to think clearly of all that had taken place since that fateful day when his mother and his friend died so violently amongst the ruins of his home. The emotional experience of these memories was far too overwhelming for Kieran to contain and he wept tears of despair as he tried in vain to comprehend the meaning of such tragic loss of life.

Linda, who was kneeling beside him, could see the tears in his eyes and she took his hand in hers and she too cried. For she understood what Kieran was going through, and had prayed that he would one day be able to give vent to the intolerable mental strain that she knew he was trying to bear.

When the Mass was over, a priest approached Mr Johnstone and signalled for him to follow. They were taken to a private room at the back of the vestry. It took Kieran some time to win back control of his emotions.

Mr Johnstone, who could see the distressed state they were both in, tried to be reassuring with his opening remarks. 'Hey! Come on now you two. You may feel like it's the end of the world now but I'm willing to bet that sometime in the near future, you'll look back on this day and see it as a turning point in your lives.'

'I'm not sure that you fully appreciate the seriousness of our situation, Mr Johnstone.'

'Now listen, son, I've heard a lot about you from my daughter and I've got some idea of what you've both been through. Believe me, I don't mean to underestimate your situation. Unless my daughter's exaggerating, it would seem that only divine intervention has kept you both alive this long. But isn't that an encouraging thought in itself? Perhaps it's time you put your faith in God? I understand that you and my daughter have been running halfway round the globe, trying to stay one jump ahead of these people.'

'That's just about the size of it,' said Kieran. 'And one jump is all we've been able to manage. We're running out of places to hide and I don't know what we're going to do or where to run next. They seem to find us, wherever we go.'

'Well, I'm not surprised, Kieran. Look what you're up against. For one thing, there's a major American corporation with links in the UK and who knows where else, not to mention an FBI agent with the facilities of the state security system at his disposal. Now you tell me that the British authorities are interested. These people all have access to powerful resources, Kieran, as you're finding out, and time and distance is no real obstacle to them. But there is a far more powerful resource, one that's just waiting to be tapped, and we're going to take full advantage of it.'

'I don't quite know what you're getting at, Mr Johnstone,' said Kieran, intrigued by Willie's apparently misplaced optimism. 'Just what is this untapped resource you are referring to?'

'Yes, Dad, what are you trying to tell us?' said Linda, sensing Kieran's frustration with her father's profoundness.

'Patience,' said Willie. 'You must let me tell this in my own way. There was a time when I once felt desperate, when I thought that my little world had crumbled. Perhaps you'll remember, Linda. It was not long before you went to America, when I lost my job in the mine. Oh, I know what you're thinking, that my problems have little bearing on the predicament you two find yourselves in today.

But as far as I was concerned then, my life was over. I was fifty-two, with no hope of ever getting another job, yet I still had a family to support. There didn't seem to be any future for me or my family then. But help did come one day and from a most unexpected source.

'Your mother and I decided to have a holiday. It was to be our last because we would certainly not be able to afford another. Your mother, for some reason, wanted to go to Yugoslavia. I think that she had heard from one of our neighbours that it was relatively inexpensive. Anyway, not long after, we were off to Dubrovnic. A couple of days after we arrived we made friends with a couple that we met in a restaurant. They were about our age and were hoping to learn some English from us. It really worked out quite well, as they in turn were teaching us their language.

'One evening when we were at their house, they told us about a place called Medjugorje. We had never heard of it before but to hear them talk, this was the new spiritual centre of the world. We were naturally intrigued.'

Linda, knowing her father's propensity for storytelling, was starting to grow impatient at this point and said, 'I don't mean to be rude, Father, but I hope you realise that Kieran and I have to be going soon.'

'Going where?' said Willie sharply.

Linda didn't answer but lowered her head to avert her eyes from Willie's steely glare.

'Listen, Linda. What took place in Medjugorje is important not only for you and Kieran but also for the whole world. If only people would take the time to listen.'

There were no further interruptions and Willie continued his story. 'Our friends told us that there had been many visitations by the Virgin Mary at this village and lots of strange phenomena had been witnessed by the local people. We were strongly urged to go and see for ourselves the profound effects that these happenings had on the local community and also on the many visitors to Medjugorje. So, the next day, your mother and I set off to visit this village. It was a considerable distance away and it took us two hours to get there. We joined a coach party of visitors who had come from many parts of the world to make the pilgrimage. When we arrived, our party was taken to the Chapel of St James and we were all ushered into the church hall for a lecture by a Franciscan priest.

'The Father began his lecture by telling us of six young people who had claimed, very convincingly and consistently over the last thirty-three months, to be in daily communication with Our Lady, Queen of Peace. He is the spiritual director of these six young people and is therefore a prime witness of the events which have transformed the spiritual life of not only his parish, but an ever increasing number of people from all over the world who have come into contact with this parish and learned what Our Lady is telling us through these young people. It has been estimated that there have been four and a half million visitors to Medjugorje. Your mother and I had been told by our friends that the priest would be giving a lecture, so we went prepared. I had taken along a tape recorder, and I have brought it with me so that you can both hear it for yourselves.'

Mr Johnstone set up the recorder and switched it on. After a few seconds they were listening to the dulcet tones of the Franciscan priest:

Now in this short time I will tell you the story of the event of the apparitions in the parish of Medjugorje with all the dynamic I can muster. This parish is more or less like every other parish in Western Herzegovina. It is mostly Catholic with a strong traditional emphasis. The people here went to church more than in other regions of Yugoslavia, but they were already on the road of a declining faith. Many young people did not pray and did not go often to church; the families did not pray; few prayed. Some prayers were not known; for instance, we have in the records a note that many young people do not know what the rosary is. The parish has 2,500 inhabitants, spread out, so that we have four churches. This is the parish church of St James.

261

On 24th June 1981, six girls and boys, that is four girls and two boys, were walking between the two villages when suddenly they saw on the hillside a phenomenon which they recognised as Our Lady, La Madonna. But at the same time they were frightened and ran away due to their fear. The following day they were moved in their hearts to go there again to pray. After praying awhile, they saw again Our Lady on the mountainside. Our Lady beckoned them to her with her hand and wanted to embrace them and gather them together. They ran with such speed that nobody could keep up with them. They themselves told us afterwards that they felt as if they were being carried by someone.

When they arrived up the mountain they saw a beautiful girl of 18 to 20 years old. One of the seers sprinkled the girl, this phenomenon, and said: 'I sprinkle you with holy water; if you are from Satan go away; if you are from God stay with us.' She smiled and said: 'I am the Virgin Mary.'

From that day until now Our Lady has continued to appear every day to the visionaries. The apparitions of which they speak are the three-dimensional type: that is, they see Our Lady like a real person – they talk to her, they can touch her, they sing and pray together. They relate to her as they would to a normal person. From the moment when Our Lady appears, they do not see anything else in front of them, nor do they react at all.

She had introduced herself to the visionaries with a specific name: 'I am the Queen of Peace.' Our Lady says that we must notify, immediately, the Sovereign Pontiff and the Bishop of the great importance of the message of Medjugorje. So a letter was written to discharge this duty. I would like now to read this letter to you:

Five visionaries (Vicka Ivankovic, Marija Pavlovic, Ivanka Ivankovic, Ivan Dragicevic, Jakov Colo) have daily apparitions of The Virgin. That they see Her is a fact which can be tested by direct observation; it has been filmed. During the apparitions the visionaries do not react to light, they hear no sound, they do not react to anyone touching them; they seem to be outside time and space. All the visionaries maintain in substance:

a. 'We see The Virgin like we would see any other person. We pray and speak with Her and we can touch Her.'

b. 'The Virgin says that world peace is in crisis. She continually invites us to reconciliation and conversion.'

c. 'She has promised to leave a visible sign at the place of the apparitions, in Medjugorje, for all humanity.'

d. 'The time preceding the sign is a period of grace for conversion and deepening of faith.'

e. 'The Virgin has promised to give us ten secrets. Up to now, eight have been confided to Vicka Ivankovic and Marija Pavlovic (who received the ninth on 8th December 1983), nine to Jakov Colo, Ivan Dragicevic and Ivanka Ivankovic; ten secrets have been given to Mirjana Dragicevic only.'

f. 'These apparitions are to be the last of The Virgin's appearances upon the earth. This is why they are over so long a period and of such frequency.'

During the apparition of 25th December 1982, Mirjana says, Our Lady confided to her the tenth and final secret, and has revealed to her the dates on which the events foretold by the secrets will be fulfilled. The Virgin has revealed to Mirjana many things about the future, up to now more than to the other visionaries. This is why I am setting down what Mirjana told me during a talk we had together on 5th November 1983. I am giving the essence of what she told me, without word-for-word quotation. Mirjana said:

a. Before the visible sign is given to humanity, there will be three warnings to the world. These warnings will be events upon the earth. Mirjana will be their witness. Three days before one of these warnings she will notify a priest of her own choice. The testimony of Mirjana will be a confirmation of the apparitions and an incentive to the conversion of the world. After the warnings, the visible sign will come upon the place of the apparition at Medjugorje, for all humanity. The sign will be given to testify to the authenticity of the apparitions and to call men back to the faith.

b. The ninth and tenth secrets are grave. They are about chastisement for the sins of the world. The punishment is inevitable because you cannot wait for the conversion of the whole world. The chastisement can be mitigated by prayer and penance; it cannot be prevented. An evil which menaced the world, the subject of the seventh secret, has been effaced because of prayer and fasting, Mirjana said. Because of that, the Virgin continues to request prayer and fasting: 'You have forgotten that, by prayer and fasting, you can avert war, suspend natural laws.'

c. After the first warning, the others will follow in a very short time. So mankind will have some time for conversion.

d. Now is a period of grace and conversion. After the visible sign, those who remain alive will have little time for conversion. That is why the Virgin urgently requests conversion and reconciliation.

e. The call to prayer and penance has as its object the avoidance of evils and war, but above all the salvation of souls.

f. According to Mirjana, we are very close to the events predicted by the Virgin. As a result of these experiences. Mirjana says to humanity: 'Turn with all speed: open your hearts to God.'

Besides this basic message, Mirjana said she had, in 1982, an apparition which throws, we think, a ray of light on the history of the Church. She tells of an apparition in which Satan came to her disguised as the Virgin. Satan told Mirjana to renounce Our Lady and to follow him so that he could give her happiness, in love and in life; whereas with the Virgin, she would have to suffer, he said. Mirjana spurned him. Immediately the Virgin came and Satan disappeared.

Then the Virgin gave, in substance, the following message: 'Sorry about that, but you must know that Satan exists. One day he presented himself before the throne of God and asked permission to test the Church for a certain time. God gave him permission to test it for a hundred years. This century is under the devil's power, but when the secrets which have been confided to you are revealed, his power will be destroyed. Already, right now, he is beginning to lose his power and is becoming aggressive: he is destroying marriages, stirring up divisions between priests, inciting obsessions and murders. You must protect yourselves by fasting and prayer; above all community prayer. Carry blessed objects. Put them in your houses. Bring back the use of holy water.'

According to certain Catholic experts who have studied these apparitions, this message of Mirjana would illuminate the vision the Sovereign Pontiff Leo XIII had. They say that after he had had an apocalyptic vision of the future of the Church, Leo XIII introduced the prayer to St Michael which the priest recited after mass up to the time of the Council, Vatican II. These experts say that the testing time foreseen by the Sovereign Pontiff Leo XIII is coming to an end.

Most Holy Father, I do not want to be responsible for the loss of a single soul. I am doing my best; the world is being asked to become converted and reconciled. In writing to you, Most Holy Father, I am merely doing my duty. Before writing this letter, I gave the draft to the visionaries so that they would ask the Virgin whether or not the contents were correct. Ivan Dragicevic brought me this reply: 'Yes, the contents of this letter are true; you must inform first the Sovereign Pontiff and then the Bishop.' This letter will be accompanied by prayers and fasting so that the Holy Spirit will guide your spirit and heart during this important period of history. By the Sacred Hearts of Jesus and Mary, accept my humble respects.

Medjugorje, 2nd December 1983

When the tape ended, Mr Johnstone switched off his recorder and said to Linda and Kieran, 'There is much more you will find out when you go over there.'

Linda and Kieran looked at each other in utter amazement.

'What? When we go over there?' said Kieran.

'Yes. It's already been arranged. Mrs Johnstone and I discussed it last night and we decided that you both should go to Yugoslavia with our tickets.'

'But Dad!' said Linda. 'We couldn't...'

'No buts, Linda, that's final. The flight is due to leave Turnhouse airport on Wednesday morning, so all we have to do now is keep you both out of sight until then.'

Kieran was rendered almost speechless by Mr Johnstone's revelations but his eyes sparkled as new hope stirred inside him. 'I don't know what to say, Mr Johnstone, or how to thank you enough.'

'There's certainly no call for that, son. It's the least we can do, considering all that you have done for our daughter. Besides, we can always have another holiday next year, now, can't we?'

Linda grabbed hold of her father and gave him a warm hug and with tears in her eyes said, 'Thanks, Dad, you and Mum both. We'll pray for you.'

'Well, there's still a lot to be done yet before you leave,' said Willie. 'There's still that little matter of finding you a place to hide for the next two days. Your mother suggested that you might be able to stay with the Morrisons.'

'The Morrisons?' said Linda. 'Who are they?'

'They're friends of ours, Betty and Graham Morrison. It was Graham who got me my job. Anyway, they live out at Newbridge which is only ten minutes' drive from Turnhouse. Look, why don't you go with Kieran and pick up your things while I phone Graham. I'll meet you both back here at about four o'clock and all going well, I'll drive you out to Newbridge.'

27

When Bill Rice and his companions arrived in London, Archie Langdon who had sent the telex was there to meet them. When they got into the car, Bill asked if a meeting had been arranged with the Irish police.

'Yes sir. As a matter of fact, I was able to persuade them to bring the prisoner over here.'

'You did? Good work, Arch, excellent. That should save us a lot of time. Tell me how on earth you managed to swing that one.'

'Oh, it wasn't too difficult. They knew that we would want to question him. I told them that we anticipated further arrests in London, arrests which will be based on statements the prisoner has already made, and that we would be needing him to corroborate his story and to give evidence.'

'I see,' said Bill. 'What's this man's name anyway?'

'Bankhead, James Bankhead. By the way, are you aware that Alex Stenton is in London at the moment? He is one of Mr Casey's entourage.'

'No, I didn't know that. That's interesting. This is my lucky day! Is he under surveillance?'

'Yes. I put a man on him as soon as he arrived.'

'Well, I think it's time we brought Mr Stenton in for questioning. We've waited long enough. I think we've got enough evidence against him, now it's time we used it. Who knows, perhaps we can persuade him to tell us something about Tom Casey's involvement in all this. And as for you, Ian, as soon as we get to the office, I'd like you to make contact with the Glasgow police. See if you can find out what's happening up there at the moment. If they're still holding the girl, then get them to wire down a picture. OK?'

'Yes sir. Will do,' said Ian.

'When can we expect the arrival of this prisoner, Arch?'

'Oh, they're here now. They came over this morning.'

'They didn't waste any time, did they?' said Bill.

'No. I think they're as anxious as we are to solve this one, especially now that they know it's more than a sectarian killing that's involved here.'

'So he's ready for interrogation, then,' said Bill. 'OK, Jim and I will get started on that right away.'

When they arrived at the London office, Bill Rice and Jim Hollis were introduced to the Irish representatives who had delivered the prisoner. After a short debriefing session, Bill and Jim prepared to interrogate their prisoner.

About an hour after the interrogation had got under way, Ian Scott appeared and asked Bill if he could have a word with him. Bill reluctantly broke off the interrogation to hear what Ian had to say.

'This better be good, Ian, I was just getting into my stride in there. What's on your mind?'

'I'm afraid it's bad news. Looks like the Glasgow police have not only released the girl but they've also released the three men.'

'What?' said Bill in disbelief.

'Apparently the three men claimed that it was all a misunderstanding. It seems that the girl was not prepared to press charges so the police had no alternative but to let them go.'

'Did they give you a description of the girl?' asked Bill.

'No, not exactly. But they did tell me that the arrest had BBC news coverage so I've sent someone over to the BBC to get a picture from the film.'

'That's good thinking. When can I expect to get it?'

'Oh, I should think in about ninety minutes or so.'

'OK. Bring it to the interrogation room as soon as it arrives and then we'll find out if it's the same girl as our Irish friend in there has seen.'

Later that day, two plain-clothes detectives arrested Alex Stenton at his hotel in the West End of London. He had been under observation since he arrived so he wasn't hard to find. The arrest was made discreetly so as not to disturb or arouse the suspicions of Tom Casey.

Alex Stenton was taken to Bill Rice's headquarters in central London. On his arrival, he protested loudly about being taken into custody without formal charges being made against him, and he claimed that as an American citizen he had a right to consult a member of the Embassy staff before he answered any questions.

When Bill was informed of Stenton's arrival, he arranged for him to be put into an adjoining interrogation room. Jim Hollis was left to continue his questioning of James Bankhead, while Bill prepared to interrogate Alex Stenton.

When Bill arrived, Alex Stenton was still protesting about his arrest. Bill reminded him that he had been brought in for questioning, although he expected that formal charges were imminent.

'Then I demand to have legal representation,' said Stenton.

'All in good time, all in good time. Right, Mr Stenton,' said Bill in a disarming manner. 'I understand you are an American citizen, over here on business. What exactly is your business?'

'I'm a security executive for Atlantic Air, an American airline company.'

'I see,' said Bill. 'And what business does Atlantic Air have over here?'

'I'm here in an advisory capacity to assist the president of CLC Industries, the company that owns Atlantic Air.'

'Ah, that would be Tom Casey, wouldn't it?'

'Yes, that's right, and our business is with the British government, who won't be pleased when they find out about your interference,' said Alex caustically.

'Is that so?' said Bill. 'I don't suppose you'd care tell us what Mr Casey's interests in the UK are now, would you?'

'No I wouldn't,' said Alex abruptly.

'I thought as much. Tell me, does the name McGuire mean anything to you'

'I can't say that it does,' said Alex impatiently. 'So what's this all about? Isn't it time you told me why you've brought me here in the first place?'

'Would you like to come over here a minute, Mr Stenton. There's something I want to show you.'

Alex followed Bill as he crossed to the opposite side of the room. Bill pulled back a sliding partition on the wall revealing a two-way mirror which looked into the adjacent room. 'Do you see that gentleman sitting at the desk, Alex?'

'Yes.'

'Do you recognise him at all?'

'Never seen him before in my life,' said Alex sharply.

'Now that's interesting,' said Bill. 'That man in there not only claims to know you but says that you travelled all the way from America specifically to see him.'

'The man's obviously mistaken,' said Alex.

'Oh! Is he now?' replied Bill. 'Do you remember being in Ireland recently, Mr Stenton?'

There was a long pause then Alex said, 'Yes. I was over there recently on business for Mr Casey.'

'Ah yes. Mr Casey. You don't wish to tell me what that business was, do you?'

'I'm not at liberty to say. It was company business,' replied Alex.

'All right then. Suppose I tell you what that business was, Mr Stenton. I suggest that you went to Ireland specifically to see this gentleman with the intention of hiring him to dispose of certain members of the McGuire family.'

'That's absolutely ridiculous,' said Alex indignantly. 'Like I said, I don't know anyone called McGuire and I certainly haven't arranged for anyone to be killed. The man's obviously lying.'

'Come on, Alex. This man's prepared to testify in open court that you hired him and others to kill these people.'

'I think it's time I saw a representative from the US Embassy. I'm a US citizen and that's my right.'

'Oh, we're talking about your rights as an American citizen again, are we?' said Bill. 'Well, now. I have a man who would be really interested to hear your views on that very subject.' Bill switched on the intercom system. 'Hello Sheila. Would you ask Mr Hollis to come in here please?'

Moments later, Jim Hollis walked into the room carrying a large folder under his arm.

'Ah Jim. I believe you have some knowledge of Mr Stenton, don't you?'

'That's right. I have his file with me.'

'This is Jim Hollis of the CIA. You could say, one of your representatives,' said Bill facetiously. 'Mr Hollis has some questions to ask you regarding your American citizenship. Can I leave him with you, Jim? Perhaps you can explain to Mr Stenton some of the discrepancies in his claim.'

'Sure,' said Jim as he put down his file and opened it.

As Bill left the interrogation room he was approached by Ian Scott.

'Hello Ian, what have you got for me?'

'The picture, I got it quicker than I thought.'

'Let me see it,' said Bill. 'So this is the young lady we've heard so much about. Right, you take it to Mr Bankhead and see if he recognises her, then see me in my office when you're ready. I've got a few phone calls to make.'

Bill wanted to get in touch with the SAS headquarters to see if they still had someone in the service who knew Alex Stenton. He figured that the best way to deal with Stenton was to confront him with one of his ex-colleagues. It took him some time and a few phone calls, but eventually it paid off. Bill got through to a retired Major who had participated in Stenton's court martial. He couldn't have hoped for more. He then arranged for the Major to be picked up and brought to his headquarters.

Bill sat back in his chair and was thinking over what his next move should be when Ian Scott burst into his office with a wide grin on his face.

'We're in luck. Our man has just identified the girl in the picture and claims that she is the same girl who was with Kieran McGuire in Ireland.'

'Well, well. My luck seems to be holding out today. Do you realise what this means?'

'Yes I do. It means that your theory about the kidnappers trying to use her as bait for McGuire is probably right. It also means that McGuire was in Edinburgh when it happened.'

'OK. I want you to go up to Edinburgh and find out what you can about this girl. Or better still, phone in advance and arrange for the local police to pick her up. Tell them that we want her taken in for further questioning. You'll have to move fast, for the chances are that they'll both be on the move again. They're not going to hang around for long now that they know the police are involved. If we can't get hold of her there's a good chance we'll get him. Look, Ian, I'm sorry about this. We're barely home a day and I've got you on the move again. Have you had a chance to speak to your wife yet?'

'Yes I have. I phoned her a little while ago.'

'Oh good, how's the baby?'

'The baby's fine.'

'That's good. I'll see that you get some extended leave when this is all over, but for the moment we've got to strike while the iron's hot. OK, Ian, on your way and report to me as soon as you can.'

By the time Jim Hollis had finished with Stenton, Bill was ready to have another go, this time armed with the time and dates of Stenton's trip to Ireland. He also informed him that the SAS were sending someone to confirm his identity and to verify that he had been dishonourably discharged. It was part of Bill's ploy to maintain a constant two-pronged attack on Stenton in an effort to strain his mental resources, thus keeping him constantly on edge. Jim Hollis had already informed him that the CIA were now aware of the circumstances under which he had left the service, and that this information was bringing his citizenship into question.

The pressure was definitely on and Alex knew it. He was now aware of how strong a case they had against him. He also knew that Tom Casey would drop him like a hot brick as soon as he found out that he had lost his US citizenship and could no longer function in the States. He might even arrange to have him blown away because of what he knew.

Despite all these threats, Alex Stenton's outer composure never wavered. He maintained a cool, controlled image but deep inside he was starting to panic like hell and desperately needed time to think, time that Bill Rice was not allowing him.

'Look, do you mind if I have a cigarette?'

'Sure. Go ahead.'

Alex made a big play of looking for his cigarettes and when he finally produced them, made an issue of lighting one. While he did this he was trying to assess from their questions how much they knew and how much they were guessing. They obviously know something about the McGuires, but what? Did they have Kieran McGuire? Was he their source or did they even know of his existence yet? It was obvious that the Irishman had made some kind of deal to turn Queen's evidence.

Alex's thoughts were abruptly disturbed by Bill firing yet another question at him. 'Well Alex. Are you ready to answer some questions now or shall we wait until your SAS colleague arrives?'

'Tell me. What exactly do you want to know?' said Alex resignedly.

'Well, first of all, I would like you to tell me why you've had men chasing Kieran McGuire clear across two continents?'

The words may have been spoken in soft even tones, but the question and the name Kieran McGuire echoed loudly in Alex Stenton's ears. He was totally unprepared for this. He was convinced that they either had Kieran or that they had heard from him. It was clear that they knew a lot more than he had realised. Bill Rice was playing the perfect hand. Just as Alex was starting to keep pace with the game, Bill would throw in another trump card.

'My men aren't chasing anyone,' said Alex.

'Come on now. How long are you going to keep this up? You know perfectly well what we're talking about. We've been on to you for a long time now and I think it's time for you to be a bit more cooperative.'

Bill knew that Stenton must be feeling pretty desperate by now so he decided to throw him a lifeline to see how he would react.

'Look, Alex, as far as we're concerned, you're small fry. We're after much bigger fish than you. Are you going to carry the can for Tom Casey? You know he'll abandon you as soon as he finds out that you've been arrested.'

'Why should he?' said Alex. 'I haven't been charged with anything.' It was Alex's turn to test the strength of Bill's hand.

'OK friend. If that's the way you want to play it, then that's the way it's gonna be.' Bill reached over to the intercom and said, 'Hello, Sheila, You can send in that detective now. We're ready to make formal charges.'

Bill was looking straight into Alex Stenton's face when he said it and could see that Stenton, for the first time, was starting to lose his cool, for there were tiny beads of sweat accumulating just above his eyebrows.

The door opened and in walked a small but heavily built man with close cropped blonde hair. He looked as if he was ex-army.

'Ah Sergeant! I want you to read this man his rights, then I want him charged on three counts: conspiring to murder Bridie McGuire and her unidentified house guest, conspiring to murder Peter McGuire, and the murder of Kevin McGuire. That should be enough to be getting on with.'

'OK! OK!' said Alex. 'You can stop this farce right now!'

'Does this mean that you are ready to cooperate, Mr Stenton?'

'I would like to speak to you alone,' he said in an almost inaudible voice.

'All right, but we're not playing games any more. Either you cooperate fully or you start serving the first of three life sentences. Do you understand me?'

Alex nodded his head in acknowledgement.

'OK, Sergeant. Leave us alone for a few minutes.'

'What about your CIA friend?' Alex said.

'He stays,' said Bill firmly.

Alex knew that it was all but over for him. His only chance now was to go for some kind of a deal. 'What's in it for me if I cooperate?' said Alex.

'That depends on how much you help us. The more you do for us, the more we can do for you. Now to start with, I want you to tell us what Tom Casey and his consortium are up to in the UK. We know that he's somehow trying to destabilise the economy but we're not sure how he plans to accomplish this.'

There was a long pause before Alex responded to Bill's question. He was determined not to be rushed into giving any information until he had had more concrete assurances than Bill Rice was offering. 'OK, OK. You've got me, but that's as much as you're gonna get unless I can get some kind of a proper deal here. I'm the only link to Tom Casey's illegal activities. Listen, guys, I can give you enough evidence to put Tom Casey away for life but it's gonna cost you and I won't settle for any of your vague promises either.'

Bill, who had been working towards this moment since the interrogation began, calmly said, 'What exactly did you have in mind?'

'I want a new identity, a small stake, and somewhere in Europe where I can start over. I want a proper contract drawn up stating these terms.'

'If we give you that kind of contract, we'll want more than Tom Casey. We'll want everything you've got and you'll have to testify in open court,' said Bill.

'That's good enough for me. I could even give you Tom Casey's Edinburgh connection.'

'And who might that be?'

'Dave Simpson. And that's just a little appetiser. What do you say, then?'

'OK, Alex, we'll see what can be done. We'll try and get a contract drawn up for you by tomorrow. All right?'

'Fine by me,' said Stenton.

'OK,' replied Bill. 'We'll continue this tomorrow.'

Immediately after the interrogation, Jim Hollis got on the phone to Frank Mariano in Washington and told him the news about Alex Stenton. He also told him about the deal that had been made and how Stenton was about to give them information that could lead to the arrest of Tom Casey.

Frank was delighted and astonished at how fast things had begun to move. He arranged for Jim to telex any relevant information to Washington as soon as he got hold of it. Frank, for his part, was able to tell Jim of his own success in obtaining higher authority to overrule the FBI's objections to his inquiries regarding Gregg Donoghue.

The next morning Alex Stenton got his contract as promised and he spent the rest of that day telling his interrogators all he knew about Tom Casey's UK operations. He started off by telling them about Kevin McGuire and how he had been recruited for the sole purpose of killing the two politicians in Edinburgh. These revelations tied in very closely with Kieran McGuire's tapes, thus giving Bill a double check on his information.

Stenton went on to tell them of the backup plan that had been implemented after Kevin McGuire had failed to fully accomplish his task. Tom Casey had persuaded the top executives of two multinational companies to cooperate in a plan to put pressure on the British economy. Once Stenton had started pouring out all this information there was no stopping him. He was able to give detailed accounts of many of the transactions that had taken place between the major companies involved.

Within days of receiving this information Bill Rice and his men went into action. A joint programme was prepared between himself and Frank Mariano for a two-pronged attack so that they could move simultaneously against the major companies. Frank was to make his move on CLC Industries and the other two multinationals in the US at exactly the same time as Bill was making his move on Tom Casey and the companies that had been set up in the UK.

A team of investigators was set up to inquire into Tom Casey's syndicate and its activities in the UK. The government was also alerted to the situation and, as an interim measure, it froze all financial aid to companies associated with the syndicate. The US government conducted a similar move and froze major assets belonging to the consortium that were invested in US banks. Further interim action was taken by UK government officials who instructed the syndicate to hand over immediate control of their UK companies to appointees of the British government.

Tom Casey himself was eventually arrested, along with several of his associates.

The remaining company heads were told that they could either, stay and make a going concern of the companies they had already started, or they could sell all their existing UK interests. They were also warned that they would not be allowed to move any of their capital equipment out of the country. Assets to the value of money they had borrowed from the British government had already been seized by the US government. These would be held until such time as repayment of that borrowed money had been made. A further measure was taken by both the US and British governments to forbid all three major corporations from participating in future government contracts, both in the UK and the US, for the next five years.

28

By the time Linda and Kieran arrived at the bedsit in Leith it was after three o'clock. While they were there, Linda took time to tell Kieran her version of the kidnapping and how she had been released by the police because of her refusal to make charges against the three men.

'I wondered why they released you so soon,' said Kieran. 'What about these people anyway? Did you manage to glean anything from them at all? I mean did they question you or threaten you in any way?'

'No,' said Linda. 'Surprisingly enough they didn't. That's what made their claim about a mistaken identity so credible, though I don't think that the police were buying that story for a minute. They didn't say a word, not even in the car. When I arrived at the building, they just pushed me into a room, locked the door and left me there. I didn't even know that there was a third man until we were leaving the building.'

'I see,' said Kieran. 'We were certainly lucky that your mother realised what was going on and had the presence of mind to take down the registration of their car. The police were on to them in no time at all.'

Linda carried on with her story. 'Well, anyway, I was in that room barely fifteen minutes when I heard all sorts of noises coming from outside. I heard a loudhailer and a voice saying that it was the police, that the building was surrounded and would the occupants leave the premises. The next thing I knew was that the door was unlocked and one of the men said, "You can go now. I'm sorry but there's been some kind of misunderstanding." You know the rest, as it was on television. Mind you, the police seemed quite angry when they realised that I was not prepared to make charges. I think that's why they kept me in overnight. They were probably hoping that I would change my mind. Of course, they also wanted time to question the three men.'

'There's only one snag about all this,' said Kieran. 'These guys are also on the loose.'

'But surely they wouldn't dare try and come after us now that the police are involved?' said Linda.

'Perhaps not, but you can bet they'll have someone watching us very closely. I wonder if you were followed from Glasgow?'

'I don't think so,' said Linda. 'They wouldn't have had time to organise anything as they were still in custody when I left. I doubt very much they would have been able to get in touch with anybody to have me followed.'

'Yes you're probably right,' said Kieran. 'So we can take it that for the moment, at least, neither they nor the police know where we are.'

'That's the way I see it.'

Kieran was sorely tempted to tell her about his own experience but decided against it. He figured that she had been through enough already. 'OK, let's get all our things together and head back to the Cathedral and see if your father's managed to arrange something for us.'

By the time they got organised and arranged for a taxi, another hour had gone by before they got back to the Cathedral.

'How did it go with the Morrisons, then?' said Kieran.

'Fine,' said Willie. 'They'll be happy to have you both and Graham said that he would take you to Turnhouse airport on Wednesday morning. But there is another problem.'

'What's that?' asked Linda.

'I'm afraid the police have been at our house looking for you, Linda. I phoned your mother and she told me that they had been there an hour ago. They want to take you in for further questioning. Your mother said there's a police car outside the house, so it looks as if they're waiting for our return.'

'Where did your wife say you and Linda were, Mr Johnstone?' asked Kieran.

'Oh, she just said that we hadn't arrived yet. She was taken so unawares that she didn't have time to prepare a story.'

'What on earth are you going to tell the police when you return without me, Dad?'

'I don't know yet, but I'll have to think of something. Anyway, first things first. Let's get you two off to the Morrisons. That's the first priority.'

'What did you tell the Morrisons about us? Won't they think it's all a bit strange asking us to stay with them for two nights and then us using your holiday tickets?'

'No, it wasn't as difficult to explain as you might think,' said Willie. 'The Morrisons had seen the news coverage on the television so they knew all about the kidnapping situation. I told them that you were dreadfully upset about the whole affair and afraid that they might try again. So I said that your mother and I had agreed to give you and your boyfriend our tickets to let you get away from it all for a while. I also told them that you thought that they knew your home address so you were afraid to go home, and that's why I was arranging for you to stop over with them. You know, Linda, I've never told so many untruths in my life!'

'Oh Dad! I'm sorry that you had to get involved in all this.'

'Don't be silly. I'm not complaining. My biggest problem at the moment is dealing with Graham's praises. He keeps telling me how noble it is of me to give up my holiday. Anyway it's time I was taking you through. You'll like Betty and Graham. They're a grand couple.'

Mr Johnstone headed straight home after he dropped them off at Newbridge. When he got back to his house he could see that there was a police car parked outside his door. The two policemen, who had watched him arrive, approached him as he entered the house. Willie told them that Linda had been very upset when he picked her up and that she was too frightened to come home so he had taken her out for a meal and they had driven around until she had calmed down a bit.

'Where is she now?' said one of the policemen impatiently.

'I don't know exactly. She said that she wanted to see her boyfriend.'

'I see,' said the policeman. 'Could you give me his address?'

'Oh, I'm sorry, officer but I'm afraid I don't know his address. Linda didn't tell us where he lives.'

'Could you give us his full name then, sir?' said the officer who seemed to be a bit frustrated by this time.

Willie was in a quandary at this point. He knew that they were bound to ask this question at some stage and he also knew that if he lied about the name, there was a good chance that they wouldn't believe the rest of his story and that just might prove a bit awkward. However, if he told them the correct name, it would give his story more credibility. The fleeting thought passed through his mind that he was getting too damn good at this lie telling.

'The boyfriend, sir,' said the policeman with his notebook open and his pen poised at the ready. 'You were about to give us his name.'

'Oh, er, I'm sorry officer, Kieran something or other. Oh yes, now I remember: Kieran McGuire.' Willie could see from the officer's reaction that the name meant something to him.

'Are you sure that's the name? Kieran McGuire, you said?'

'Yes. Oh yes, I'm quite sure that's the name.'

'And you don't know where he lives?' said the policeman.

'No. I'm sorry, I don't.'

'All right, Mr Johnstone. Thank you for your help,' said the officer as he folded his note book and tucked it firmly into his breast pocket. 'You will inform us when she returns, won't you sir?'

'Yes, of course I will. It just occurred to me though that she sometimes stops over at her boyfriend's place so I can't say for sure that she will come home tonight. You know what these young people are like. They've all got minds of their own when it comes to relationships. Not that I approve, mind you, but they're adults now and we have to allow them to make their own decisions about these things.'

'Yes, I know what you mean, sir. Well, we'll leave a car at the door just in case she comes back later.'

About eight o'clock that evening Ian Scott arrived in Edinburgh, feeling very tired and travel-weary after his long rail journey. He had taken the train because the weather at Gatwick airport had made flying conditions uncertain and all scheduled flights were already two hours behind. This meant that he had spent six hours travelling.

When he got to Edinburgh he took a taxi to Fettes Row police station, the main Edinburgh headquarters, where he met Chief Inspector Angus McLean. Angus was a tall, heavily built grey-haired gentleman who spoke with a Highland accent. He originally came from the Isle of Skye and, although he had spent the last 14 years in Edinburgh, he had never lost his Highland lilt. After some brief introductions and a large mug of hot tea for Ian, Angus began putting him in the picture.

'I'm afraid I've got good news and bad news for you, Mr Scott.'

'OK, Inspector, let's hear it.'

'Well now, the bad news is that we haven't been able to get hold of the girl yet although we've got a car waiting at her address. The good news is that we've established that her boyfriend's name is Kieran McGuire.' Angus paused for a moment, waiting for some kind of response.

'Yes, go on,' said Ian.

'Aye well, she's supposed to be staying at his place at the moment. At least that's what her father tells us.'

'And where is his place?'

'Ah well, we don't exactly know that yet.'

'I see,' said Ian. 'OK. The first thing I want you to do is to get that police car away from her door. We don't want to frighten them away now, do we? Put a plain-clothes officer in an unmarked car somewhere near the house and get him to check in every hour.'

'Maybe if you'd told us what this was all about in the first place, Mr Scott, we could have arranged to be less conspicuous, but if you insist on keeping us in the dark, then you'll have to take the consequences. We're not bloody mind-readers you know.'

'I'm sorry. We haven't really had time to put you fully in the picture but I intend to do that now that I'm here. But first of all, what steps have you taken to locate her boyfriend?'

'There's not a lot we can do until we have some idea of what part of the city he's in, but we have put out his description. We'll just have to wait and see what happens next. Anyway, how badly do you want these people?'

'I'll tell you how badly we want them, Angus. I want people who can identify them at the airport, the docks, the railway stations and the bus station. That has to be organised tonight. OK?'

Angus looked at him with an expression of anger and disbelief. 'Have you any idea what you're asking?'

'I'm well aware of what I'm asking, Inspector, but this is a priority situation.'

'And a costly one, but that'll be your responsibility from now on. I hope you realise that,' said Angus as he picked up his cap and stormed out of the room.

Meanwhile, at the Morrisons' house, Linda and Kieran were alone in their room, discussing the tape that Linda's father had played.

'Yes, I never really got a chance to take it all in,' said Kieran. 'When your father played that tape, I was absolutely stunned. I didn't know what to think. And when he told us that we were going over there ... well, I was just so relieved that we had another place to run to that I didn't stop to think about it.'

'Well, take time now,' said Linda. 'What are your thoughts on the subject?'

'I honestly don't know what to think, Linda, I really don't. I usually like to keep an open mind about these things but ... wow! This seems different somehow,' said Kieran thoughtfully. 'It's as if we were being asked to make up our minds now, to make a stand, and being warned that time is running out. That's what it sounded like to me, but I guess we'll know more when we actually get over there. It certainly looks like your parents are convinced.'

'Have you always been a practising Catholic, Kieran?'

'Yes, I have, at least until I left Ireland and got myself into this mess. Talking of which, we've certainly been in some near disastrous situations haven't we? I can't tell you how many times I thought that it was all over for us. Mind you, there were times when I wondered if divine intervention was at work. What about you? What's your reaction to the Medjugorje message?'

'Like you, Kieran, I'm not sure but I do want to believe. The message says that the world is in great turmoil and when you look around you, there's certainly plenty evidence to support this. Look what's happening in the Gulf, Beirut and Central America, and it's only a matter of time before South Africa ignites with the blacks and whites confronting each other.'

'Yes,' said Kieran, 'and it won't be long before the superpowers are involved in some of these confrontations.'

'What do you think about going to a communist country?'

'I should think that's the least of my concerns at the moment. Our survival is far more important. Besides, I prefer to look at it more as a Catholic country than a communist one. Apart from that, people from all over the world go to Yugoslavia on holiday, don't they? Anyway, our immediate concern is getting as far away as possible from our pursuers.'

'Do you think that we will have to stay over there?'

'That depends largely on what happens while we're there. Anyway, who says that the Yugoslavians are going to let us stay?'

'Oh, I don't know,' said Linda, 'but I can see the Western press making great news coverage out of this story if they ever get hold of it: "Young couple seeks political asylum in communist country".'

'Like I said, that's the least of our concerns at the moment.'

The next day was uneventful for Linda and Kieran as there was nothing much they could do but stay indoors and out of sight. A great deal of their time was spent trying to avoid lengthy discussions with the Morrisons, just in case they should ask some awkward questions. Fortunately, the Morrisons had decided that they should be left to spend some time on their own.

It was quite a different situation at Edinburgh police headquarters, where Ian Scott was becoming concerned about the cost of having all these men covering the city exits, especially on a 24-hour basis. Angus had already suggested to him that the horse had probably bolted by this time and that it was probably too late to close the stable door. 'It's your own damn fault anyway,' said Angus, 'for not putting us in the picture sooner.'

Ian was hard pushed not to argue the point as he didn't want to alienate Angus any further. He was also aware that there was a limit to how long he could ask for such expensive blanket cover of the area. 'I'll tell you what, Angus. Give me cover for one more night, then unless we get information regarding their whereabouts, you can recall your men first thing tomorrow morning.'

'That suits me fine,' said Angus tersely and left the office. As Angus left, Ian Scott's phone rang. The call was from London and Bill Rice's voice came on the line.

'Hi Ian. How are you doing up there?'

'Not so good, Bill. We haven't been able to get hold of the girl yet. She didn't go home last night and her father tells us that she was with Kieran McGuire. However, I've covered all the major city exits.'

'That's most unfortunate. I rather suspect that they've probably bolted by now. They wouldn't hang around now that they know the police are involved. Never mind, we're having better luck down this end. This guy Stenton has started to open up. He's singing his head off and it looks like he's going to be a prime witness. That's what I'm phoning you about. Stenton has given us the background to the Edinburgh set-up and has implicated Dave Simpson as the man who orchestrated the Edinburgh Parade killing, so I want you to bring him in right away. I want to question him myself, so I'll be up there some time later today. Whatever you do, Ian, don't let this one get away for we've got enough on this guy to make formal charges.'

'OK, Bill, leave it with me.'

Ian immediately got in touch with Angus who arranged for two uniformed men to accompany him while he picked up Dave Simpson in Glasgow. Ian was taking no chances this time. He wanted to be on the scene himself when the arrest was made. As it turned out, he had little cause for concern for everything went like clockwork.

Dave Simpson was still in his office when they arrived and didn't seem too worried when Ian told him that he was wanted through in Edinburgh for further questioning. He seemed to think that the questioning was in connection with the supposed kidnapping and was quite relaxed about the whole affair. He obviously thought he was on safe ground in that respect. Ian decided not to discourage his line of thought and so didn't enlighten him about the true nature of their inquiries.

Bill Rice had been luckier than Ian with his travel arrangements to Edinburgh for he had managed to fly up and was in the city for six o'clock that evening. When Bill met up with Ian Scott at police headquarters, he was brimming with enthusiasm about the way the case was going.

'Well, Ian, it's all starting to fit together nicely. I think we've got the whole story now and, thanks to Stenton, we've even got Tom Casey in the bag.'

'You've actually arrested him then?' said Ian.

'Yes we have, and I think we've got enough evidence for a conviction on at least three counts.'

'Great!' Ian said. 'You have been moving fast.'

'We sure have and I don't see many obstacles in our way now. It's only a matter of time before we sew this one up. By the way, Frank Mariano is coming over tomorrow to interview Tom Casey. He called last night. The FBI has come up with information tying Gregg Donoghue to Tom Casey. It looks like they've been working together for quite some time. We'll get the full details when Frank comes over. We've also made a breakthrough against the syndicate: you know, the one Tom Casey organised. According to Frank, one of the major corporations has put forward a few sacrificial lambs in their attempts to clear themselves. Talk about a domino effect! When we toppled Stenton and then Tom Casey, we certainly started a domino run.'

'What about the other corporation, sir? Is there any headway in that direction?'

'All in good time, Ian. We're getting there. I'm expecting to hear more about them from Frank when he comes over. You wouldn't believe what's been going on in the last two days. For one thing, the government has already called a cabinet meeting over this and the corporation heads have been confronted by representatives from both the US and our own governments. They've even frozen major assets belonging to the corporations involved. Anyway, what about this Dave Simpson fellow I came up to see? Have you brought him in yet?'

'Oh yes, I have. By the way, he thinks you want to question him about the kidnapping.'

'Oh does he now! Boy, am I going to spoil his day! I'm going to throw the book at this guy. For one thing, he's to be charged with being an accessory to murder, and that's just for openers. I've got all the evidence I need to put him away for a very long time.'

On Wednesday morning, Graham Morrison was on his way to Turnhouse airport with Linda and Kieran. As they neared the airport they saw two police cars leaving the area. 'Well, I wonder who they've been looking for at this time of the morning?' said Graham. 'Mind you, it's typical isn't it? When you want a policeman you can never find one and when you're not, the place seems to be crawling with them. Never mind, I shouldn't think you'll be bothering about that where you're going, eh? Two weeks in sunny Yugoslavia sure sounds great to me. Have you been there before, Linda?'

'No I haven't, but my mother told me that she and my father enjoyed their stay. I'm just looking forward to a holiday. I can't wait to get over there. Just getting away will be enough.'

Graham was being very tactful and was careful not to mention Linda's ordeal. 'Well then, here we are,' he said as he pulled into the airport car park. He helped them take their luggage to the terminal and stayed with them until they were safely booked in. 'OK, you two, have a nice trip. Hope you enjoy your holiday. I'm afraid I'll have to rush off. Oh, by the way, I nearly forgot. Your father gave me a letter for you since he couldn't make it to the airport.'

Linda took the letter and they said their goodbyes. Once they were in the air and safely on their way to Yugoslavia, Linda opened the letter.

Dear Linda

Your mother and I are deeply sorry that we were unable to see you both off at the airport but I'm sure you'll understand that we daren't risk being followed by the police. However, we both take heart in the knowledge that by the time you read this letter, you will be well on the way to safety. Well, pet, I hope that perhaps this letter can make up in some small way for our absence.

Your mother is already crying as I write but I don't think they are tears of sadness, although we are both very sad that you are leaving us at all. No, your mother is just so relieved that at last you and Kieran have found a safe haven to go to and she is shedding tears of joy.

I expect that by now you feel God has tested you both severely but I want you to remember that all the anxiety and torment that you have experienced has not been in vain. It has led you to seek refuge in God and now you are surely in the safest hands of all, so let God be your final refuge for there is no other, and say a prayer thanking him for helping you in your hour of need.

Well, Linda, I'll say goodbye for now. We both pray that you have a safe journey and that you find peace in Medjugorje. We love you very much.

Your ever loving father

PS We have phoned our friends in Dubrovnic and have

arranged for them to look after you while you are over there. They will be meeting you at the airport.

After they had read the letter, Linda and Kieran sat in silence for quite a while, thinking over all that they had been through together.

Then Kieran took her hand in his and said, 'Linda. Will you marry me?'

Linda didn't answer immediately. She simply threw her arms around him and hugged him very tightly for a moment.

Then she said, 'Yes! Yes! Of course I'll marry you.'

'Some proposal,' said Kieran. 'I haven't got a home to take you to or a means of support. Never mind, perhaps we can write our story when this is all over. How about that for an idea?'

'And who on earth would ever believe all the things that have happened to us, Kieran? If you were able to convince someone, I shouldn't think that you'd find a publisher willing to risk putting our story into print anyway. Isn't the truth really stranger than fiction?'

Further information on the Medjugorje story can be found at www.medjugorge.org/medpage.htm

A Nature Walk in the Woods

Louise and Richard Spilsbury

Raintree

Raintree is an imprint of Capstone Global Library Limited, a company incorporated in England and Wales having its registered office at 7 Pilgrim Street, London, EC4V 6LB – Registered company number: 6695582

www.raintreepublishers.co.uk
myorders@raintreepublishers.co.uk

Text © Capstone Global Library Limited 2015
First published in hardback in 2014
The moral rights of the proprietor have been asserted.

Edited by Joanna Issa, Penny West, Krissy Mohn, and Gina Kammer
Designed by Cynthia Akiyoshi
Picture research by Elizabeth Alexander and Tracy Cummins
Production by Helen McCreath
Originated by Capstone Global Library Ltd
Printed and bound in China by Leo Paper Group

ISBN 978 1 406 28219 1
18 17 16 15 14
10 9 8 7 6 5 4 3 2 1

British Library Cataloguing in Publication Data
A full catalogue record for this book is available from the British Library.

Acknowledgements
We would like to thank the following for permission to reproduce photographs:

Alamy: © incamerastock, 7, © Tim Graham, 18; FLPA: Jules Cox, 5, Michael Rose, 6, Steve Gettle/Minden Pictures/FLPA, 9; naturepl.com: Ben Hall, 12, Tim Martin, 14; Shutterstock: Alena Brozova, design element (nest), Antonio Clemens, 17, clearimages, 19, Eduard Kyslynskyy, 20, Eric Isselee, design element (deer), (earwig), front cover, Fedorov Oleksiy, design element (leaf), Garsya, design element (moss), Imageman, design element (moss), Jakkrit Orrasri, 13, Jason Patrick Ross, 15, back cover left, Kletr, 21, Kuttelvaserova Stuchelova, design element (moss), Madlen, design element (branch), (moss), Nadiia Korol, 22 top left, Nekrasov Andrey, design element (caterpillar), Oleksiy Mark, 22 bottom right, Piotr Krzeslak, 4, Richard Griffin, design element (fungi), romrf, 22 bottom left, Sergey Kelin, front cover, Sergey Peterman, 16, T Cassidy, 22 top right, TessarTheTegu, 11, back cover right, xpixel, design element (moth); SuperStock: Craig Joiner/age fotostock, 10, John Cancalosi/National Geographic, 8.

We would like to thank Michael Bright for his invaluable help in the preparation of this book.

Every effort has been made to contact copyright holders of material reproduced in this book. Any omissions will be rectified in subsequent printings if notice is given to the publisher.

All the Internet addresses (URLs) given in this book were valid at the time of going to press. However, due to the dynamic nature of the Internet, some addresses may have changed, or sites may have changed or ceased to exist since publication. While the author and publisher regret any inconvenience this may cause readers, no responsibility for any such changes can be accepted by either the author or the publisher.

Contents

Some words are shown in bold, **like this**. You can find out what they mean by looking in the glossary.

Where are we going?

We are going on a nature walk in the woods. Woods are places where lots of trees grow closely together.

It can be cool and muddy in woods, so wear a coat and rubber boots. If you walk quietly, you should spot some amazing woodland wildlife.

What lives in the woods?

Look down at the ground as you walk in the woods. Can you spot marks like this in the mud? What do you think they are?

When deer walk, their hooves make marks like this. Deer are brown. They wander in woods, feeding on leaves, **nuts**, and berries.

What lives in the trees?

Use your binoculars to spot animals in the treetops. Which animal do you think made the hole in this old tree? Why do you think it made the hole?

Some birds make holes in dead trees and
build **nests** inside using feathers and leaves.
Some birds make nests up high to keep
eggs and **chicks** safe from **predators**.

What nibbles nuts?

Look at the **nuts** that fall from the tree branches. Something has nibbled these nuts. What type of animal do you think eats these nuts?

Squirrels have strong front teeth that can bite through the shells of hard nuts. Then they eat the nut inside. In autumn squirrels bury nuts in the ground to eat in winter.

What lives on the tree trunk?

Look around the tree trunk. What do you see? Nuthatches climb head first down a tree trunk, feeding on **insects** that live in the **bark**.

Insects protect themselves from hungry
birds in different ways. You have to look
very closely to see patterned moths like this
because they hide against the tree bark.

What eats the leaves?

Take a close look at the leaves on this tree. What do you notice? What do you think made the holes in these leaves?

Caterpillars eat leaves, so they can grow fast and change into butterflies. Their **jaws** slide sideways to mash up leaves. Can you see the little hooks on their legs that hold on to the leaves while they eat?

What is in the dead leaves?

Use your magnifying glass to spot **insects** under the dead leaves. Insects live in the damp, dark leaves to keep the sun from drying them out and to hide from **predators**.

You might see an earwig resting in the dead leaves. Earwigs move at night, eating leaves, dead animals, and animal droppings. They use the **pincers** at the end of their body to nip predators!

Which trees are these?

A nature spotter's guide helps you to name trees by the shape of their leaves. You can tell this is an oak tree because its leaves are long with curly edges. Oaks also have **nuts** called acorns.

Take a close look at these leaves. Long,
narrow leaves like this grow on pine trees.
Pine leaves are tough, thick, and sharp with
a shiny, waxy surface.

How can I protect the woods?

Lots of animals live on trees and in the woods. You can help to protect the woods by never dropping litter. Walk quietly so you don't disturb the wildlife.

You can also protect woods by saving paper. People cut down trees to make paper. If you use **recycled** paper, people will cut down fewer trees.

Exploring nature

These things will help you explore the woods on a nature walk.

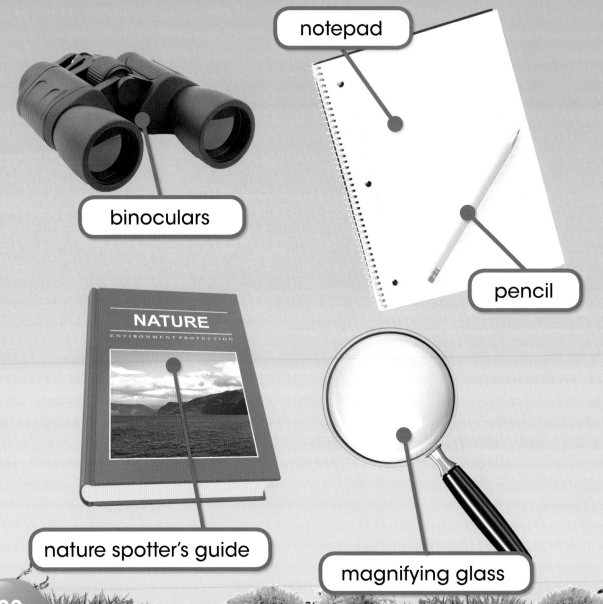

notepad

binoculars

pencil

NATURE
ENVIRONMENT PROTECTION

nature spotter's guide

magnifying glass

Glossary

bark tough layer around a tree trunk

chick baby bird

insect small animal that has six legs when it is an adult

jaw part of the body that opens and shuts the mouth

nest place where an animal has its babies

nut hard-shelled seed that grows on trees

pincers two animal claws that work together to grab things

predator animal that eats other animals

recycle to change waste so that it can be used again

Find out more

Books

In the Woods (Nature Walks), Clare Collinson (Franklin Watts, 2010)

Woodlands (Nature Trails), Anita Ganeri (Heinemann Library, 2010)

Websites

http://www.bbc.co.uk/nature/habitats/Temperate_broadleaf_and_mixed_forests

Find out more about ancient woodlands and the animals that live in them.

www.naturedetectives.org.uk

Become a woodland nature detective using spotter sheets, insect packs, and other facts and information on this website.

Index